S0-AWE-091

THE COMPLETE WOMAN RUNNER

Recommended Reading:
Runner's World Magazine, Box 366
Mountain View, CA 94043; $9.50/year
Write for a free catalog of publications
and supplies for runners and other athletes.

World Publications
1400 Stierlin Road, Mountain View, CA 94043

Library of Congress No. 78-58048
ISBN No. 0-89037-143-1

Table of Contents

Introduction

It is apparent to anyone who walks through the modern world with eyes open that women are running in unprecedented numbers. Whether with their dogs, with husbands, with friends, or alone, women are filling the streets and the roads and the bike paths on runs that have become a very important part of their daily lives.

At one time almost the total domain of men, running is now a sport and a lifestyle that easily accepts participation by either sex. Women need no longer feel shy about entering the sports world for fear of being labeled "masculine" or "tomboy." Women are finding in running a new freedom and a new road to individuality.

Running requires no great investment of money, demands no previous athletic excellence, asks very little yet asks everything. It is universal and individual. It is pleasure and pain, and then pleasure again. It requires no set patterns and no great expenditure of time; it can be done at noon or at midnight.

It can be whatever the runner makes it.

William Butler Yeats once wrote that dance is the perfect art because "it is impossible to separate the dancer from the dance." Similarly, running may be the perfect sport—because the runner *is* the run. It is easy to see why running has become the sport of women who are interested in self-awareness. In a world dictated by machines and schedules, running once again puts the individual first...it changes spectators into participants.

Women at all levels of running have found a common bond with each other—an island of time in the mainstream of the day in which they can make friends and escape the pressures of life in these United States. Men have accepted running for much the same reasons: It provides very real protection against stress, overweight, nervousness, heart attack, and other diseases.

Running among women is special. Yet, when you read this book, you will discover that running for men and women is virtually the same in every aspect.

For the unique joy and health of it, men and women are running on common ground.

The Editors of *Runner's World* Magazine

Part 1

The Journey: Starting Out and Persevering

1

Training to Run

How to begin: choosing the right shoes, equipment, warm-up exercises, schedules

Sue Stricklin

I have been communicating on the joys and tribulations of women and running for over two years now. This chapter is designed not only to answer basic questions of how and why, but to let you know that we all have the same shared experiences. These shared experiences are to a great extent what running is about and what ties us together as runners. Charts and graphs you can find any day, but they don't communicate in the same way as others who have "been through it."

We all go through the physical, psychological, and social problems that are peculiarly associated with women running. Although we solve these problems in our own style, they give women runners a unique togetherness. Women need inspiration and reassurance in the beginning because they come from a relatively impoverished athletic background. I want to give you the necessary reassurance not only to *get* you going as a runner, but to *keep* you going.

You are, as George Sheehan asserts, an experiment of one. You will have to find what works the best for you. What works for me or someone else may not be right for you. That is why there will be no charts and graphs in this chapter.

So read, ask questions, and build a strong foundation and you will find your own running style in something you can do very well. Out there on the road you will find and come to terms with yourself. It is an exciting and growing experience. Only you can do it for yourself. So come with me and find out about this very old form of physical activity or madness that seems to be, if you will forgive me, over-running the country.

REASONS TO BEGIN

Why start running? It is certainly easier to watch other people running instead of doing it yourself. Is it really as great as everyone says it is? It's cold in the mornings, you get hot and sweaty, there are aches and pains, you are rained on and stared at, it requires time and planning, and what are you supposed to think about when you are running?

There are a lot of books written about running, but when you finally put on your shorts and tennis shoes and try it, it certainly is not like anything you read about. Especially that "euphoric feeling" runners talk about experiencing. And yet, there must be something to it. So many people seem to be doing it. When they are finished running they talk about how great the run was even though they didn't feel that way, or look that way, while they were doing it.

Then you begin to notice other changes in your running friends. They start buying books on training, nutrition, and medical advice. There are discussions about hard-fast, fartlek, intervals, LSD, Lydiard, Bowerman, aerobic, and anaerobic. Good grief. And then the former life of the party starts yawning and leaves at 9:30 pm on a Saturday night, just after dessert, muttering that "tomorrow is Sunday and a long one." *A long one?* What are they talking about?

Then you discover, to your amazement or horror, depending on your attitude, that they have not only risen at an impossible early hour (the kind that only fishermen see) but they have gone out and run a distance that seems insane. They claim to have enjoyed it and recount every step. They talk, of course, afterward, in replacing all the protein, carbohydrate, and fluid lost during the run. Actually, that part of running is a very nice side benefit. Especially when your friends seem to be losing weight and firming up. Perhaps there might be something to running that is not readily apparent until you sort of ease into it. Maybe tomorrow you'll go out and give it another try.

As you stand poised with your hand on the door knob, ready to take the first step, you wonder, How do I *begin*?

Is there a right and wrong way? Once you begin, how do you stay motivated, and as you continue, what are some of the changes, problems, and ideas that occur? Let's go out that door and explore a new, long, winding, sundappled, rain splattered, physically and psychologically frustrating and satisfying road.

Why are you going out there? Maybe to lose weight, to firm

up the flab which suddenly appeared, because all those magazine pictures look so good, you heard it will make you feel better, all your friends are doing it, you need some time alone, your dog needs exercise, your teenager is driving you up the wall, something is wrong somewhere but you don't know where, if you can't fight them join them, and maybe there is something to it if so many runners keep running.

These are probably some of the reasons you begin, but what is important is that you give running a fair chance. A fair chance means doing it faithfully for at least three months. Before you start, remember all the words of warning you have read and take them seriously. Have a checkup by your doctor and, most important, a stress (treadmill) test, which will show up any irregularities. Learn how to take your pulse and monitor your progress. After a medical okay and knowing that you are a beginner and have certain limits, you are ready to start.

Shoe Science

The most important part of success at the start, other than your commitment and motivation, will be your shoes. Tennis shoes, old shoes, and pseudo-running shoes will not do. I ran in my tennis shoes for four months when I began and it's a wonder that I did not injure myself. It is the difference between wearing concrete boots and cushioned comfort. Anyway, why make yourself feel worse than you have to?

Go to a runners' store where the salespeople are also runners. Try on a lot of shoes. There is no "best" shoe—only what feels best on your foot. They should feel good when you walk around in them. Never buy a pair of shoes that need to "stretch out"—you'll wind up with blisters. Be careful: Do not buy racing flats even though they feel light and wonderful; buy training flats with enough cushioning and support for everyday running.

Of course, the question of "what do I wear?" comes up. In the time I have been running, I have seen runners' dress change from nylon boxer shorts and cut-offs, cotton T-shirts in a variety of mismatched colors to a veritable fashion show of bodysuits, matched running outfits, and fancy warmups. A minor note: warmups were originally called sweats, were baggy and gray in color. That was before. Now they are polyester, tailored, and come in multi-colors, stripes, and zig-zags, with or without leg zippers. Don't go overboard to begin with. You can probably make do with a pair of loose, comfortable shorts and a cotton T-shirt.

What you wear will also depend on where you live, what the weather is like, and what time of the day you run. I happen to run in Hawaii where it is both warm and humid and sometimes rainy in the mornings. Because cotton really chafes, I have found that nylon tricot is the best material to wear for both shorts and top. It doesn't matter when they get wet, and they don't become heavy like cotton does—essentially you are running drip dry. Nylon tricot and mesh also have the added advantage of continually drying out as you run and sweat, thereby keeping a constant cooling process going. That, of course, is not so important when it is 45° with a cold rain. My experience has mostly been with warm-weather running. I find that in cooler places, by putting a cotton T-shirt on instead of, or under a nylon top, which keeps the upper body warm, I stay warm enough. Also, you become warmer as you run, so don't overdress. Above all, choose comfort, not looks!

While we are on the distinction between comfort and looks, let me add a note about makeup. I have noticed a lot of beginning runners out in full foundation, mascara, and blusher. Eventually there are little rivers of sweat running through the foundation and the mascara begins to smudge. You don't need to wear all that stuff, advertising to the contrary. It is not necessary when you are running. You will acquire a glow of your own that is very natural. I also believe there is a side benefit of firming up the skin. All that is really necessary is a good moisturizer and skin protection against the sun. A lot of extra stuff on your face doesn't help you run better; besides, it tastes terrible.

A last word about women's clothing: whether or not to wear a bra. Yes, by all means wear one when you run. It is important for support. The problem will be in finding something comfortable. Stay away from cotton, underwires, and an excess of metal in the way of fasteners. Look for nylon, stretch elastic and comfort with no feeling of constriction. If you have something tight around you it is hard to breathe properly and deeply when you run.

Now, let's go out the door and take the first steps.

FIRST STEPS

It is said that the first step is the hardest, and in large part that is true. At about the fortieth step though, your body, if it is unused to physical activity, will suddenly realize something is different and begin to protest. To ease these first steps and to begin your running program correctly, take about 10 minutes to stretch and warm up your muscles. I'm not talking about calisthenics and jumping jacks, but slow limbering up yoga-type exercises. There are a number of good stretching exercises demonstrated in magazines and books.* Pick a variety concentrating on your leg muscles, since that is what you will be using. You need to watch yourself, though. Stretching exercises can be used to put off actually beginning what you are out there to do—which is to start running slowly.

I use the phrase "start running slowly," deliberately. Your tendency may be to determinedly "keep up" with a faster friend, husband, or boyfriend. Don't. Go your own speed and stay comfortable. Running is just like walking. One foot in front of the other, alternating feet. So begin by walking faster and faster, and you will find yourself running.

Probably the most enjoyable way to begin is to run with a friend who is also beginning. That way you can share your mutual development as runners and provide moral support when needed. There are side-benefits, also. Joe Henderson claims that running has done more for the lost art of conversation than any other sport. He is correct. As you run along, talk. Not only will the time fly by and the whole process seem easier, but it will be thoroughly enjoyable. You would be surprised at the conversation and topics covered.

One of my best friends, who leads a busy life, and I have a standard running date every Friday morning at 5:30 a.m. for a 10-mile run. Very specifically, all others are "disinvited" to join us. We cruise along a familiar and lovely hilly route and talk nonstop. It is fun catching up with each other's activities, working out problems, and just enjoying what we are doing. It's our time to stay in touch. I still run with people I started running with three-and-a-half years ago.

Your running friends are special and different because you share a lot of miles, talk, sweat, and very good days together and that forms a special bond. This doesn't mean that you always have to run with someone. Sometimes running by yourself is your only chance to find time to yourself. It can be and is

---

* See *New Exercises for Runners* by the Editors of *Runner's World* Magazine (World Publications: Mountain View, Ca.).

very enjoyable to run alone. I regularly run alone, by choice, at least four days a week. I value my own time and the opportunity to be in tune with myself. I experience the surrounding beauty of where I am running. I have my favorite flower gardens, wooded areas, and store displays.

One of the most unique and neatest running experiences I have ever had was a two-mile leg of a 140-mile relay. I ran at about 2 a.m. through a wooded area with the wind blowing and the rain pelting down. It was elemental and fantastic. I'm not saying that it is always that neat, but you do get in tune with yourself and what you are doing.

Form and Style

There are some basics of running called *form* and *style* that can help you run easier. Your posture greatly affects your ease in running. Watch how other people look when they run. Some of them appear to be fighting what they are doing and look very uncomfortable. They hold their arms high right in front of their chest with their hands clenched. They frown. They lean far forward or backward and sway from side to side with each step. It not only looks hard and uncomfortable, it is hard and uncomfortable.

Instead, imagine yourself in a relatively straight line balanced over your knees and legs. Your center of gravity, which you can think of as placed in your pelvis, moves right over your feet as you stride with a bent knee. Your head is up and shoulders relaxed. Your arms are bent at about waist height and move partly across your front at an easy angle. Your hands are gently cupped, not clenched. Experiment. Clench your fist and see how it tightens up all your muscles. As you stride, don't attempt to reach out beyond your natural stride length. Everyone has a different frequency pattern that is right for them depending on factors such as height, leg length, knee lift, and so on. As your foot strikes the ground, it should be an easy motion: heel, across the ball of the foot to the toe, off.

There is no special secret way of running. You should not get trapped in the track runners' syndrome of bounding up and down on the ball of the foot. Men are particularly prone to this technique.

Now that you're out there, what happens? You've stretched, warmed up, and are off down the road. How long are you supposed to run? There are, of course, many answers. I want to

295
10 000 METERS

give you a few guidelines to follow that will allow you to progress and develop to an intermediate running level.

One of the basic ideas in running is slowly building up your endurance and conditioning level. Face it, women as a general rule lead somewhat nonathletic lives. And most of us did not participate in school sports other than our P.E. classes—not because we did not want to but because it was not offered. Commitment to a regular program of running slowly builds up your general physical endurance and conditioning. As you progress it becomes easier, and you will begin to notice some interesting and enjoyable side effects.

Although there are several ways of starting, there is one basic premise: Start slowly. Be aware of how you are running as you go along. Are you relaxed, with your arms swinging easily and your posture good? It's easy to begin too fast because we all want to look good and being a beginner generally bothers us. Remember, though, in running it simply doesn't matter. There are no experts; some people are able to run faster only because they have been running longer, but it is all relative. There are days I run fast and days I run slowly; that is part of my training and building up my conditioning. And all runners run the same way, one foot in front of the other. Nothing fancy.

As a beginner, I think the best way to start is to run by time only. Do not try to run certain distances. By running time you do not get caught up in the "how far did you run" syndrome. In 40 minutes you can go two miles or five miles or eight miles. On different days you will run different distances in the same amount of time, depending on how you feel. So run by your watch only.

I think 30 minutes is satisfactory both physically and mentally. Run 15 minutes out your front door and then turn around and come back. You can explore your neighborhood when you run for time and discover things you had never noticed when you drove by. You can run anywhere when you run by time, and as you become more experienced you will know approximately how far you run in that time. Simply because we are all curious and will go out and measure where we run just to find out the distance!

At the Honolulu Marathon Clinic we start people running one hour, three times a week. Our weather and life pace is conducive to that way of running. It is obviously easier to handle 30 minutes of running time than an hour. Ideally, you should stick to a minimum of 30 minutes to accustom yourself to a definite period of time. In that time frame you can run slowly the entire time, or combine running with walking. Alternate the two in a walk-fifty-pace, run-fifty-pace and gradually lengthen your running time. You will be surprised how quickly your body adapts itself.

Remember, man is basically a running animal and running is basic to almost all sports. Perhaps that is why we like doing it so much. By running every other day you are following the stress/adaptation theory of building up your endurance. In the beginning, running is a stress because it is a new physical activity. In allowing your body to rest and adapt, your progress will be steady. Of course, there are almost as many ideas on how to run as there are runners. You will find this particularly true for beginners. I personally believe that one half-hour every other day, four times a week provides the best beginning foundation.

The first eight weeks of beginning running will not be great fun. It will not live up to the advance billing you have read about in various articles. You are building up a habit of exercise. There will be vague aches and pains as you move from a passive to an active way of life. You will find, too, that it is easier to run at certain times of the day. Some people are morning runners and some are afternoon runners.

Personally, I find it is much easier to run in the morning. The day begins well and the run leaves me refreshed with the feeling that I have "done it." Then, if I want I can run again in the afternoon. If you wait until the afternoon, it is easy to find excuses not to run. You're tired after a day's work, the kids need you, dinner has to be taken care of, a party to get ready for, and on and on. Do it early. You will find that the early mornings are incredibly lovely and the air fresh and sweet. Some adjustments may have to be made in family life, but it does seem easier to deal with in the morning than late in the afternoon.

A WOMAN'S STRENGTH

Women are incredibly strong, stronger than they think, and with a careful, slow start, building a good base, you will be very pleased with your progress. Some will adapt more quickly than others, and age is not so much a factor as your basic level of physical capabilities.

As you progress and suddenly feel good and your program is

beginning to work, what do you do? Take it easy. We all seem to believe that if a little bit is good, more must be better. Again, the key is stress and adaptation. If you are feeling good and suddenly increase your running time without allowing for adaptation, your body will fight back with signs of overstress. These include a feeling of almost overwhelming fatigue, aches and pains that don't go away, colds, a desire for sweets and sometimes a feeling of depression and the "blahs."

Pay attention and listen to your body. I find that women generally are much more in tune with their bodies than men are and will notice subtle signs more readily. Slowly increase your time/mileage buildup, after your first eight weeks of running. Your schedule would then include a longer run on Sundays, which is traditionally the "long one" or whatever day works best for you, and then have a rest day. If you are running mainly for recreational purposes and to become more physically fit, then your goal does not need to exceed the maintenance level of 40 minutes every other day, four days a week. That will really provide you with all the basic conditioning and exercise necessary.

However, if you are entertaining more serious thoughts and are running with a goal of five days a week and a longer Sunday run, then there are some variations you might employ to add interest to your runs.

One is known as the *hard-easy* schedule. You run longer on one day and then shorter on the next, allowing your body to rest and then run longer again. Sometimes this fits into a personal schedule more easily. Then, there is the concept of *fartlek* running. *Fartlek* is Swedish for "speed play." After you have been running for awhile you will notice that there are times during your run when you seem to run faster and easier and then you slow down again. What you are doing is a form of fartlek. After your first 30 minutes of running, when you are thoroughly warmed up, try picking up your pace for a certain distance. Focus on a telephone pole down the street, or anything you like, and run to that object, gradually picking up your pace until you are breathing harder, then slow down when you get there and run slowly and easily, recovering to your normal pace and breathing.

It is simply playing with going faster.

When you run fartlek you will notice the difference between running aerobically (when you are not out of breath or breathing hard) and anaerobically (when you are breathing hard and need oxygen). You are teaching your body to run in different ways and it will feel heavy and awkward at first. You should not do too much or feel that you must run fartlek. Simply run as you feel and take advantage of your natural running rhythm when you are feeling good.

At this point I can hear the question "But how do I breathe?" There is nothing magical about breathing. Basically, you need oxygen and your system sees that you get it. The harder and faster you are breathing, the more oxygen you are using up at a faster rate. Thus the "talk test" is employed when you are running to make sure that you are not running too fast. That does not apply to race situations, of course.

You see, there is nothing hard about running. It is easy. Running becomes hard only when we make it hard.

SCHEDULES

I hesitate to suggest specific schedules because people tend to take them as gospel, not as suggestions. I will offer some advice in setting up a schedule that will fit into your life.

I have suggested starting with 30 minutes four times a week. The key is to go slowly and allow for the stress adaptation process. You may feel just great after the first two weeks and decide to go farther and longer. Contain your enthusiasm; instead, increase one of your runs timewise by 15-20 minutes and hold that for several weeks. Then increase again and hold and repeat the process until you are running four or five times a week for 40 minutes each time. One day should be a longer run, perhaps one hour. I find that it takes at least three weeks to adapt to what is essentially greater mileage when you increase your time.

You will slip into thinking miles or distance after awhile instead of time. This is all right once you have built up your endurance. In the beginning, though, run time and not mileage. The endurance and mileage will come as a function of running time.

When you start thinking about mileage, a reasonable goal is to run 40 minutes or five miles on a run. The five miles will come with training, so don't push; allow it to happen as a function of time.

Another good rule of thumb is not to increase your mileage by more than five miles in a week and then hold that new mileage for at least three weeks. You will be able to tell if you have adapted if you don't have signs of overstress. Then you can increase again in the same pattern. Be very aware of how you are feeling. The major reason for slow build-up of endurance is to avoid injury. Injuries are primarily caused by your body's reaction to overstress. There is never anything wrong in cutting back or laying off for awhile until that Achilles tendonitis, shin pain, or whatever goes away. There is no such thing as "running through pain." If it hurts, pay attention; your body is telling you something, so treat it properly. To stay uninjured is smart running.

Still, there are minor problems that can affect the beginning runner's attitude. One is menstrual periods. I have found that with increased physical activity and fitness, your period is much easier to handle. If you are prone to edema, you will probably still have it but not as badly. And right before your period your pace may slow down and you will huff and puff more, but no matter, just think you are sweating off all that water and how much better you will feel. And although you may start out with some cramping, generally that tends to disappear as you run. The improved muscle tone from running seems to alleviate a lot of problems we always took for granted. Most nylon tricot shorts have a little pocket in which to put a tampon or carry an old sock with supplies inside.

Another problem that I rarely see covered in books about running is diarrhea. It afflicts new runners and experienced runners alike. I have no magic solutions, just some ideas to help solve the problem. As part of your better physical conditioning your system changes in many ways. One change is increased susceptibility to certain foods. The first solution is to find all the rest rooms along your route. If necessary, change your route to include them. Notice if the problem is greater in the morning or evening and change your running time if that helps. Then, start examining your diet. Keep a record of what you have eaten. Perhaps certain foods the night before, like a huge salad, caused the problem. Or it may be milk, wheat, gluten, chocolate, or something else. It may take time to pinpoint the cause but it is worth the effort. You can also carry a supply of toilet paper for emergencies. This is one subject I have found most people simply don't communicate about because they become embarrassed. Because it is so common, ask other women for their solutions and pass on the information.

Family Relations

You may experience tremendous guilt attacks about neglecting family responsibilities. If you are going to run, other members of the household need to learn to do their share. It will be hard at first, but the end result is good for everyone. Kids and husbands discover they are capable of becoming more self-reliant doing things they had never before considered. They are proud of their achievements and your personal achievements as well. Another way of solving the problem with very little children is to team up with friends to babysit on a rotation basis.

Your social life will change, too. It is really tied up with the physical changes that affect your diet and sleep needs. You also will find yourself very happy to excuse yourself at 9:30 on a Saturday night. Nonrunners find it harder to accept and have a tendency to think it is strange, tinged with a bit of envy. Particularly when you eat a second helping of carrot cake, commenting that you are running long tomorrow.

You will find that the stresses and strains in your personal life are very real because you are changing. But change is for the better because you are in the process of feeling better about yourself.

In the two years that I have taught and coached women runners, I have found there is a very definite cycle of changes that women runners go through psychologically. In essence it can be summed up as getting to know yourself and feeling your worth as a person. Running is often said to be a cheap form of therapy—this is probably very true. You have a unique opportunity combining the physiological changes that happen when you are out running and the psychological changes that produce some very beneficial results. When you have been running for a while, things seem to fall into perspective easier. Your worries, concerns, fears, and everyday stresses resolve themselves not only more quickly, but often more imaginatively. You will experience those sudden flashes of insight and wonder why you didn't think of it before.

Every day out there on the roads will not be a wonderful day, but good days happen often enough to begin to notice that on the days you don't run you have a sort of edgy feeling. Or if you have something to work on and need to make some decisions you will find yourself giving the runner's reply, "Let me run on it." It is both literal and figurative. I find that when you start out, review the problem so it is set in your mind, then turn to zero, think about nothing, enjoy the scenery or something else. After about 30 minutes or so, answers and ideas suddenly start bubbling up. It is a wonderful process. Sometimes, after a very stressful day of kids, new puppies, school, the office, or an IRS audit you will feel physically and emotionally drained. Put on your shoes and head out the door before you can tell yourself how badly you feel and take a short run. You will return recharged and ready to deal with the world. Then take your bubble bath!

What is subtly happening to you is what you have read about. Running, which you began in order to improve yourself physically for diet or health reasons, has become something else. You have become dependent on it. You have become, as William Glasser says, positively addicted. Not bad for a beginner's modest hope in just being able to do it.

Now that you have your basic foundation of conditioning you may want to enter competitions. This requires not only your basic long slow distance (LSD) running, which you have been doing, but a different mind set. Actually you have been developing this without being aware of it. Basically it is the knowledge that on that particular day you have done your best and some days are faster or slower than others. Everybody who goes out there and finishes what they set out to do is a winner. That is the most significant thing that women can learn in running. You are only running against and with yourself, no one else. There will be days you will run very well and do what is known as a PR or personal record. There are days you will do a PW or personal worst. What is important is that you have gone out there and done it. That makes you a winner in the satisfaction of having pushed and achieved.

My last thought for you as a beginning runner is to always remember that you are an experiment of one. It is an ongoing evaluation of joy and pain. Running will bring you satisfactions that are too wonderful to communicate. It is that elusive feeling that will keep us out there on the road in all kinds of weather all over the world. It also makes up for all the in-between moments when you are not any too positive about being a winner or a grand experiment of one. Commit yourself to the first eight weeks and then keep going. When you begin to feel the very positive changes that are happening to you in many areas you will discover that your experiment of one is not only worthwhile continuing; it is developing capabilities in yourself that you never thought were possible. You are no longer running for "your health" but because you want to run. When you want to run you are no longer a beginning runner. You are a runner. Stay with it and enjoy it.

2

Beyond Jogging

From jogger to runner: increasing workouts, adapting diet, keeping running logs

Mark Cockrill

Dr. Jack Scaff of the Honolulu Marathon Clinic has said a commitment of eight to twelve weeks, consisting of three to four one-hour runs per week, is typically adequate to transform the dilettante jogger into a committed runner. From my experience you cross the threshold into serious running when you realize you have used your discretionary time for running and have voluntarily set aside other activities that you used to enjoy. The story included here concerns a group of women who found themselves at this stage of development when they decided to seek something more to improve their running performances.

SATURDAY AT THE TRACK

Even in Hawaii an early Saturday morning in January can occasionally feel cold. But the shivers I felt standing alone on the University of Hawaii's synthetic track were more from apprehension than the gusty trade winds. Yet gradually over the next ten minutes a small group of women runners assembled, and the warmth of their enthusiasm quickly dissipated the chill of apprehension I felt earlier.

While we waited for everyone to arrive, I went over a mental list of the women who had come into The Running Room looking more for advice than shoes or running gear. It was just a month before Hawaii's first all-women's race, and the question I was hearing repeatedly was, "How do I run faster?" Most of these women were "graduates" of the Honolulu Marathon Clinic in that they had finished at least one marathon, but now were realizing there might be something more. These women had entered running from the top down, or as joggers who gradually increased their mileage (using the principles Sue Stricklin outlined earlier), building endurance until they were ready for their first major race, the Honolulu Marathon. This approach, although now becoming commonplace, is the reverse of that used by the traditional marathoner. In the past the competitor had moved upward from high school or college track teams, often limited to races of eight laps around a quarter-mile track, to cross-country or road races of ten to twenty kilometers, and finally (usually after years of endurance training and speed workouts) to race his or her first marathon.

This group had learned to finish, to run for fun, to run to simply accomplish the task of completing the distance. The traditional racer knew, that if he was willing to go slow enough, he could run twenty-six miles; his objective was to "race," to maintain a challenging pace, to finish within a given time, or to beat a fellow runner. For the most part, these competitive urges were not primary motivators for this group of female runners, but that would change.

In organizing the Saturday At the Track (SAT) group, we initially focused our attention on the all-women's ten-kilometer race that was scheduled for a month away. The women in the group ranged in age from nineteen to forty-eight. Almost all had completed at least one marathon with their "best" times ranging from 3:40 to 5:29. While a few had earlier run weekly mileage as high as fifty, for the most part their average total weekly runs were about twenty-five miles. The primary purpose was to take these endurance-based runners and improve their "short-distance" speed. Since none of the runners had any track background, we started with a basic discussion regarding the concept behind interval or speedwork and then simply let the format of each weekly meeting evolve from there. In a short time it became apparent that one hour was adequate for both the track workout and the question-answer session that inevitably followed. Since runners love to talk about running, I was pleased to find that I had an eager audience for the information I had acquired both from marathoning and from co-managing a store for runners. When we agreed to meet every Saturday morning at the same time, SAT was born.

Because of the limited amount of time, the speedwork buildup for the 10-K race was, by necessity, abbreviated and probably resulted in only marginal physical gains. But this is not to say that considerable improvements were not made in the individual race results, because the psychological and mental gains were substantial. More than anything else, these women discovered how much faster they could run over a given distance *if they were willing to endure a higher level of discomfort.* They found they wouldn't die by running hard—it just felt like it sometimes. Their awareness came about by considerable trial and effort, seeking to find that level of pace within each individual where oxygen transport systems vacillate between the aerobic and anaerobic levels. Probably if one success had to be singled out from the SAT meetings, it would be a gaining of this race-pace awareness. In addition, we started to share considerable information regarding stretching, injuries, running gear, and overall training programs.

Although our time had been limited, it appeared to have been well spent. In a starting field of 650 runners, seven members of SAT who ran finished as high as the top seven percent, and all were in the top forty percent.

Success Breeds Success

With this taste of success, the women began to appreciate the benefits of a formalized training program and were then ready to commit themselves to a more serious challenge. Their next major goal was the upcoming Big Island Marathon scheduled for four-and-a-half months away. So as to better advise each runner, I asked her to set her own goal in terms of a particular finishing time, and also to determine what her level of base weekly mileage was at that point in her training. Once we had established where the runner was and where she wanted to go, we had the two focal points necessary to map out this new and exciting journey.

Most runners set a goal of under four hours for the first marathon and had an average training base of thirty to thirty-five miles per week. Depending on each individual's natural strengths and weaknesses, we set up a schedule that spelled out both the weekly mileage and each week's longest run. From that the runner could spread her daily runs throughout the week as was compatible with her work schedule. The typical mileage buildup consisted of adding five miles to the weekly total and then holding this mileage constant for three weeks before another five miles would be added. Particular attention was paid to the runner's general well-being at the beginning of each new buildup period because we often found that stress-related injuries or illnesses (colds and sore throats mostly) would be more likely at this time.

Over the years I have found that this practice of increasing mileage by adding an absolute number rather than increasing by a fixed percentage is much more successful. It seems as the runner in transition increases her mileage, it is much less risky to have this increase, although constant in miles, actually be proportionally less to the existing base (for example, a five-mile increase from twenty-five to thirty miles per week is a twenty percent heavier load, whereas the gain from fifty-five to sixty is only a 9.1 percent increase). Although it is very individualistic, it seems that the three-week period of fixed mileage works well: the first week to ten days being a period of new stress; the second week less stress and increased adaptation; while the third week the runner feels good, is consolidating her energy and is physically and mentally ready to consider another step up.

In addition to successful results on this program by a number of male runners, this was basically the mileage buildup/weekly long run program Sue Stricklin used to lower the national marathon record for thirty-nine-year-old females by more than fourteen minutes, in the warm, humid 1977 Big Island Marathon.

As for weekly runs, we found it very important to integrate these into the three-week segments so that the longest of the long runs would come at a point when the runner was most rested. For example, if a runner had found she could handle 18 miles without undue stress, her schedule would be advanced to a 19-miler the week before her new buildup, then back to a 17-mile run at the beginning of her second week when her resistance would be the lowest. Then it was raised to an 18-miler at the beginning of the third after she had begun to adjust to her new higher weekly mileage and had the psychological benefit of knowing she had handled this distance successfully in the past.

Our Saturday morning track workouts continued to stress moderate to substantial effort in the speed workouts but always with an awareness of how the individual was standing up to increased weekly mileage. I varied the track workouts by both distance and time to avoid the mental drudgery that can come with the contemplation of one more side-splitting Saturday morning grind. At least every other week we would spend a portion of the hour doing some off-the-track fartlek type running in the form of follow-the-leader or catch-the-rabbit games. The University's track is located in what was once an old quarry area, so we had an opportunity to do some modified hill work in the form of going up numerous flights of stairs.

As the women were exposed to more variation in their running, they asked about hill workouts and in particular the Tantalus run many of Hawaii's serious road racers used for one of their "hard" days during the week. From my experience, most areas of the country where there is any gathering of serious runners have one major run that really requires an extra effort to complete. This is the run that the unwary out-of-towner is always invited to come along on, and is often an informal test of fitness (both physical and mental) of the visitor. On Oahu, the 10-mile Tantalus loop certainly qualifies. I knew the group had reached a new plateau when they decided to meet one afternoon a week to run Tantalus voluntarily, which gains over 1,600 feet in approximately five miles of switchbacks, then descends over the remaining five miles of knee-jarring macadam.

Approaching the Marathon

As we approached the eight-weeks-to-go mark before the marathon, we increased the intensity of our track workouts and became even more serious about monitoring how our bodies were standing up to the new levels of stress. Some runners were reaching sixty to sixty-five miles per week and minor stress problems were inevitable. Hawaii is extremely fortunate in that in addition to having two orthopedic specialists who run, Dr. Kent Davenport and Dr. Bob Smith, we are also regularly visited by Dr. John Pagliano, an outstanding sports podiatrist from southern California. Suggestions and remedies obtained from these physicians were often exchanged during the lecture portion of our SAT meetings, and it is to their credit that much of our progress was relatively injury-free. Also at about this time, I included initial thoughts on how we would start to taper our weekly mileage, how dehydration could be avoided by the judicious use of replacement fluids, and how very important it would be to reduce body weight as much as possible.

Individually the women were having more and more success

in small local races, and a new competitive side was starting to emerge. Sharing these newly-experienced aggressive feelings with other members of the group appeared to be very beneficial for all. It was gradually becoming accepted that it was right and maybe even good to become competitive. So the growth continued—mentally and physically.

As we approached the final few weeks, lecture time was spent helping individual runners develop their race pace estimates and to make decisions about the marathon pace. To this end, I referred the group to Chapters 18 and 19 in *The Complete Marathoner* as well as to an excellent article by Dan Moore entitled "Proper Pace for the Long Race." The article appeared in the December, 1974 issue of *Runner's World.*

In the final week before the Big Island Marathon, I was amazed by the increase in phone calls I received with questions regarding pre-race diet, tapering of mileage, hotel accommodations, and what I was going to do about the weather conditions! These calls were really a welcome interruption to my own pre-race fretting and SAT grew in unity as the members shared their mutual apprehensions.

Thursday evening prior to the race, SAT members met for a carbohydrate-loading party, which turned out to be the beginning of an eating binge that continued through the remainder of the week and was only slightly interrupted by the Sunday morning marathon. After seeing this continual intake of food, it was suggested that the group's logo be "the shark's jaws" from the recent hit movie. At this evening gathering each of the nine runners who had decided to run the marathon put their predicted finish times in an envelope. These envelopes were then sealed and set aside until after the race. The woman who most closely estimated her actual finish time would receive a prize of new running shorts. The eventual winner's estimate varied by less than one percent from her actual time.

Unlike conditions in the previous two years, the 1978 Big Island Marathon did not provide the women with an ideal running environment. Like most marathons in Hawaii, the race started at 6:00 a.m. to avoid the heat later in the morning; but unfortunately, six o'clock arrived in the middle of a very heavy downpour. Within less than two miles, the slippage and weight of our shoes felt more typical of conditions at twenty-two miles. This early downpour was severe enough that in one case a woman's insoles in both shoes delaminated from the mid-sole

Zebra Room
1370
899

and she was forced to change shoes in the middle of the race. Fortunately, she was able to request, through aid from a support group, that her training shoes, left in the hotel room, be picked up and delivered to her along the marathon route. Unbelievably, this was successfully accomplished and she was able to comfortably finish the race, albeit with some loss of time, in a dry pair of shoes.

Eight of the nine SAT runners finished the marathon and established new personal records. The ninth runner was held back by a reoccurring hip injury, yet still finished fast enough to earn third place in her age group. Even more amazing was the fact that as a group, *the runners improved their marathon times by an average of 27 minutes!*

To confirm that we were on the right track, I held a number of informal critique sessions to review what the runners felt were their successes and failures as well as what they felt about Saturday At the Track and the various techniques used. From this feedback, I have established some of the more important points from this successful and exciting five-month experiment.

FROM JOGGER TO RUNNER

Now that we have seen what successes are obtainable by women runners who do not necessarily have exceptional natural abilities, but rather are willing to help in setting up and following a logical buildup schedule, I would like to suggest some of the less obvious keys to their successes. Although these points are not as apparent, they are no less important than the increasing weekly mileage or the long run. The SAT group learned that successful serious running requires a holistic approach or the neglected areas will become the weak links in the chain and breakdown will follow. Note that I have not gone into great detail on these points as other writers will expand on many of these items throughout this book.

As mentioned earlier, runners love to talk about their avocation and are delighted when they can give advice to a willing listener. But as an eager student, I urge you to *evaluate your teacher* closely. It is of paramount importance that you recognize whether or not the information being laid before you is appropriate to your level of conditioning. From personal experience, I can attest to the importance of this determination. I was less than two years into running when I had the good fortune to make the acquaintance of some outstanding national and international caliber racers, including Olympian Jeff Galloway, marathoner Ron Wayne, and Boston-winner Jack Fultz. Following the 1976 Honolulu Marathon, a group of us (including these runners) vacationed together for a week on the neighboring island of Maui. While this was a unique opportunity to share experiences and pick brains about running philosophy and training concepts, I came to realize that I could not directly apply their approaches to endurance or speed training to anything I was capable of doing at that time. This is not to say their information was without value, but rather that it was necessary to store it away until the day arose when I could successfully apply it to my own running program.

An extension of this same know-your-source concept applied when, as co-manager of The Running Room, I would have to continue to find out the individual jogger/runner's background before I could be of any real assistance either in making recommendations for running gear or answering questions as to training programs or running related injuries. With this caveat in the back of your mind, let's look at some other points that the women of SAT found valuable.

Sleep. Too often the blanket statement is made "Runners need less sleep." Although it may be true that a runner who has reached a given mileage base and has been maintaining that base for some time has developed a more efficient system needing less rest, it certainly is not true that the runner in the middle of a mileage buildup program that is taking her to new levels of performance can get by on less sleep. I believe the reverse to be true. I suggest you consider rest as a nutriment that has to be supplied in greater quantities in relationship to increased effort. Therefore, as your mileage increases, do not be surprised that there will be a need to increase your rest period. The best support of this is the ease with which vacationing women runners build up their mileage, as opposed to the struggle these same females experience while carrying a full workload and not having a schedule that would easily allow additional rest in the form of more overnight sleep or daily naps.

Nutrition. SAT successfully experimented with liquid diets prior to major races as a form of keeping the carbohydrate intake up but reducing the residual bulk before race day. Although the timing varies from one individual to another, it seems that twenty-four to thirty-six hours before a race is adequate for most runners to clear their lower intestines. We have had good success with Nutriment, a canned, flavored drink, and recommend that runners experiment with this or similar products to determine what works best for them. Other than this liquid diet, the standard carbohydrate-depleting and loading, and making an effort to stay completely hydrated in the warm Hawaiian climate, the only other nutritional recommendation given at SAT was a continued admonition to lose weight.

Weight Loss. Although I hesitate to use the word "easy" along with weight loss, I think it can safety be said that the easiest way to improve your long-distance running performance is by reducing your fat-body mass. You will be amazed at the amount of stress that can be avoided by substantial weight loss.

Another way we reduced pre-race stress and allowed our physical system to maximize the benefits of the higher mileage and faster running was to *taper pre-race workouts* starting earlier than normally recommended. Like most of these suggestions, the tapering period will vary from one runner to the next and even the same runner will find that as she progresses in endurance maturity, she may need less tapering. Nevertheless, we worked on a schedule that called for eighty percent (of the maximum mileage previously obtained) for the seven day period two weeks prior to the race and approximately fifty percent (of maximum mileage) for the week immediately before the race. For example, if the maximum weekly mileage for the last three-week period was sixty miles per week, then counting down Week II would consist of approximately forty-eight miles and Week I would equal thirty miles. With time and maturity, I expect the individuals will modify this concept but feel comfortable in using it as a starting point.

Keeping a Running Log. As can be seen, considerable emphasis is placed on the individual's ability to evaluate her own situation and to be able to convey that to her coach. It is very important that the runner keep a *daily written log* covering not only time and distance run, but also less specific characteristics of the run such as general feeling before and after, minor stresses that might grow into more serious problems, and an overview of how the particular workout fit in with the long-term objective. I personally find it also valuable to keep track of which shoes I wore for each run so that occasionally I can calculate the total mileage I'm getting out of each different model. As the mid-soles gradually lose their resilience, it is very helpful to know if a particular pair of trainers is getting near its mileage limit.

On a weekly meeting basis, this written diary will give a good frame of reference for discussions between runner and advisor. Possibly even more important is the information that can be gleaned out of the diary when the time comes for planning the next buildup schedule. I have found that a daily business diary that allows a separate page for each day plus room for a weekly summary is ideal. This historical record should also include detailed information on the races entered, covering such items as distance, pace, total time, environmental conditions, running shoes, and clothing; all of which would be evaluated as to degree of success or failure so that improvements could be made next time.

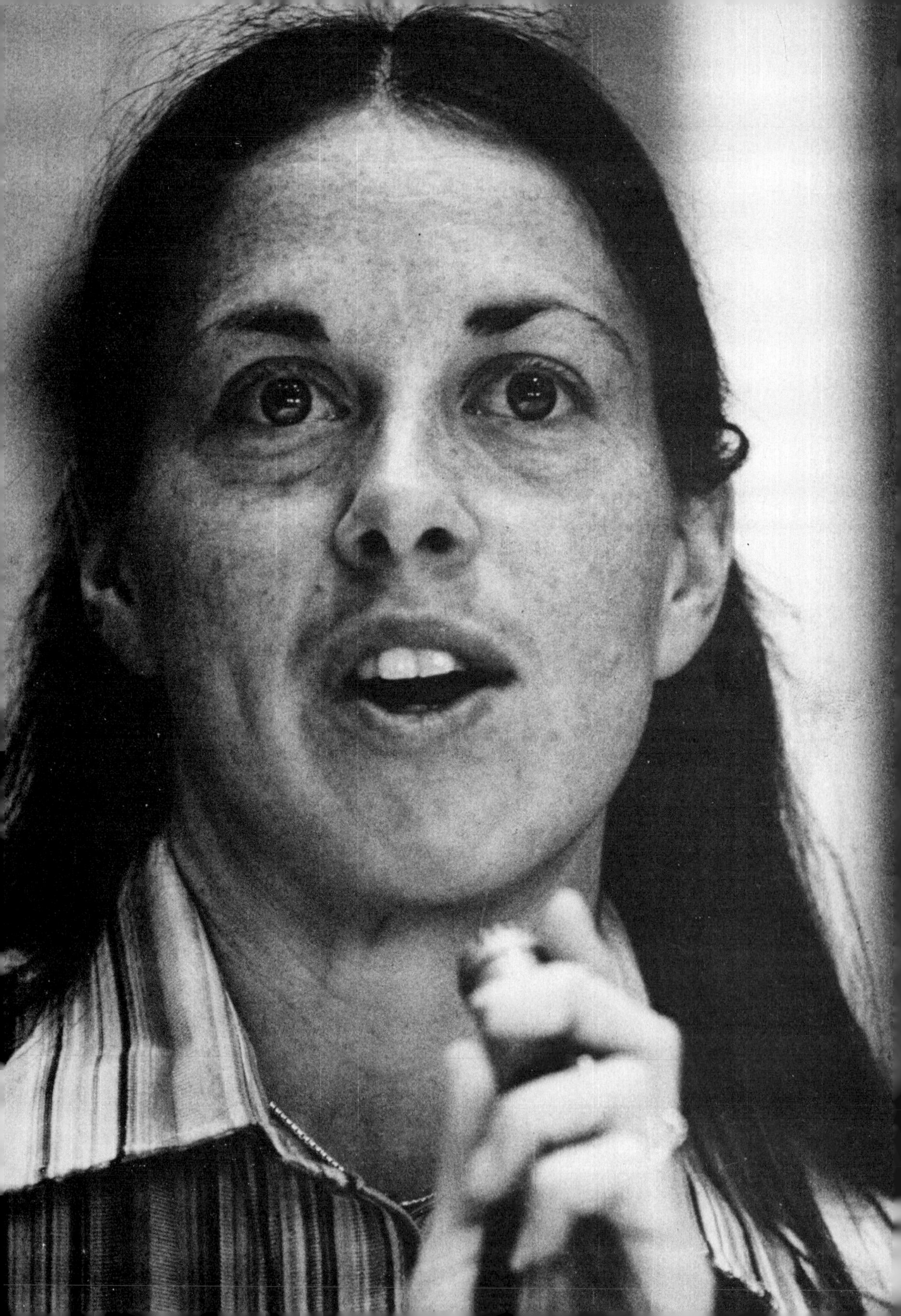

3

Coaching for Women

A coach's contributions: experience, knowledge, enthusiasm and the will to win

Jacqueline Hansen

I did not spend my last year in college in the usual program of classes. Instead, I enrolled in a single experimental course entitled "Search for Identity." By the end of the course, I had chosen to identify myself as "a runner." Few other interests in life attracted me with the intensity and discipline I found in running. Few other activities were so rewarding.

This "self-identity" was not defined overnight. Neither was it pre-destined from childhood. I chanced upon a sport I could play well, and I chanced upon a coach who helped me achieve lofty goals.

My exposure to women's running came so late in life and so haphazardly, I was quite unaware of other female athletes and totally naive about any existing women's sports programs in this country. In my limited knowledge, the only track-coaching of women was happening at Tennessee State, where Ed Temple trained the Cinderbelles. In 1964 and 1968, I watched the Olympic Games on television and followed results in the newspapers; in my mind, Olympic athletes were professionals and I could no more relate to them than I could to Billie Jean King.

Even though I watched and listened intently to the Games, I was not inspired to go out and run. Instead, I acquired knowledge to keep pace with my friends (all male) on the school track team. For boys, running it seemed was quite natural. They were encouraged and expected to participate in competitive sports from junior high school years on. For girls, such activities were unheard of. Small wonder that my interest in the track team amounted to no more than an occasional flirtation. I was always a mere spectator.

All through junior and senior high school, girls' sports took second position to boys'. For example, on a rainy day, the girls' P.E. classes typically listened to records while the boys played in the gym. Not only did we receive no encouragement to compete, we were blocked at every possible opportunity. Certain after-school sports were acceptable for young girls—sports like volleyball and such; but we played with other schools on a non-scoring basis. The emphasis was always on "fun" and "non-strenuous" activity. By the time I reached my senior year in high school, I was so inexperienced and poor in athletics, I avoided all sports, seeking safe haven in dance, marching band, and a meek attempt at tennis.

FROM GROUPIE TO RUNNER

Then a P.E. teacher at my high school, Dixie Griffin, made a breakthrough, establishing the first track and field class for girls in the Los Angeles City Schools system. I quickly made the transition from "track groupie" to "participant," based on nothing more than a slight aptitude for running in my physical fitness tests. I was far from being a star, but track class was challenging and a seed of interest was planted. Dixie's forte was the shot put, certainly not my best event. In fact, I never did find an event I excelled at in those early days (1966). Women were limited to sprinting dashes and doing certain field events, and I wasn't even good enough to compete in an all-city meet.

After high school, I attended junior college and later a four-year institution, but found very little in the way of coaching at either place. For example, at the junior college, the women's track and field class consisted of two 40-minute sessions per week less shower time, roll call, and passing period. Our instructor's specialty was golf, and mostly we studied for skills tests from a textbook. Nothing improved when I moved on to a four-year state college. Because I was the only one to sign up for track class, I was told to continue running as I pleased, that I could compete for the school when meets were available, and that I would receive class credit for work done—on my own.

Running was only secondary to my studies, but I persisted on my own, whenever the mood struck me. I became a fair-weather jogger. I often wonder how many other women like me were out there jogging, just needing a coach, some encouragement, some instruction.

I suppose the lack of coaching in the college system was due to several interrelated conditions. There was little call for a track team, because so few young women turned out to join one. On the other hand, few P.E. teachers seemed capable of coaching and developing a team. Furthermore, there was little opportunity to compete. Perhaps the absence of talented coaches was due to the fact that no talented female track athletes had advanced to coaching positions. It's difficult to coach while still competing, even if you're capable of teaching.

I don't regret my college years without a track team and a scholarship. It's conceivable that I might have burned out my interest in the sport had I been pushed through an intense track career early on. Instead, I benefitted from participating in a variety of events. When I finally did find a coach and began to train properly, it was from pure desire to excel and not to fulfill a scholastic commitment or to earn credits.

My meandering persistence in running finally found a channel when by chance I met the cross-country coach at Valley Junior College in Van Nuys, California. Had I graduated "on time" with my peers at Cal-State University Northridge, my chance meeting with Laszlo Tabori might never have taken place. Jogging around the athletic fields of CSUN, I met a woman runner one day, who introduced me to yet another woman runner—this one a real competitor—trained by an experienced coach.

Judy Graham's invitation to run with her and to train with Tabori and possibly even to compete for the Los Angeles Track Club was an overwhelming prospect at the time. I had no notion of pursuing running to such an extent, but out of curiosity I attended a workout. I was enough of a track buff to recognize and respect the likes of Chi Cheng, Una Morris, Martha Watson, and other notables on the LATC roster. I could hardly imagine joining *their* ranks. Laszlo was the middle-distance cross-country coach on the LATC staff. It quickly became obvious that to train with him, meant to compete *for* him. Also obvious was the exciting realization that it mattered not what caliber runner you might be, because Laszlo himself had become a champion the hard way—under the stern tutelage of the renowned Hungarian coach, Mihaly Igloi. Tabori seemed to take it as a personal pledge to let the nonstars have an opportunity to shine whenever the possibility arose.

Thus, I found myself running my first cross-country race in the California State Championships at Ventura, over a hard, "mountainous" course. I would hardly say I was "shining" that day—I barely finished, nauseous and aching in every muscle. The second time I ran a cross-country race, I fell down, stumbling from fatigue, got a sprained ankle, and did not even finish. It took me two months to gather the courage (and heal my ankle) to return to Laszlo's workouts after this trauma. From January of 1971 to the present, we count our "anniversaries" together. As he is fond of saying, it's a 50-50 contribution.

A COACH'S CONTRIBUTIONS

My contribution: time, effort, dedication. His contribution: vast experience and firsthand knowledge of the sport, given unselfishly. It's impossible to know what direction my energies would have taken me had he not directed them to the track. It never occurs to me that I might have made the wrong choice. My running career has been more than rewarding, even without records or trophies. And I have reaped more than my share of those.

Faced with the question of why I have gained so much success under Laszlo's training, I have to admit that I honestly don't know. I am aware of certain contributing factors: Laszlo observes no sex barriers among his athletes. We are trained alike, although at varying levels of speed, regardless of sex. In theory, men and women can run together in an interval workout. In reality, the only women I have known capable of interval training in this way have been Judy Graham and (more recently) Debbie Heald. On rare occasions, Laszlo puts me with a group of men to encourage me to run faster. Most of the time, I train alone—by choice. I'm convinced that my workouts are as hard as any of my teammates', male or female. And I think this lack of sexual discrimination helps to make Tabori's women runners strong.

Another contributing factor is the inherent difficulty of Tabori's workouts. Some say his top-notch athletes are simply the product of raw survival. Maybe yes, maybe no. Early on, Laszlo gained a notorious reputation for being a slavedriver—a reputation that has been hard to shake. It's part of his mystique. He *is* very demanding. Laszlo will accept any athlete willing to train consistently according to *his* methods and then he will do his utmost to help that athlete reach his or her potential.

In the beginning of his part-time coaching career, Tabori helped junior college athletes to improve enough in a two-year career to go on to university teams, sometimes on scholarships. Later he helped women like myself to train for AAU championship races. More recent, as mentor of the San Fernando Valley Track Club, he has helped cardiac rehabilitation patients, housewives, business people, children, anyone simply willing to learn to run. With the influx of such casual runners, training alongside his serious competitors, Laszlo's "slavedriver" image has mellowed. He has made a place for everyone at his track, and has found a method for each individual.

Sometimes I think Laszlo made the transition to long-distance coaching along with me. When I first came to him, I trained intervals three times weekly to be a middle-distance runner. In those days (1971-1973), Laszlo never trained anyone for distances beyond 5000 meters.

Both workouts and races were always intense, serious matters done to shouted commands like "dog eat dog" and "put the guts to it!" Only off the track did Laszlo seem at all "approachable." Eventually I discovered a warm, humane man whose pride ran deep—too deep to allow himself to "run for fun," to come out of his retirement. Retirement struck me as an odd note connected with running. I considered my newly-found way of life a healthy means of living out my years to the fullest. But for Laszlo, running under Igloi had been an all-consuming career that one day came to a halt. Now he was giving freely of himself to help others achieve extraordinary goals. So that once I took up marathon running, he accepted the double challenge of coaching longer events *and* women.

In the summer of 1972, while doing my usual off-day six-mile run on the dirt trails and grass fields of a flood-control basin, I met an older runner by the name of Monty Montgomery. He was usually accompanied by a block of runners on long, late afternoon and early Sunday morning street runs—something foreign to me; I knew nothing but track workouts and hour runs on grass. Watching these guys on their long runs finally touched my soul and I had to try it for myself. I don't know if Monty remembers the first time I tagged along with his group, but I always will. It was a daring venture out of my cage. Not knowing if I could keep up the pace, I memorized the streets as we went along, in case I had to retrace my steps alone. Instead, I found the gentle, even pace very pleasant; and the stories this man could tell made the run come alive. Monty provided my first inspiration to run a marathon and remains a personal hero to this day. I can only hope to be half the runner he is when I reach his age. (At seventy-two years old, he still runs marathons consistently near the three-hour mark.)

BEING COACHED FOR THE MARATHON

Other than a couple of long jogs that summer, my only training before my first marathon was a season of cross-country. Then, on a week's notice, I decided to attempt the Culver City Marathon in December 1972. I would never advise anyone to approach distance running the way I did. Laszlo certainly did not encourage this folly, but I must say he was very tolerant of my impulsive decision. After a long talk, he consented to my wishes, bestowing a strange blessing: "You are so very stubborn, I am sure you will go far." I didn't know whether to take this to mean I had a great future or that I'd go a fair distance in this race and drop out.

Whatever Laszlo intended with that statement, I am extremely grateful for his decision to let me pursue my own inner feelings about my running. At first, he reacted like any sensible coach and thought the idea of my running a marathon was preposterous. Yet, he let me know that he understood how it was eating away at me. He momentarily revealed his own lost dreams, saying there were things he wished he had tried as a runner, things he'd never know. The conclusion was that I should be free to try anything.

I won't launch into another "my first marathon" essay. The world doesn't need any more. But I will say that "cherished" experience was a painful one. In spite of Joan Ullyot's theory about women never experiencing "hitting the wall," I ran into *something* between 20 and 22 miles that slowed me to a crawl. But finishing my first one and winning the women's division provided enough positive reinforcement to make me say "Next time..." only moments after I'd said "Never again."

I stated that Laszlo seemed to make the transition to distance running along with me. Once it was obvious I was an addicted marathoner, he was forced to modify my workouts. The first change was double workouts to increase overall weekly mileage. Next, the hour jogs "only on grass" had to go. In their stead came one-and-a-half to two hour runs on the streets combined with trails when possible. The only things that remained the same were the interval workouts, two or three times a week. In addition to the usual 2½ miles warmup, 15 x 100 "Shakeups," and lots of stretching exercises, my workouts consisted of longer and more plentiful sets on the track, covering distances ranging from 150 meters to 6 laps at a time with "interval" rests of 2 laps easy between sets. These workouts could total as much as 15 miles or more over a 2½ to 3 hour period.

Though I do not pretend to suggest that Laszlo's methods are the "only" way to train, I do believe that the combination of speed and distance work to prepare for a marathon seems essential and consonant with the various training methods used by most successful marathoners.

I know that as much as Laszlo may secretly yearn to recreate in our club workouts the intensity and absolute dedication of his own competitive days under Igloi, he has come to terms with the reality of coping with a group of independent, self-sufficient Americans, including many who are content simply to fit some exercise or limited competitive goals into their busy schedules. He has adapted remarkably well. What else can he do? For me, the most recent reward of my relationship with my coach is that he—and his wife, Kata—have taken to the roads, running distance themselves.

4

Being Your Own Coach

You can do it all yourself: forming training schedules, learning from others, racing

Nina Kuscsik

Not every woman runner needs a coach. Some women appreciate the direction offered by a coach, but often none is available. Others prefer to learn by doing. Perhaps the philosophical milieu that propels a woman into the running world biases the formation of her running lifestyle.

I spoke to a woman who ran competitively during college and continues to be prominent in marathon events. When I asked her about her training schedule she said she ran easy mileage in the morning and got her workout from her coach every afternoon at the track. When I asked if she had any idea what type of workout she would receive on any given day, she replied, "None at all, I let the coach do all the work for me."

Ursula, the receptionist at my dentist's office, is a runner. She has been at it over two years, and averages 30 miles a week. "At first I found it hard to get up at six in the morning to run so I only ran weekends and one night during the week," she said. "Now I love the quiet and beauty of the early morning and it starts my day off just right." And when it's time to make our routine checkups with the dentist, she fills me in on her running progress. "I changed routes a while ago, because I found some roads without any dogs," she said, "but there were more hills, and I had a tenderness in my calf for a long time. Finally I reduced my running to the track until the tenderness went away."

Whenever I see Ursula in her Clark Kent existence, it reminds me that there is no great secret to training for long distance running. Ursula's running has become as basic to her activities of daily living as brushing her teeth. Meanwhile, she is following one of the basic principles of long distance training: consistency. Ursula laughed when I mentioned to her the idea of having a coach.

Most of us fit in between these two extremes. How often I have heard, "Running is something that is my very own. It belongs only to me. I like running by myself. It bothers me when I can't run." This personal commitment to running can be race-oriented or not and can allow for the involvement of a coach—if the runner's integrity for pursuing the sport for her own satisfaction is not interfered with.

We all march to a different drum. I look upon my running as the most independent workmanship of my life. And my evolution from this course of study into myself and life continues. The freedoms in this area are endless; to run or not to run, to run fast or slowly. I can be as flighty in my goals as my needs require, can change priorities at a whim, make no commitments except to myself. My inner life is rich. I am strong. I have a need to be my own coach. At the same time I'll listen to advice from those I respect.

Experiment of One

In 1967, as the mother of two toddlers, I sought a convenient method of remaining physically fit. After competing in various sports over fifteen years, I wanted to feel physically good about myself without having to plan travel time to a sports facility, meet practice times inconvenient to me, and spend time with sophisticated equipment. Small wonder I took to running. Get the babysitter and go. One-half hour free time meant one-half hour running time. No travel time, no traffic jams, no waiting for practice time for my team. And in my running half-hour I reaped more benefits than equal time in any other sport could give me. Of course that's still true today and the reason that so many have turned to the earthy rejuvenation that comes from running.

I built up mileage, and after running the only race I knew about, the Boston Marathon, I learned from other runners that there were local and shorter events in my own area. I soon joined a women's running club, where I was the oldest member of the active team. (The supportive team for cake sales and transportation were my teammates' mothers and closer to me in age.) I raced with the team and occasionally practiced with them. We did speed workouts together; they were scheduled for 6 p.m. and were one-half hour driving distance away. So the children would eat an early dinner and off we would go to practice. While I gained much from the workouts, there was something wrong. I chose to run for fitness and while improvement was satisfying, there I was once again, battling traffic to make scheduled group workouts. My attendance at practice grew more sparse, and I began to feel guilty. "Didn't I want to improve?" and "Where was my team spirit?" were questions I asked myself. After a lot of thought I realized I ran to run, to feel good, to be fit, to know that I could run the next day and the next. I knew that my running had become something that was more my own than anything I ever had or wanted in life and whatever level of running I could bring myself to by my own doing was the level I would aspire to and be happy with. I would not seek any more.

I stopped practicing with the team, though I continued to run with them in competitions. Soon I learned that most distance runners were self-coached and were generous with advice when asked. So I became, as Dr. George Sheehan says, "an experiment of one." I learned much by trial and error and I am still learning. Most recently I've learned that no one can be superwoman all year round. My biological clock parallels that of the bear. I function better in the heat of the summer, so I no longer try to be in great shape during the winter months. I take off for a few weeks (not completely), skip many races, build up my mileage gradually, and find that my approach to the remainder of the year's running is vigorous.

TRAINING

A brief consideration of the top women distance runners suggests that we still have a long way to go to find the ideal combination of emotional and physical characteristics and the most effective method of training that would produce a single route to top performance in all runners. Training methods, attitudes and mileage vary from runner to runner, but most simply the way to train for running is to run. And the most benefit is to be derived from following the basic principles of consistency, adaptation to overload, and recuperation.

The human body is made to improve with use. Any program of consistent running will result in improvement. An endurance base is established through regular running and the body becomes stronger to meet additional demands. Improvements seem to come in spurts, but what is responsible for the gains is the regular dose of running.

To overload is to stress the body beyond its current abilities. To constantly overload is to produce a tired and possibly injured athlete. But if the body is allowed adequate time for recuperation, it can overcompensate and become stronger. This gradual adaptation to stress can and should be a part of the general philosophy of training, regardless of the distances and speeds used. This adaptation does not occur immediately; it is a slow process measurable by weeks or months.

The basic ingredients for a runner are endurance, stamina, and speed. Pure speed is largely determined genetically and does not concern itself with the delicate balance of keeping the workload within the body's ability to provide oxygen to burn fuel for energy.

At the point that the runner exceeds her maximal aerobic capacity and begins to run anaerobically she begins to build up lactic acid. The lactic acid cannot be reprocessed without oxygen so it accumulates in the muscles. It becomes the limiting factor in a runner's performance as the accumulation progressively impairs the muscle's ability to contract. The difference, then, is that if one runner can run aerobically at 6:30-per-mile pace and another marathoner hoping to stay with her also runs at 6:30 pace but does not have the same maximal aerobic capacity and so maintains this pace by running anaerobically, the second runner will accumulate lactic acid. This will progressively reduce her performance level while the first runner continues to run even pace and aerobically. So our greatest goal when training for endurance and stamina events is to strive for increasing the maximal speed at which we can run aerobically. This is the goal of endurance or aerobic conditioning.

Base Training

A runner can attempt her first marathon after completing base training. This consists solely of building mileage. Let's look at some of the limiting factors to building optimum mileage. The cardiovascular system may be ready, but the body mechanics are not. Tendons and joints must be given time to adapt to the demands of running. At this level, a runner may benefit most by skipping days during the week, running perhaps two days with one day off to insure adequate recuperation. For the veteran runner a more real limiting factor is finding the time to put in the mileage.

Making Time to Run

Not having a coach and specific group workouts allows for more flexibility in your running schedule. Although this should be an advantage, it takes some discipline and continual shuffling of priorities and motivation to implement workout plans. Seventy miles a week at eight minutes a mile breaks down to an hour and 20 minutes a day. If you run a twenty-mile and a twelve-mile workout each week, the other days of running will take less than one hour. Splitting the daily mileage into two sessions is fine for keeping up the mileage as long as at least two of the longer runs are kept intact. The cardiac efficiency and muscle adaptation developed by these long runs cannot be achieved any other way. I find that alternating daily mileage not only helps my running but breaks up routines that may become monotonous.

At some point in her training every runner inevitably finds herself lacking the energy either to sustain or increase mileage. If this happens to you, you may find that you've been trying to maintain a pace that is too fast to run each day, or you may find that you've been getting in your mileage at the expense of rest time. You can cheat on sleep occasionally and get away with it, but if cutting sleep to get in planned mileage becomes a habit and the result is a lower energy level, you should re-examine your goals. Chronic fatigue precludes enjoyment of your running time and makes you more susceptible to injury, and will eventually impede performance. When I find myself in this situation, I remedy it by cutting mileage and making sleep a higher priority.

The Warm-Up

In addition to running time, an allotment is necessary to prepare the body for running and to cool-down the body after the run. The traditional gym class "warm-up" was basically a cardiovascular preparation for activity. Runners can incorporate this warm-up into their actual run by starting the run at a slightly slower pace. Generally 6-9 minutes are sufficient for this warm-up, and the production of sweat usually signals that the completion of this phase is near. Additional time before running should be utilized for relaxing the muscles and then stretching. Warm muscles stretch better so ideally a few minutes of slow jogging should be done before stretching. The how's and why's of stretching are not within the scope of this chapter but have become increasingly important in maintaining flexibility and prevention of injury.

The Cool-Down

The cool-down after running is pretty much the same as the warm-up but in reverse. How many times have you returned from running with just enough time to shower and dress; and when you come out of the shower you find that you are still sweating and as hot as before? That's because your body has not had adequate time to cool down. If you're really lacking time you can start your cool-down in your last mile by running a little slower. Otherwise, stop running before reaching your final post-run destination and walk some. This assists your body in returning to its pre-exercise level and helps prevent muscle stiffness. After a few minutes breathing returns to normal, heart rate resumes a level near the pre-exercise rate, and you can go through the post-run stretching and relaxation exercises.

I try to make productive use of my cool-downs. If I'm returning home after the completion of my run, I'll use that passively active period to pickup around the house, sweep the floor, or vacuum. After a long run in the summer, my favorite cool-down is mowing the lawn. It not only stretches the hamstrings and calves but seems perfectly paced for my cool-down needs.

WHAT WE WANT FROM THE MILEAGE

Unless you are planning to run your races with someone who will pace you or will work together with you, you should be mentally prepared to race alone. If you are preparing for an all-women's race, you will most likely not be paced. To race alone, you want to have a good feel of your body's timetable for distribution of energy. The best time to learn about your body and the changes it undergoes during long runs is when you run alone. Once running distances of up to twenty miles become comfortable rather than marathons in themselves, I think it's good to leave the watch home or use it only to mark what you've done, not to pace yourself. One learns much more in hindsight. Instead of trying to run a marked mile on your course in a certain time, you may elect to mark the time it takes you to run a certain mile. Then you can concentrate on relaxing, retaining momentum, stride rate, and stance. The last piece of the puzzle will be your pace. Changes inside your body can be observed on these long runs. Last year I learned that all was fine for the first two hours of my runs. Then I got hungry, followed about twenty minutes later by a brief feeling of nausea, then a few minutes later by tiredness. As I continued to run, I would become more comfortable. With each successive long run I would observe the same pattern. When the symptoms recurred during the marathon race, I had no fear of them knowing they would pass and were not disaster signals.

Running alone is a good time to notice your breathing habits. Most runners breathe in and out, and I think too much is made of sophisticated breathing techniques. If you develop particular problems that you might relate to your breathing, you will want to read up on this area. Breathing should be rhythmic, usually inspirations taking a slightly longer count than expirations. At times you may find that your stride rhythm and your breathing rhythm are the same. It has a nice efficient feeling. I believe it is just a phase of that particular run and you can no more hold on to that breathing pattern than you could catch the wind. Invariably soon after you become conscious of this rhythm it begins to disintegrate, much the same as when attempting to count your own respirations, they become unnatural.

Relaxation techniques can be experimented with. Tightness in the shoulders is one of my problems, so to relax them I alternate shrugging and relaxing for several moments. One of my favorites to relax shoulders (I hate to do this when running alone where anyone may have even so much as telescopic access to me, but I don't mind at all doing it in a race) is to drop my wrists and let them dangle and at the same time drop my jaw, sort of like a puppet with loose strings. You will find it impossible to have tight shoulders when your jaw is dropped. Then I try to think of the movements of particular parts of my body. I do a forward rotation of my hips and pretend that I am advancing pubic bone first. I begin to notice changes in my arm movements; they are swinging through slightly lower. Next I relax and think only about the arm movements. This is especially interesting going up and down hills. I notice the changes in position that occur spontaneously. Do my arms cross my midline? I try to avoid that but allow my arms to swing across my body to the midline. This movement seems to be most efficient for me for long-distance running. Arms are used mainly for balance in long-distance running and arm movements usually conform to body build.

Sometimes I find myself in complete harmony with the environment. I feel effortless; there is no change in speed or effort but I am flowing. I try to memorize the feeling as if in doing so I could duplicate it at will. Where are my arms? How high are my legs swinging through? What is my stride rate? If you are fortunate enough to live near the beach you can check foot placement in the sand (substitute snow if you must). Your feet should land directly in front of each other, not on each side of a midline.

Did you ever run on the sand and find someone else's footsteps not yet washed away by the tides? I always consider this a great find. Generally the strides are longer than mine. I try to place my feet in the prints. If they are longer than my natural stride I begin to lift my legs higher to get more ground between steps. I go faster; print after print, because in order to match the longer stride I have picked up momentum. After a while I can't keep up the pace and I settle back into my own stride and compare the difference in stride length. I do this because I learn more about the relationship of speed to stride length. I do this because I learn more about the relationship of speed to stride length. It is natural that as you increase your speed your stride will get longer, so I don't think this is a change to work on. When I run on the track at 8:00-per-mile pace, I take about 88 steps per 110 yards. At a 6:00 minute pace I take about 69 steps. I don't think about it, but I do note the difference.

Sometimes when a runner gets tired, she will decrease her stride rate (because of tired hip flexors) and will try to compensate by increasing her stride length. This is counterproductive. I try to retain the cadence of my stride even going up hills. To remember this rule, many New York runners only have to remember being passed by Jim McDonough in a race. Jim is an ultramarathoner about five feet tall who races with a shamrock pinned to his right shoulder. As he passes you, you understand why he is known as "pitter-patter." Many times I've tried to match his small strides, but after a while I have to let up and he pulls away.

The pace of your daily run can vary from day to day as well as the distance. Also you can vary the pace within a run. Any changes in pace should be the result of a planned effort, rather than having to drag one day because you ran too hard the day preceding. These changes in pace give you more knowledge of how your body feels and how it functions at different speeds.

After weeks of accumulating mileage (mostly alone) I find I've become quite familiar with the working processes of my body. About that time I usually find that my training pace has dropped 15-30 seconds per mile, regardless of the distance run. Even in the dissociative state ("the wandering mind syndrome") my pace remains lower.

TRAINING GOALS

No one could say this in more simple terms than does Ron Daws in *The Self-Made Olympian.*

> To understand training, one must realize that in a strict sense the primary goal of the distance runner's training is not to make him faster. He wants to get to the finish line faster, but that doesn't require more speed as much as it does stamina . . . Stamina is the ability to run relatively fast, relatively far. It differs from endurance which is exercising moderately for great periods of time. If I wanted to break the record for running from Los Angeles to New York, I'd want endurance. If it was the 10 kilometer world record, I'd want stamina, and if I wanted the 100 meter record, I would need speed.

If you are training for a specific race that is longer than any distance you've already run, your highest priority is your endurance condition. If you know you can go the distance, then the question is how fast? Stamina and speed can play a significant role in training to race.

ANAEROBIC TRAINING

Running for speed is the opposite of aerobic running. Any pace faster than maximal aerobic pace is speed work. This type of running prepares you for running at a faster pace. Many theories abound on speed work, but all of them are aimed at building a tolerance for anaerobic running. The theory is that the body can be taught to increase its ability to withstand oxygen debt and that the maximal anaerobic capacity of the runner can be developed through speed training. Arthur Lydiard proposes that following his base program of aerobic training, 8-10 weeks of anaerobic running three times weekly (includes hill and track periods) will develop a runner's anaerobic capacity to its maximum.

Under Lydiard's cyclical approach to peak performances he begins with weeks of endurance work followed by a transition period of six weeks of hill training. This is his runner's first venture into anaerobic training and the purpose of this type of resistance training is to convert the endurance into stamina and power. When Lydiard-trained runners finally approach the track for race preparation, they begin with capitalizing on their strong points, endurance and stamina. The track training evolves from a beginning of high volume, relatively slow speed with short rests to faster, shorter workouts with more rest and finally to fast workouts with little rest.

The goals of speed work are to develop the body's anaerobic capacity and to develop speed. Intensive anaerobic workouts will not necessarily develop speed but will build a capacity for anaerobic exercise. Shorter and lighter workloads (Arthur Lydiard suggests fast relaxed running for 100-150 meters with a three-minute recovery) with longer recoveries can help develop speed. Other distances run should not be faster than race pace and usually a few seconds slower. For marathon runners race pace may be considered their best 10,000-meter time. When repetitions are lessened and recovery time increased, you can calculate race pace from your best time at a shorter distance. A classic example would be 20 x 440 or 5 x 1 mile (with half-distance recovery), where your pace would be set according to 10,000-meter pace. For further sharpening or training for shorter distance races a 10 x 440 with equal-distance recovery, can be run at a pace a few seconds slower than your best two-mile time.

Time trials are another form of anaerobic training that are of value. Rather than running and recovering and then running again, a time trial strings together the mileage into one continuous run. Pace here becomes extremely important. Road runners frequently jump into a short distance race and call it a time trial, but it is advantageous to do time trials alone on the track where you can concentrate on evenness of pace rather than aim for a good time at the finish.

Everything you read about speed should be adapted to your own needs. A fatigue can be experienced in anaerobic training that differs from the fatigue of high mileage. Adequate recovery is extremely important. Listen to your own body. If your body is still tired two or three days after a speed session, you are probably running too hard. Speed work is an opportunity to learn pace and get to know your body and how it functions under anaerobic conditions. The exciting and important thing to remember is that speed work is not a race. The speed at which you do your anaerobic training depends on your basic abilities and your present level of conditioning. And just as you vary your efforts in aerobic training you can also vary your efforts in speed workouts.

LOS
ALAMITOS
MARATHON
MARCH 5, 1977

RACING

A road runner's racing program can become a scheduling nightmare if she takes every race as a serious effort. Racing often plays havoc with a training schedule. You cannot train hard and race hard. If your racing timetable calls for weekly races for a period of time, training must be eased. The hard work for any particular race should be done weeks before and fatiguing work the week before a race will not positively affect the outcome of the performance.

If you are gearing yourself for a significant race, mental preparation becomes important. This is the time to take yourself seriously. If your preparation has been consistent and planned well, you should think positively about your race effort. The beauty of the road race is that anyone who achieves her goals becomes the winner. Marathons used to be rather pleasant experiences for me at least until the 20 mile mark—sort of like training but with many other runners to talk to on the way. However, as the competition gets keener and my own abilities improve I find myself "working" the entire race. Not working in the sense of pushing harder, but rather directing effort to monitoring pace, effort, the mind, and later the discomforts. I try to control negative thoughts when someone passes me. I try to remember that running uphill is as uncomfortable for everyone as it is for me.

Many runners find it reassuring to know as many race conditions as possible. Will there be splits? At what points? Is there a wind factor? At what points? It helps if you can run over the course before race day. If this is not practical, a ride over the course can give you a good feeling for it. You may choose to run up some hill that appears awesome, or one at a strategic point. Also, it helps to know the location of the finish line. If there are significant turns or markers along the course, you might take a little time to note at what mileage point they occur. If splits are to be given or mile markers posted this won't be necessary. If you don't mind computing in your head during the run, you can wear a watch and check it at the mileage checkpoints. Some runners don't want to be bothered by math problems and they write down on their arms the splits they plan to run. I always wonder what happens when they're off pace. How do they make adjustment for the next split?

The habit of stretching before you run will remind you to allow time for adequate warmup and stretching before competition. The shorter the race, the longer the warmup, because the starting pace of the shorter race is that much faster and the body must be ready to take on the immediate demands of the race pace. You can be a little more elaborate in your pre-race warmup than you might be in training because you have already arrived at the race, have your clothes on to run, number pinned, and you have nothing else to do. Jog a little to warm up the muscles. Then do your stretching and finish with several minutes of slow running perhaps with a few short 50-100 yard pickups. If the warmup is completed within ten minutes of race time, your body will be ready to go at the gun. Because of the large starting fields it becomes increasingly harder to begin a race in the properly warmed-up condition, as so much time is spent saving your place among the starters.

When you finish a race, it is also important to cool down. Some races, because of their size and finish line layout, force you to come to an abrupt stop at the finish line. You are directed into a chute on the heels of another runner. You will breathe heavily, and may feel exhilarated but awful. The best thing that can happen at that point is for the chute to move quickly and release you to an area where you can continue to jog for another ten minutes. This aids the transfer of lactic acid for the muscles, lessening impending leg stiffness. Ten minutes of jogging will probably leave you feeling better than if you sat for the ten minutes while trying to rid your body of waste products.

The best way to run a good race is with consistent pacing. The effort needed to stay on a pace will change. At first you may feel that you are holding back; later no pace is comfortable. Tension mounts. This is when it helps to know the accurate distance to the finish line. Unless you have a particular strategy in mind and you feel you have a stronger finish kick than your competitor, it's wiser not to save anything for that final drive to the finish. That energy could be better used elsewhere and somehow the pace quickens anyway when the finish banner is in sight.

After finishing an important race successfully, especially a marathon, you should take a recovery period of 7-10 days. Some fast running can be done but over short distances. Sometimes the prouder you are of your accomplishment the worse you feel a few days later. This seems to be a normal response after the exhilaration of achieving a goal. It happens in areas outside of sport but with us there is a reorganization going on within our bodies as they recover and at the same time an adjustment to make from the tension of the pre-race days and in setting new goals. This is known as post-race depression and may last a few days.

Fatigue

In the race situation, feeling tired must be treated differently than in the training situation. You may feel tired long before your performance level drops. Sometimes to *feel* tired is not actually to *be* tired. If, in the hours before a significant competition you feel fatigue, it can actually be a sign of appropriate nervous tension. That feeling of fatigue is absent following the race and for the remainder of the day.

Tiredness before a training run is often erased once the blood sugars are elevated after a few miles of running. On the other hand, sometimes you feel good at the start of a workout only to have to drag through those last few miles. Why this happens often defies explanation and you should not judge yourself too harshly. The next day can be as different as your mood when a rainy morning turns to a sunny afternoon.

Sometimes there is a fatigue that lasts for several days. It is difficult to know whether it is psychological or physiological. Usually a diversion from the ordinary will suffice in bringing back energies. Skipping a workout or cutting one short will give you some time to spend doing one of your other favorite activities. Perhaps sleeping late or going to the theater or shopping or having a relaxed dinner with an old friend will be the change you need. Occasionally I find that simply running on new courses where I have no idea of the mileage or route will revive me.

ON KEEPING A DIARY

Many runners keep a diary that records much of the technical and subjective information of their running life. It becomes a motivational factor as an exciting story of increasing abilities for mileage and lessening fatigue. My running diary showed me there was no need to take the day off before race day. If I want to take a day off now, I usually do it two days prior. This is learned only by trial and error for each individual, but the diary documents previous experiences for you to draw on. It also proved to me that no running for several days because of illness did not matter in the overall training program. Other women found by keeping the diary that during some months menstruation can sneak up on them. The situation was validated by remarks like "feeling great" during a sparkling workout or competition one or two days before menses. Periodic recording of weight and resting pulse rate (before you rise in the morning) show changes that can be related to performance. You can record your planned run and what you actually did or you can just record your actual run and assume that was your plan. In this case any deviations from your plan should be recorded; e.g., "planned 8 miles but train was late and only did 6," or "planned 10 but felt awful; cut it to 6."

Also, plan to record anything that affected your planned pleasure or pain level. Perhaps you completed the planned workout but developed a stitch or your legs felt heavy, or the run felt better each mile and you felt light as a feather. It's a good idea to note any changes that may affect your biomechanics such as running on sand, snow, dirt, or wearing new shoes. A diary made in the form of a calendar clearly shows progress and weekly mileage totals can be referred to easily.

EXTRAS

Running with Others

Sometimes in training it's enjoyable to run with others. It's good to agree on pace ahead of time. Best of all is training occasionally in an area where lots of runners train, perhaps in a park or on a lake front. For example, at the reservoir in Central Park in New York City there are hundreds of runners circling two loops just under two miles each. They are there every night between 5 and 8 p.m. You can elect to run with someone for part of your run. You can run someone else's pace merely by catching them and following them or sticking with them when they pass you. When you've had enough let go. I try to run with people my size and make comparisons in style.

Learning from Others

Reading helps understanding immeasurably, and many good books about running are now available to us. Usually others helped us pick out our first pair of running shoes. Before the days of carbohydrate-loading I learned from other runners to take sugar during the run, not before, and found it effective when taken at regular intervals during the last half of a marathon.

Comparison

When you admire the performance of another woman runner, don't think that if you follow her training program you can run like her. Take into consideration the other runner's age, physical build, lifestyle, and running experience. Then try to discover how she trained when she was at your level, and adapt that information into your running program.

Improvement

An athlete following a consistent program will continue to improve her fitness level and her performance level. It takes several years to establish an endurance base. The tremendous potential for improvement makes women's running the exciting sport that it is now. Each time a world record is broken, serious runners wonder about their own ultimate goals and take some time to re-evaluate them. Dr. Joan Ullyot says in *The Complete Marathoner*, "Everyone who lowers the record to a new standard makes us, too, realize our potential and run faster or farther than we ever believed we could—until someone older, or heavier, or more awkward than ourselves shows us the way."

The Last Extra

Running well, like practicing good medicine, is an art as well as a science. The art is a careful blending of physical background, basic speed, proper training, and motivation. We have a smorgasbord of levels at which we can run and/or compete and we can interchange them throughout our life as our needs and desires change. We are free to experiment with different mileage quotas and with intensities of speed work if we choose to do speed work at all.

Arthur Lydiard has said, "I believe most men and women go through life never knowing what it is to be really fit. They never know that vigorous feeling of well being, the unlimited sources of energy, the morale boost of never being really tired."

Being fit exudes an energy that tells us that being fit and being women are congruous. The activity of distance running is of a very personal nature. Today's woman allows herself to probe without restrains into who she is, and when she reaches that center through her running experiences she has become her own prototype. Then she can most freely decide what satisfactions she will derive from her running.

SCHEDULES

Here is a brief sampling of schedules. The long weekly runs are important to progress and keeping your aerobic fitness. A runner doing speed work two or three times weekly should lessen her weekly mileage, but keep the long run. It's best to have a training plan and deviate from it when your body tells you. For beginning runners mileage should be increased at a rate no higher than ten percent weekly.

Total Mileage	Mon.	Tues.	Wed.	Thurs.	Fri.	Sat.	Sun.
40	6	2	5-8	4	8	–	12-15
70	6	10	6	12-15	6	10	18-20
100	12	8	6+12	15	6+8	3+10	20

BONNE BELL
83
10 000 METERS

5

Dealing with the Family

How to find the time: cooperative babysitting, getting to workouts, taking the kids

Ellen Clark

Any woman who has a family to care for, a house to manage, and who still wants to embark on a running program will soon discover it's tough going. However, I'm here to give hope and to tell her that it can be done. It's not always easy, but I'm living proof that "where there's a will, there's a way." If a woman wants to become physically fit or if her goals are to compete in races and improve her times, it is possible to fit running into a hectic family lifestyle.

If a woman wants to run, my advice to her is *don't get bogged down in excuses*, such as "my kids won't let me" or "I have too much housework" or "I don't have enough time." If I had dwelled on all the potential reasons for not getting started, I probably would have never made it out the door in the first place. So, go forth! Delay no longer. Do it.

Once the decision has been made to run, then it becomes a matter of scheduling and dealing with the family in a cooperative spirit. I've devised a few loose rules, and perhaps some of them will help wives and mothers who happen to be runners. The rules are as follows: (1) be flexible, (2) be willing to compromise, (3) keep your running in perspective, (4) plan ahead, and (5) be understanding.

BE FLEXIBLE

The first rule is "be flexible." I have two children: Willie is five and Teresa eight. Also, my husband Bill runs. I must schedule my runs when the kids are in school, when Bill can watch the kids or when I can get a babysitter. Of course, I cannot always count on any of these arrangements. Babysitters get sick, have commitments of their own or (this has happened many times) they have forgotten all about having to babysit. Children get sick and cannot go to school and your idea of a nice 10-miler in the hills goes down the drain.

Bill is receptive to the idea of watching the kids while I run but sometimes he is late getting home from work; or on the weekends he may want to run with his friends. I can't just say, "Well, I'm going to go run at 9 a.m. and that's final!" I try to be as flexible as I can. I plan my running around Bill's on weekends. He has to run early in the morning or after 5:30 p.m. He cannot run during my mid-morning "prime time" when I'm fully awake and the day is fresh and cool. So, if Bill wants to get in a long run Saturday or Sunday at a certain time that's fine. I'll wait until he gets back and run at the less desirable noon or mid-afternoon or I'll get a babysitter if the budget allows.

My rule of "being flexible" was tested to its fullest when I embarked on my long road to fitness. Willie was a tiny baby and Teresa was three. Bill had his usual 45-minute commute to work, was going to night school, and was also running. Our mornings were on split-second timing. One foul-up and the whole show came to a stop. Bill would get up and run at 5:15. He'd get me up after his run and I'd run while he was in the shower, but I'd run no more than fifteen minutes so I could get back and fix breakfast and pack a lunch. With Bill successfully out the door, both kids would wake up and it was time to give Willie his bottle and Teresa her breakfast.

If either Bill or I overslept in the morning, I'd forget the running. I would wait until 9 p.m., after Bill's running or school, after dinner, and after tucking the kids in bed. It took all my will power to plod two slow miles around the neighborhood in the dark and cold, but I was motivated to get in shape. I kept up my running during the week and welcomed the weekends when I could run in the wonderful sunshine.

In families where the wife has a career and she desires to run, the matter of flexibility is even more important. Her husband may be able to take over some household chores and childcare, so she can run near home. Perhaps the woman can also squeeze in a workout during lunch time or on her way home from work. If the husband and wife put a little thought to the subject and are willing to run when the opportunity presents itself, I'm sure it is possible for both to get in their daily runs.

COMPROMISE

As my children got older, running became somewhat easier. Nursery school, and then kindergarten became my babysitter.

I have learned how to be a little selfish because running is a selfish activity. The running I do is mine. Mine alone. It has opened a whole new dimension to my life. Yet this self-directed activity cannot be done at the expense of my family. I can afford to be selfish but not too selfish. There is a delicate balance and here is where the compromise comes in.

An example of where I compromise is in the amount of volunteer work I do at Teresa's school. Anyone who has children in grade school knows how easily one can get roped into various projects. I'm sure the school would be happy to have me volunteer every day, but I compromise with them. I give them *some* of my time, but not *all* of it. I'm careful to set aside time for my running.

I use the art of compromise with my husband. Not long ago, Bill did not want to go to a 20-mile race in Sacramento, but I did. So, we worked it out. I went to the race with friends and he played with the kids all day. Then he was free the following weekend to go to a race without dragging us along.

IN PERSPECTIVE

For my third rule, the key word is "perspective." It's important to keep running in perspective and not let it take over my life. Once a person is caught up in the sport, the temptation is to read every page of track material around, talk running every available minute, leave sweaty running clothes all over the house, and talk splits and times to family acquaintances and friends who aren't into running.

It's okay to be enthusiastic about the sport but a woman must be careful not to overdo it.

I put running very high on my list of priorities; something that I want to do every day, but it isn't the only thing I enjoy. I like giving piano lessons, studying and reading about current events, playing baseball with the kids, taking history classes, and numerous other activities. I like to look on my running as a hobby, something I enjoy immensely. I don't mind being identified as "Ellen the Runner" (in fact, it's quite complimentary). But I am more than a one-dimensional person: I'm a wife, a mother, a reader, a fair pianist, a good seamstress, and I am a runner, too.

PLAN AHEAD

Without rule four, planning ahead, the woman runner can throw flexibility, compromise, and perspective out the window because she won't get out the door in the first place. If the woman has not made arrangements with a babysitter or husband, she will not be able to run. It's as simple as that.

Now, how does one go about planning for runs? For myself, I make out a chart. The chart usually covers 8 to 12 weeks. I pencil in the races I want to run, then Bill and I decide what workouts I should do for one week. I like to fit in a hill workout, a track workout, and a long run interspersed with easy runs. From the chart, I can plan when to get a babysitter and when to run with friends. I can also look ahead to races and start thinking about what we'll do with the children on that day. There are various ways to take care of the children for both workouts and races. First, I'll cover workouts, then races, because they both have their own special problems.

Getting to Workouts

There are numerous babysitting arrangements that will get the lady runner out the door for her training run. The most popular is the teenage babysitter. A drawback is that most teenagers can only babysit after school. Therefore, your running is confined usually to midafternoon. As a birthday gift to me when the children were very small, Bill said I could get a babysitter once a week so I could do a long run. He never stipulated when this ongoing present would end so my birthday present has continued for five years. In fact, 4 p.m. Tuesday has become a tradition when many of my friends join me for a long run that day.

Another drawback to teenage sitters is that it is sometimes difficult finding one who is willing to work on a regular basis and at a specific hour. When we moved to our present neighborhood, I talked to mothers in the area to get their recommendations on good sitters. I then tried several sitters and got their recommendations on more sitters. I soon had a whole list of names on which to draw.

I've learned that teenagers usually aren't happy about sitting for less than 30 minutes so I make it worthwhile for her by running 90 minutes or so. Also, I figure if I'm not too chintzy with the cash, she'll be willing to come back!

I never assume that my sitter will show up on Tuesday at 4,

so I always call Monday and ask if she is coming. I've decided it was much easier on my nerves to make the phone call than to be left stranded Tuesday afternoon, which has happened numerous times.

COOPERATIVE BABYSITTING

Besides the teenage babysitter, there are the cooperative sitting services. Co-ops are ideal for mothers of preschool children. I wish I could have used the co-op when Willie was a baby, but there were none in our old neighborhood. The advantage of a co-op is that, because it is composed of mothers in your area, you always have a willing adult to take care of your child. It all works very simply: If you use the service for an hour, you must babysit another person's child in your home or theirs for an hour. The co-op bookkeeper keeps track of all transactions.

No money is exchanged and you can fit in a run any time a mother is free to babysit. For people on a budget (and who isn't these days) the co-op is a good idea. In Los Altos, there are numerous co-ops. One is connected with the Association of American University Women. It has forty members and was organized ten years ago. For information on co-ops in your area, call the local elementary school, the AAUW, or find out by word-of-mouth. Babysitting co-ops are not listed in phone directories.

A less desirable way of obtaining childcare is to simply ask a neighbor to babysit. I'm reluctant to do this, though, unless it's an emergency. I don't like taking advantage of other people and somehow I always have that feeling when I ask a neighbor.

The worst method of handling the babysitting problem is rounding up the kids and the toys and taking them with you to the track where you do your workout. I've done this when I've had to, but I never liked it. For one thing, the kids were bored after five minutes. Every time I circled the track one or the other would ask when it was time to go. I could never concentrate on my running because I was afraid one of the kids would fall off the bleachers or get in some kind of trouble. When Willie was a year old, he'd cry as I started a 440 because he thought I was running away from him forever!

Most (not all) of my babysitting problems were settled when Willie went to kindergarten and Teresa to third grade this year. New mothers will find they outgrow their need for sitters very slowly!

Mothers and Races

Races provide moms with many challenges, and not just in running them. Running is often easier than finding a babysitter at an early hour. Almost all races start at 9 or 10 on a Saturday or Sunday morning. I usually have to do a lot of fast talking to get a sitter to come at 6:30 or 7. It's a good idea to start calling potential babysitters a week in advance of a race, and then call them the day before as a reminder. Bill and I consider the expense as chargeable to entertainment, similar to going to a movie and dinner. We usually stop for breakfast and socialize with other runners. We can really run up a tab after being gone five or six hours; but none of our sitters will take Master Charge!

Coming home to the kids, they are genuinely interested in how we do and are especially interested in daddy's trophies. (I rarely get anything; my reward is the race itself!)

We like taking the kids with us to races if it is going to be a short race and if they can be in a safe area while we're running. I often ask some friend who isn't running if he or she would look after the kids. This works okay if it's a loop course and the start and finish are in the same spot.

This "asking a friend to babysit" reminds me of one of the reasons I got started in racing. I thought it would be much more fun out there running the race than staying behind and holding everyone's sweats and babysitting their kids!

We like taking the kids with us to races in San Francisco because there is so much to do after the races. We have had some funny experiences when we've taken the kids. During the days when I was trying to potty-train Teresa, she had trouble waiting longer than a minute to get to a toilet. So the solution was that we brought her potty-chair with us to races. We set up her chair near the bleachers at a track meet in Santa Barbara, and when Mother Nature called, Teresa had only ten feet to walk. Although our set-up might have appeared a little strange to some folks, most runners are used to taking advantage of toilets whenever and wherever they exist.

Taking the Kids

When the children come with us to races, it usually involves a great deal of preparation. The younger they are, the more junk you have to load in the car—diapers, bottles, toys, stroller, extra clothes, food, and running gear. It's a wonder we ever made it to races on time, after all the hassles of prerace car-loading. My advice to anyone with small kids is to allow more time than you think necessary and then you'll still just make it!

Though taking the children to races can be work, it's fun having them along. Every year Bill and I put on the Pacific Association 15-Kilo championship race in Los Altos Hills, Calif., and they help with the aid station. One of the drinks last year happened to be Body Punch, but little Willie kept referring to it as "Potty Punch." As a runner would approach the station, Willie would yell, "Potty Punch, Potty Punch here." The expressions on some of the faces of the runners seemed to say, "I'm drinking *what?!*"

With Bill and I co-race directors for the 15-kilo race, we've learned it's difficult enough to direct a race without worrying about providing for child care. Most races in which we compete do not have babysitting; however, sometimes I am surprised. The Avenue of the Giants Marathon during April in northern California, does provide a childcare center during the race. You can leave the kids; they'll be served lunch and "babysat," all for $5. For Bill and I, though, we had left the kids with friends in a "kid-swap" arrangement. The "kid-swap" is a marvelous way of getting away alone for a couple days. Bill and I cared for the children of our friends, the Pikes, for a weekend. Then the following weekend Barb and Herb took ours. It all worked out satisfactorily. They played together quite well and we didn't have to pay huge sums to a babysitter, either.

It is very important to think of the child and whether he or she will enjoy a race. To *make* a child watch a long race such as a marathon is ridiculous. Watching a marathon can be downright boring to a child. For the parents' mental health and the child's too, it is better to let the child stay with friends for a couple days or with a sitter if the marathon is near your home.

Unusual Solutions

There are other ways of having children cared for during races but these ways are a little unusual. I have a friend who used to run three-mile road races while pushing her son in a stroller. Winnie Jebian claims that she only had one stroller mishap when the baby fell out but most of the time her son really enjoyed moving rapidly! Procrastination has its benefits, though. Her three sons now are all too big for the stroller.

Run with your children if all babysitting methods fail. In my case, it means SSD (Short Slow Distance) because I don't receive much training benefit in a short jog, but they like it once in a while and it's fun for me to accompany them.

Age-Group Running

Running with your children leads me into the subject of age-group running where children from the age of four or five can run for a track club and compete in track meets and cross-country. Many parents are quite successful at getting their children involved with running in a positive manner. The child must be old enough to decide to take up the sport. A parent can set an example, but the motivation to run must come from the child. I've seen youngsters who were forced to run in their preteens. The child will lose interest and quit if he or she cannot meet the expectations of coach or parents. Because Bill and I enjoy running so much and because Willie and Teresa see the satisfaction we've gained from running, they may want to participate some time in the future.

With the comments I've made on children and sports, I want to emphasize that I believe in vigorous activities for children. It is wise to let the child experiment with many sports and to let the child's interest be the spark for his continued participation. Family harmony (at least in regard to sports) should then be easily achieved.

BE UNDERSTANDING

There are three situations where my fifth rule of "be understanding" comes into play: (1) The wife takes up running and the husband does not, (2) the wife or husband cannot run because of a running-related injury, and (3) the woman runner becomes famous for her running.

To this point, I have written mainly about the problems of husbands and wives who both run. What about the wife who takes up running alone? In some ways it is easier on a marriage for everyone in the family to be running rather than just one person. With the recent boom in running, though, it has become acceptable for women to be running. Many women have taken up the sport regardless of whether their husbands are running.

Once a woman gets involved in running, she will discover it takes a lot of understanding on her part to live with the fact her husband may not want to jump on the running bandwagon.

How, then, does a wife deal with this? I've come up with a few suggestions:

A woman does not get her husband interested in running by talking about running night and day. She also should tone down her talk about how slim and fit she feels, and how much better and less flabby he would be if he were out running. The desire to run must come from within. A wife can leave some good books on beginning running around the house (Dr. Kenneth Cooper's book, *Aerobics*, is a good one) or *invite* her husband to races.

Race directors often need help at aid stations or registration, and welcome volunteer help. A husband may want to try it himself after seeing others out there running. It isn't the end of the world, though, if he never likes running. The wife can still pursue her interest in running. But be careful about when and with whom she runs! A wife who runs only with one male companion can get herself in a lot of hot water with her nonrunning husband. The wife can insist the relationship with the other guy is platonic and a matter of convenience ("He lives around the corner...") but that may not end her husband's doubts. The husband may be resentful that he is being left out of the running or that his wife prefers the company of another man. The wife should determine if running exclusively with a male companion is worth the risk of alienating her husband and having him turn against the sport of running.

Nothing takes more understanding than living through an injury of your own or your husband's. This is especially true when the woman is feeling great and everything is clicking for her but it is not for her husband. It takes every bit of understanding to know how lousy her husband must feel both physiologically and psychologically.

Running becomes a habit; when you can't run it is exasperating. If your husband is injured and you are not, help him find answers to his injuries through books, physicians, running friends, or any means you can think of. Open yourself up to him. Let him talk out how he feels. Be a good listener. At the same time don't remind him of his injury all the time by saying, "how's the ol' injury coming along today, dear?"

The husband of a friend of mine has been injured for quite a while. My friend must be very careful not to play up her running or be "overexuberant" or boastful about her accomplishments. She doesn't want to make her husband feel any worse for not running.

I have been very lucky in that I have never had an injury. If I ever get one, I will hopefully restrain myself from punishing my family for my lack of running. My friend, Dave Himmelberger, had an injury a few years back that put him in a cast for a few months. He stepped in a hole and broke his ankle while running on the Stanford golf course. When his wife, Kathy, saw the cast she teased him with, "I hope you don't take this out on me!" It has been three years but Dave finally got back at Kathy. Dave has given her a "disability" where she has had to delay most of her running. She is pregnant.

THE FAMOUS WIFE

What happens in a family when the wife becomes famous for her running while the husband, to put it kindly, is not as well recognized by the public? Wouldn't this be a situation where a great deal of understanding is required by both husband and wife to cope with the problems of notoriety?

While Penny DeMoss is well-known in track circles, it took her second-place finish at the Boston Marathon with her spectacular time of 2:44:52 for race promoters and the media to take notice. She was the Tracy Austin of running, the new star on the scene. Suddenly she was barraged with telephone calls from race promoters asking her to come to this or that race. Newspapers were very interested in obtaining interviews. It got to the point where Penny was telling herself, "Please, not another interview!"

Although not many of us can expect to become world-class runners like Penny, it is interesting to see how the DeMoss family copes with success.

Some newspapers made a big deal out of the fact that Harold finished 17 minutes behind Penny at Boston. Yet Harold said it didn't matter where he finished in relation to Penny. He has run a 2:34 marathon as a master (when he was 40) and he feels that if he were motivated in that direction and if he desired to run faster than he is now, he could. Harold finds joy in simply training and picking a few favorite races to compete in. He feels that it shouldn't matter where he finishes in relation to his wife as long as he's satisfied with his performances. To illustrate his point he told the story of how some of his fellow Pan Am pilots have asked him after races, "Did Penny beat you this time?"

Harold says he answers them with, "Running is not pro football. No one beats any one. Penny just happened to get to the other end first. Anyone who runs is a winner."

Harold takes great pride in his wife's races. But what about those people who constantly refer to him as "Penny's husband or Mr. Penny DeMoss?" I asked, "Doesn't that get to you after awhile?" His response was, "Na!" Then Penny interjected, "What bugs him are the ones who ask 'how did your daughter run today?' "

Harold says there is no tension between Penny and him as a result of all the publicity. Yet, it can be a bother when it robs them of time for relaxation together. Race promoters are quite willing to invite Penny but not "Penny's husband" to races. Harold cannot always accompany Penny, anyway, because of his job. Penny says it takes a great deal of time going to various running events while keeping up with her work as a graphic artist. As an example of what they were talking about, Penny said she would be attending a high-altitude training camp in the Sierra this summer without Harold for a couple weeks. Harold says he won't be able to go because of flying commitments but may be able to squeeze in a weekend.

It was quite evident in talking with Harold and Penny that they do not take themselves all that seriously, that they can laugh about their present situation. Harold asked me if I had seen the movie, *A Star is Born.* Harold said, "In one sense that movie parallels our lives. When I met Penny, I was Kris Kristofferson and she was Barbra Streisand. I was the star on the descent. I ran my 2:34 marathon and my times weren't getting any faster. Penny, though, was on the ascent. I knew she had a three-hour marathon in her somewhere and she certainly has done that!" To my way of thinking it's both Harold and Penny's mature attitude toward the sport of running and their understanding of each other that helps them to cope so well with the pressures of being famous!

VACATIONS AND RUNNING

Bill and I never pass up the opportunity to be participants in running events while on vacation. Sometimes, the running event has been the focus of our trip. For example, I have been lucky enough to accompany Bill on his various track trips. I've seen him run in the Boston Marathon a couple times and watched him in the Olympic Trials in Oregon. We've been to various races all over California, and one trip that holds very fond memories was to the City to Surf Race in Sydney, Australia.

In the past, I've been a spectator on our "running vacations," but no longer. When we go to Tahoe, we run the Tahoe Relays. When we visit grandma and grandpa in Colorado, we climb Mt. Elbert or run the Pikes Peak Marathon. Our vacations aren't fun if we sit around relaxing.

One of our vacations that will go down as the least relaxing was our trip up to Mammoth Mountain in the heart of the Sierra. Along with three other families and a trio of babysitters, we rented two condominiums. In the morning the babysitters would watch all seven children while the ladies and men would go on "run-a-hikes." Our friend Tom Bache is credited with creation of this special sport, otherwise known as Demolition Running. For the run-a-hikes, a person dresses in normal running attire, then arms himself with a topographical map of all the trails in the area and sets off on an 8-15 mile journey on hiking trails that in the Back Packers Guide say three, four, or five day journey! Lish Bache and I would be gone as long as four hours and climb to elevations of 11,000 feet. The combination of running at altitude, picking our way over rough terrain and just being out there for hours without water was very taxing on the ol' bod. Seeing the guys come in after one of their "run-a-hikes" was a sight to behold. Bill looked more exhausted than if he had run a 2:22 marathon. He'd drag himself to a chair and sit and sit and sit. His tongue would be hanging out and we could hear faint whispers of, "Give me carbos, water, carbos." He would feel more human after he'd been replenished with his usual supply of pretzels, beer, and more pretzels.

I'm not suggesting that "run-a-hike" vacations are for everyone, but having the babysitters along was a great idea. We were able to do our running in the morning and in the afternoon go fishing, hiking, or swimming with the kids. I have never looked upon running as something I had to do on vacation to stay fit. Rather, the running has always been a part of the vacation itself and has remained a fun leisure-time activity.

If families want to continue running on vacation, I do not see this as a problem. There are races and running camps available or a person can simply get out of the car and run wherever he or she is vacationing. Running while on vacation offers me the opportunity to see other parts of the country on something more than a superficial level. I have more of a feel for the land than if I were whipping by in a car.

Throughout my running years, I have frequently heard the adage, "You get as much out of running as you put into it." I would have to modify that to, "My family gets as much out of running as I put into it." My running does not affect me alone. It affects my whole family and I believe it does so in many positive ways. First of all, the satisfaction I derive from running shapes my outlook on life, my whole attitude. I feel that I am a more relaxed person, a less tense person.

Second, running has given me a communication tool between Bill and myself. In many ways it has drawn us closer. We love to talk about running and we do so daily. We talk about each other's workouts and we talk about how we feel on our runs. We talk about others' races and we talk about our own races. In short, we never run out of things to talk about when it comes to running.

Third, my running has made me more knowledgeable about the sport and therefore I can more readily identify with Bill and his running experiences.

I guess my story is not all that untypical, but when I met Bill he had come very close to making the 1968 Olympic Team in the 10,000-meter and had finished second in the Boston Marathon. I have to admit I didn't even know what 10-K was, nor how anyone could run 26 miles without stopping. Being married all these years to a runner and with me running six-mile races and marathons myself, I can no longer plead ignorance. It has come down to Bill and I fighting over the track and running magazines that arrive in the mail. I realize there's always more to learn. It's a sport that continues to capture my interest.

The one effect of my running that really gives me an "upper" is the interest and the pride my family has shown me in my running endeavors. I will never be a world-class runner nor even a "San Francisco Bay Area-Class Runner," but to my family I'm a star. For me, running has been good for me and most assuredly, it has been good for my family. I encourage women with families not to be timid about starting a running program. There are problems with obtaining babysitters and scheduling runs, but the benefits derived from running far outweigh any of the hassles.

ONNE BELL
553
000 METERS
BONNE BELL
1135
000 METERS

6

Dressing, Coping and Racing

Buying the right clothes, fighting the elements, pre-race eating, masters races

Barbara Pike

There are considerations for female runners beyond learning basic training schedules and running techniques. The mechanics are important, but so are the selection of proper clothing for running, attention to cosmetics that have traditionally been important to women, and the avoidance of certain pitfalls that will help make and keep running enjoyable.

Herein is a guide to things to wear and to beware as you take up running as an avocation and a lifestyle.

CLOTHING

Shoes

Invest in a good pair of running shoes ($20-$40). Your feet need the cushioning and support of well-built shoes. I have a friend who ran in a pair of plaid sneakers discarded by his daughter. Most people cannot get by very long in their old tennies, however; my friend bought jogging shoes before his feet gave out.

Do some research before you actually buy shoes. Start with the annual shoe issue of *Runner's World* (October). Look for a training flat sturdy enough to last hundreds of training miles. Racing flats are much lighter but do not have the support or durability for daily running.

Although RW rates the top shoes numerically, no shoe is number one for everybody. Shoe stores report that the top-rated shoe is often hard to get, and may have substandard workmanship because of the factory rush to fill orders. Any of the top rated shoes may be best for you. Some of the better shoes in women's sizes are Adidas (Runner), Brooks (Vantage, Women's Villanova, Victress), Converse (World Class Trainer), Etonic (KM, Street Fighter), New Balance (320), Nike (Lady Waffle Trainer), and Tiger (Tigress).

Because many shoe companies are now making women's models, you should find several in your size and width. Check their ratings for good cushioning in the heel and forefoot, particularly if you will be running on sidewalks or streets. Weight is not as important in a training flat as sole durability, of course. You can get a lot more mileage from any shoe, however, by diligent attention to repair. More on that later.

Don't be confused by all the different sole tread designs: any of them will probably be fine for you. The "waffle" or nubby design adds cushioning and traction but tends to wear down rather quickly.

Do not order by mail unless you absolutely must. Getting the proper fit could be difficult because shoe sizes seem to vary. My husband's shoes were one whole size from one model to another of the same brand.

Take the socks you will run in when you go to the store, plus anything else that will go into the shoe such as insoles or foot supports. No store will have all shoes in all sizes. If the store doesn't have your size, ask them to order it for you or try another store. Make sure the shoes are comfortable, that they feel good on your feet. Shoes should have plenty of toe room, both in length and width. Pick the larger one when choosing between two sizes: you can always wear thicker socks or put in insoles to take up extra room.

Bend the shoe to make sure it's not too stiff. You can fix a shoe that's too stiff by cutting across the forefoot with a razor or hacksaw but not too many people want to start chopping up their brand new shoes. Be sure to try the shoes on a hard surface, not the store's soft carpet. One running-shoe store in our area has installed a strip of artificial track on their floor to provide a good "test-bed."

Two other considerations which may sway you in the final analysis are price and looks: higher price tag does not necessarily mean better shoe. Women's models are coming out in fashion colors, so pick shoes that make you feel good about wearing them. Check the pair you have selected for flaws; feel inside the shoe for creases or lumps which may cause blisters.

Any shoe should have a stiff heel counter (the wraparound material in the back of the shoe that keeps the heel in place). The heel should be slightly elevated to take the strain off the Achilles tendon. Again, check sole cushioning and stiffness.

You can't tell what's inside the shoe, but a few minutes of inspection will give you some clues. I recently saw what looked like jogging shoes in the grocery store above the frozen food section. They were blue nylon and leather with yellow stripes and a ripple sole for only nine dollars. They seemed like a good buy until I looked closely at them. The heel had a wraparound piece of leather but no stiff counter. Forefoot flexibility was terrific, because the sole probably had no cushioning material at all. The only cushioning in the shoe was easily compressible. Those were not shoes you would want to run in!

Pay attention to your feet and legs regardless of which shoes you buy, particularly the cheaper "look-alikes." Consider different shoes if you develop persistent pains.

Finally, when you get your new shoes the arch supports are usually easy to take out, move around, or replace if they don't feel right. Running shoe stores and drug stores have a variety of arch supports, arch "cookies," heel cups, and the like to customize the interior of your shoe. When trying placement and types of arch and heel supports, glue them in temporarily with white glue. Use waterproof glue after you have decided where you want them, though, or they will come off the next time you run in the rain. I found that out the hard way when the insoles I had added for cushioning wound up in the toes of my shoes one rainy day.

Prolong the life of your shoes by keeping the worn areas built up. Warm glue, melted in a glue gun, can be applied to the soles. I like to squirt the glue on, then smooth it out with the hot tip of the gun. Glue guns and glue pellets are available at most hardware stores and running-shoe stores. Share the cost with a friend or fix your children's toys with it and consider it money well spent.

Do not make the patch thicker than the original sole. You could be inviting a leg injury.

Hot glue adheres relatively well, especially if you clean the sole first with medium sandpaper, but the patch may mark your floors if you scuff your feet across them. My son's teacher could not understand why her classroom floor was always scarred by heel marks. I knew, but wasn't telling!

A new product, Goo, is particularly effective on uppers but doesn't wear as well on soles. It is also cheaper at the beginning because you don't need special equipment. Just spread it on and let it harden overnight.

After some experimentation (with four runners in the family there's plenty of opportunity!), I found that I could get a more durable patch by applying a layer of Goo from the tube, then building up the rest of the worn area with hot glue. I don't know why, but the patches seem to last longer.

Any patching should be started when the shoe first starts to show signs of wear. Waffle soles, in particular, need early attention. Look for wear on the outside of the heel. Being run upon doesn't seem to wear the sole out as fast as being scuffed a little with each step. Apply thin layers of Goo or glue frequently, rather than as a thick patch after your shoe is badly worn. Wear out the Goo, not the shoe.

Despite diligent maintenance, your soles may wear out before the rest of the shoe. Numerous shops specialize in running-shoe repair. They will replace soles, mend uppers, replace insoles, and put in new laces, generally for under $15. You may also have a choice of different tread design. Decide if your shoes are worth resoling based on replacement cost and shoe condition.

Do-it-yourselfers can put their own new soles on. Nike sells waffle soling material by the sheet. (If you can't get it in your local area, write to Ron Wayne, The Athletic Department, 2114 Addison Avenue, Berkeley, Ca., 94704.) Remove the old sole by holding the shoe above, not on, an electric stove. Pull off the old sole when the glue melts. Or dissolve the glue with lighter fluid. Using the old sole as a pattern, cut out the new sole. Glue the new sole in place with your Goo. Also Goo around the edges for a tight seal. Each sheet is usually enough for a pair of soles. If your shoes are small, however, you might be able to get two pair.

To dry your shoes if they get wet, stuff wadded newspapers into the toes to absorb the water. Replace with dry newspapers after a couple of hours. Leave your shoes in a warm place to dry (not the clothes dryer!). I like to put mine on the hot water heater or over a hot air vent on the floor. A blow-type hair dryer dries the insides very quickly, but it may overheat the shoe if left in the shoe too long. Shoes can mildew and smell musty if left wet too long.

In the Elements

Consider the weather when dressing for your run. On cold days wear layers of sweatshirts and a light jacket rather than one heavy jacket. Clothing that seems warm enough at the start of a run may be inadequate after the sun sets or when the wind comes up. The outer layers should open down the front to allow you to regulate heat buildup. Remove one layer at a time if you get too hot; tie extra clothing around your waist. Wear long underwear, panty hose, tights, or sweats on your legs. Wear a knit hat or ski cap to keep your head and ears warm; use gloves, mittens or sweat socks on your hands.

Don't overdress; your body produces a great deal of heat when you exercise vigorously.

Air temperature, wind velocity, and running speed all influence how much clothing you will need. On a calm, sunny day you probably won't need more than your shorts and shirt if the temperature is above 50. Even if you feel a little chilly at the start of a brisk run, you'll be comfortable after the first few minutes. Wear your sweats and you may soon be looking for a place to leave them.

Contrary to what your mother always told you, running in the rain will not make you sick. You can be perfectly warm and comfortable even when soaking wet. Use discretion about running when you are not in good health, however; and don't sit around in your wet clothes after your run.

Experiment with different combinations of sweat shirts, windbreakers, and rain jackets. Rubberized clothing is not recommended because it allows a dangerous buildup of body heat. Your legs will need less protection; you may be comfortable in just your shorts. Don't wear cotton sweatpants, which get very heavy and droopy when wet.

A brimmed tennis hat will not keep your head dry but will help keep the rain from dripping down your face and the back of your neck. I do not like to use the hood on my jacket because it cuts down my side vision and is surprisingly noisy!

After your run, get warm and dry as soon as you can. A hot shower is the perfect ending to a rainy day run.

Do not minimize the danger of running in the heat, particularly when the humidity is also high. Heat can kill. Acclimate yourself to hot weather by taking easy runs of increasing length. Your body will adjust after about two weeks.

Dehydration occurs long before you actually feel thirsty.

Drink fluids before, during, and after your run. Weight loss during a run is almost all liquid, which needs to be replaced.

Learn to recognize the danger signals your body is sending you. Chills, cramps, dizziness, light-headedness, dry, "cottony" mouth are all signs that you must slow down or stop.

Clothing on hot days should protect your skin from the sun's rays and allow air circulation to the skin. Wear a white shirt that is lightweight and loose fitting. The "fish-net" type of fabric screens the sun and allows ventilation of the skin. Avoid dark-colored, heavy cotton T-shirts. They absorb more heat from the sun.

Wear a light-colored hat, cap, or scarf that does not bind, yet is snug enough to stay on. When you stop for water, soak your hat too.

Above all, be sensible about racing and training in very hot weather. Pace yourself and stop before you become a victim of heat exhaustion. On the hottest days plan your runs for evening or early morning.

Clothes: Dollars and Cents

Running clothes need not be expensive. Try out the shirts and shorts you already have to see which are comfortable for running. Or check the selection of patterns at your fabric store. Clothing that is tight or binds causes chafing, particularly on the inside of the legs and around the armpits.

Wear a cotton or cotton-blend T-shirt, one that does not bind under the arms or at the neck. Once you start going to races you will acquire quite a collection of shirts. Some shirts cling and become almost transparent when wet. Try yours out in the shower before a rainy day run.

I like the woven nylon running shorts with short slits on the sides. They are inexpensive (about four dollars), light-weight, and come in a variety of colors. Some shorts are made specifically for women, but these tend to be more expensive.

Try on new shorts before buying them. Look in a mirror at all angles, not just the front. How do they look in back when you touch your toes? Men's shorts, even the "unisex" styles, do not fit all of us. In particular they seem to be short-waisted and cut very high. I felt positively indecent in some that I tried on! Try different makes to find the one that fits you best.

You don't need an expensive sweatsuit. Any light sweater and stretch slacks will do. Look in the boys' or men's departments of department stores for sweat tops and pants (about five dollars each). Warm-ups range in price from twenty to sixty dollars. Fleece-lined sweats will be fine on cold days but will keep you too hot in more moderate weather. Pockets (especially with a zipper) are a handy feature.

Whether or not you wear socks is an individual matter. I feel more comfortable in socks. They help absorb moisture and are softer than shoe lining. I used to wear sweat socks but have recently switched to low cut tennis socks. In the rain the sweat socks got heavy and droopy. The higher tops, however, may help keep pebbles out of your socks and protect your ankles from low-lying branches, prickles, and poison oak. Some people feel that synthetic fibers cut up their feet, but I have not found this to be so. Socks with holes in them, that wrinkle or slip down can form blisters. Try different styles and form your own opinion.

The amount of support you need from a bra depends upon your build. Women with small chests may be perfectly comfortable running without any bra. Large-breasted women usually need the support of a sturdy bra.

If you have a medium build, wear your usual bra. "Runners bras," similar to teen bras, are light-weight yet will keep you from feeling uncomfortably bouncy.

Underpants should be cotton, or at least have a cotton crotch. Cotton absorbs moisture and helps prevent vaginal infection.

As you run more, you will develop your own preferences in clothing. The basic criteria are that the clothes feel comfortable and that you feel good wearing them.

Always try new clothes on short runs before wearing them on a long run or in a race. Pick weather conditions that will duplicate as closely as possible the actual conditions you will encounter. A friend wore a new pair of shorts during a rainy marathon. The stretch nylon fabric that felt so soft when dry stretched and sagged when it got wet. The insides of her legs were chafed until they were raw and bleeding. In the same marathon another friend wore an all-nylon tank top that chafed her neck and arms. When in doubt wear clothes you are sure of even though you may have a new outfit for the race.

Cosmetics

Don't bother with makeup before you run. Exercise itself gives your skin a healthy glow. Also perspiration may cause your makeup to smear and run.

Nor do you need to use a deodorant before a run. The body actually has two kinds of sweat glands. One kind, located all over the body, acts as the body's air-conditioning system and helps cool the body. It's the other kind, located under the arm pits, that causes body odor. The cooling type is activated during exercise, not the odor-causing type.

Vaseline (petroleum jelly) will protect your skin from chafing, especially on hot or rainy days. Smear a generous layer anywhere clothing is likely to rub: on the insides of your legs, under your bra straps, on your upper arms. Put some on your crotch if you wear a pad during your period. Use it, too, to protect areas that have already been rubbed sore. This versatile jelly is truly "first aid in a bottle."

Particularly in the summer, be conscientious about using suntan lotion. Overexposure to the sun results not only in burning but also in longterm effects such as premature aging and skin cancer. Protection is needed particularly for exposure between the hours of 10 a.m. and 3 p.m. Suntan lotions vary in their degree of protection. Some lotions are astringent for oily skins; others are creamy for dry skin.

According to a recent study by *Good Housekeeping* magazine, the following offer the most protection, listed alphabetically:

Highest Protection: Block Out by Sea & Ski, Coppertone Super Shade by Plough, PreSun by Westwood, Sun Bloc Gel by Almay, Sun Bloc by Bonne Bell, Sun Protection (Extra Protection) by Helena Rubenstein, Sundown by Johnson & Johnson, Ultra Bloc by Bristol-Myers, and UVAL by Miles Labs.

High Protection: Coppertone Noskote by Plough, Coppertone Shade by Plough, Coppertone Sun Tan Foam by Plough, Sun Lotion by Almay, Sure Tan by Bonne Bell.

The label will usually indicate the degree of protection you can expect. Most of the lotions providing highest protection contain PABA. Products with names like "Dark Tan" or "Sudden Tan" usually have low protection.

Select a sunscreen appropriate for your type of skin. Apply over exposed areas, especially face, neck, and arms. Use it regularly.

Feet

Pay special attention to your feet. You could run with a broken arm, but even the smallest cut or blister on your foot can be disabling.

Trim your toe nails close and straight across. Most runners who train on hills have had a toenail darken and eventually come off. Until the new nail comes in, consider the black nail a status symbol of running.

Use skin lotion to keep your feet from becoming dry and cracked. Put adhesive tape or moleskin directly over a cut or crack until it heals. Women susceptible to fungus diseases, such as athlete's foot, should put on dry socks and shoes after running. Consult a podiatrist for more serious skin problems.

BEYOND THE FIRST STEP

As you progress beyond the beginning stages of running, add some variety to your training. Run with a group of friends to help the training miles pass more quickly.

Join a jogging class or running club to find compatible runners. Jogging and fitness classes are frequently offered by high school or junior college adult education programs, city recreation departments, the YMCA or YWCA. A knowledgeable instructor will get you tuned in to running in your area.

Ask the AAU or Road Runners Clubs of America for the names of clubs in your area. Many are family oriented and sponsor fun runs and barbeques. Some may offer coaching for both beginner and veteran runners. Your YMCA may have a low-key running club.

The National Jogging Association (1910 K St. NW, Suite 202, Washington, DC 20006) national challenge program awards ribbons or patches to participants who run from 365 km (226.8 miles) to 1978 miles during the year. Your regular effort will be rewarded with an increasing total of miles in the log book.

Look in your own neighborhood for women runners. More experienced runners are usually happy to help you and run with you occasionally. Informal groups often spring up among women with similar schedules and abilities.

Don't feel antisocial if you enjoy running alone. Social runs with friends, however, will add a stimulating new dimension to your running.

2263
1764

ETIQUETTE

For variety you may occasionally run at a track. So that runners of all speeds can be accommodated on the track, a few unwritten rules of track etiquette have emerged.

Synthetic tracks, in particular, are very expensive to install and repair. Because the first three lanes get the most use during races, those of us doing laps for a workout should run on the outer lanes to equalize the wear.

The cardinal rule is to avoid interfering with other runners. Let the serious runners doing timed, repeat intervals have the inner lanes. Move out a lane when a faster runner is overtaking you. Don't let them intimidate you, however, if you had intended to do some intervals yourself. Most tracks have marks called staggers showing where to start for a 220 or 440 in the different lanes. Use the staggers in the outer lanes or just fit your intervals in between other runners' intervals.

Ordinarily one runs counterclockwise on a track. Running the other direction can result in a head-on collision with another runner. At the very least it is distracting to keep dodging out of the way.

Naturally if you're the only runner at the track you can run however you please. When other runners are also using the track, use courtesy and common sense.

RACES

Races give you a chance to expand your horizons, meet different runners, run different courses, test yourself. Run your first race with a friend if you can. Your goal is to finish and enjoy the experience rather than finish in a specific time.

Opportunities for distance racing are plentiful in most areas. *Runner's World* lists over 200 Fun-Run sites each month, along with some other races. Check at local running stores for information on upcoming races.

Many areas have local publications that list races. *Northern California Running Review* and *Yankee Runner* cover Northern California and New England, as their names suggest. Find out if such a magazine covers your locality. Check your local paper for a community sponsored Pumpkin Run, Turkey Trot, or Fourth of July Run. Get on the mailing list of a local running club.

Entering

Joining the AAU (about $4 per year) is required for entering all AAU-sanctioned races. Apply through your AAU office before race day. Do not count on getting your AAU card at the race. In a pinch, however, you can usually get by with writing "pending" instead of your AAU number. Then apply. The entry blank should tell you whether or not the race is sanctioned.

Fun-Runs are simply low-key races. Most have no entry fee or form and are not sanctioned by the AAU. Men, women, and children, fast and not-so-fast, run a measured course and get their finishing time. Awards are not given; however, a certificate or ribbon may be available for each finisher.

Most other races charge an entry fee, generally $2 to $3. Races with higher entry fees may give T-shirts or patches to all participants. Fees of $4 to $5 (tax-deductible) are not uncommon for charity runs.

Get a copy of the entry blank by sending a self-addressed stamped envelope to the race director. Preregister if you can. Not only will you save time and hassle on race day, but you also might pay a lower fee. In fact, some races will not accept post entries on race day. Having your money invested in the entry fee may also keep your determination to run from wavering as race day approaches.

Most clubs sponsoring races do not expect to make a large profit. Here are the typical expenses for a race with 440 runners with a $2 entry fee: trophies and ribbons $292, AAU $98, printing and postage $283, labels $25, and safety pins $12. Net profit was $170 for hours of dedicated work.

Be a bona fide registered runner. Your entry fees are used to provide a good race. Unofficial runners are not eligible for prizes and interfere with those who have registered. One San Francisco area race director threatens to bodily remove from the course any runners not wearing race numbers. The greatest sin of the unofficial runner, however, is to cross the finish line. Having unregistered runners take a finishing place makes correlating names, places, and times nearly impossible.

Pre-Race Eating

Do not eat a big meal before your race, especially food high in fat and protein. Eating before the race will not give you extra energy and may cause stomach or bowel problems. Drinking, especially on hot days, is more important. Water and fruit juice are fine, or try one of the athletic replacement drinks such as ERG or Body Punch. I prefer iced tea.

Take your own beer, cola, or other beverage to drink after the race. Even though you skipped breakfast, do not expect to be very hungry afterward. Dieters take note!

Getting to the Race

Even when a race is 2 to 3 hours drive, I like to dress in my racing clothes at home. That way I'm sure to remember everything. Also, availability of dressing rooms at the race is uncertain. Or cool days sweats will keep you warm en route. Particularly if you anticipate rain, pack a *complete* change of clothes (including underwear and shoes).

Plan to arrive at the race at least an hour before the start. Even preregistered runners must check in on race day. At many races you will be given a number to wear. Pin it on the front of your shirt with at least two pins. Tear off or fold under edges that get in the way of your arms as you run.

Find the toilet; the lines tend to get longer closer to the start. Find out about the course, the route, the terrain. Often you will need to self-address an envelope in order to receive results.

At the Race

A few definitions will help you understand runners' jargon:

- **Pace:** speed, in minutes per mile
- **PR:** personal record, best time for that distance
- **Aid** (aid station): water or other concoction given during longer races
- **Split:** time given partway through the race, useful for determining pace
- **Finishing chute:** funnel to get finishers into single file

In cool weather warm up in your sweats. Jog slowly for a few minutes, then stretch to loosen up. Generally speaking, the longer the race the shorter the warmup. Marathoners may use the first miles of the race as their warmup. Milers may spend half an hour or more getting warmed up.

Jog down the course 200 to 300 yards from the finish line. Pick out a landmark you can remember. Knowing that the finish line is near will give you more confidence at the end of the race.

Five to ten minutes before the race is to begin lock your sweats and other gear in your car. I like to remove the car key from my key ring and tie it in my shoe laces. Some runners stick their keys on a tire or under the car hood. Don't be like a fellow I knew; he locked them in his trunk. Double knot your shoe laces to keep them from coming untied during the race.

Pick a spot at the start that roughly approximates where you expect to finish. Leave the front line to the fast runners or risk being trampled at the gun. If you think you will finish about half-way back, start in the middle of the pack. Slower runners should start at the back. It's much more fun to pass runners than to be passed, anyway.

Though you may not have much running room at first, runners are usually courteous and avoid unnecessary jostling. Try to run at the pace of those around you until the pack spreads out. Use the splits given as an indicator of your pace. Splits are not always to be believed, however; either the time or distance could be wrong. For a long race like a marathon I not only figure out my splits for a certain pace but write them on the back of my hand. You'd be surprised how hard it is to remember them after 15 or 20 miles! Use waterproof ink to keep the numbers from smearing.

As you finish, listen for your time. It may take several weeks to get the results. If you are given a numbered stick, turn it in with your name. When the results are compiled, your finishing order will be correlated with your time.

It's best to keep moving around for a while after you have stopped running. Standing still can cause faintness because of blood pooling in the legs. On cool days put on your sweats after you cool down.

Runners are a gregarious lot after a race. They would be flattered to be asked their advice about almost anything. Don't be shy about joining in.

An awards ceremony is usually held after all the runners have finished. Although prizes are only awarded to a few, each runner is a winner, accomplishing a significant feat in her own way.

When you get home, record your time in your training diary and mark your calendar for the next race.

Masters Races

Masters track-and-field is rapidly growing in popularity. It offers competition to women (and men) over 40 on the local, national, and international level, mostly during the spring and summer. In fact, many masters athletes plan their vacations to include the international meet each year.

Track events (from 100-meter dash to mile run) and field events (such as the long and high jump, shot put, and javelin throw) are usually included. Men and women are divided into groups by five-year age increments. Some meets include sub-masters (30-39) categories as well.

I recently went to a couple of local masters meets where the atmosphere was relaxed and supportive. Fast and slow alike were cheered and encouraged. I could see the camaraderie as old friends greeted each other.

I asked one 50-year old woman who competes in the 100- and 200-meter dashes how she trains for the sprints. She said she starts each workout with an easy 1-2 mile run, then stretches for 15-20 minutes before doing speed work. Masters athletes should pay special attention to stretching and warming up properly, especially before sprinting or jumping events.

Masters track might hold special appeal if you don't like putting in the miles required for the longer road runs. Write to the AAU for information about meets in your area.

Some women are accepting the challenge of ultramarathoning, with distances ranging from 50 kilometers to 100 miles. In 1978, Pat Smythe from San Francisco was the first woman to complete the Western States 100, a grueling course over rugged mountain terrain. Four others started, two of whom covered 92 miles before getting lost. Another who got to 57 miles has vowed to finish next time.

For those with varied athletic interests, biathlon and triathlon events combine running with bicycling, swimming, horseback riding, or even kayaking and Nordic skiing.

In short there's almost no end to the variety of opportunities for women. Road races from 5 kilometers to 26 miles are the most common, but ultradistance, masters track, and "combination" races are also becoming popular.

FACTS OF LIFE

Runners encounter many hazards, and learning to circumvent these problems will add to your enjoyment of running. Most of these problems are found in our running environment (but some, such as painful stitches, are very personal). Animals can pose a threat to the enjoyment and safety of your run, particularly dogs and snakes. If you and a horse are sharing the same trail, it only makes sense to get out of the way. Walk around it and give it as much room as possible. Some horses are easily spooked by runners.

Don't dwell on these few unpleasant facts of a runner's life. Use your ingenuity to devise creative solutions to the situations as they arise. Most of us will log thousands of miles without being seriously endangered.

Stitches

Stitches are sharp pains located generally, but not always, in the upper abdominal area.

Although stitches can occur for different reasons, one common cause is faulty breathing. Breathe from the diaphragm rather than the chest. To check yourself lie flat on the floor with a book on your stomach. The book should move up when you inhale and down when you exhale.

These stitches are likely to occur when you are overbreathing; that is, reducing your effort without slowing your breathing. When running downhill, with the wind, or just slowing down, slow your breathing, too.

I am one of those people who have more problems with stitches than most. I have devised some techniques that work for me. Improvise on my ideas to find out what works best for you.

Most of my friends do not breathe rhythmically but I learned it at my first jogging class and find it helps keep me from overbreathing. For easy running breathe in for four steps and out for four steps. Change to 4-3, 2-2 or whatever, depending on your pace.

The key to prevention of stitches is early detection. At the first twinge check your breathing, pick up the pace, run up a hill. Exhale forcefully by creating resistance with your lips or tongue. Try exhaling in 2 or 3 short pants instead of one long breath. Squeeze your side forcefully.

This variation of fartlek may work even if you are tired. Run 50 to 100 yards at a brisk pace or until you are tired. Walk to recover. Alternate fast running with walking until you get home. If you are a beginner plagued by stitches, you may have to start with this fartlek and progress towards the slow, continuous run.

Stitches may occur when you least expect them. I was coasting downhill at the end of a recent marathon when I started to feel a stitch. Running faster was out of the question. I got lightheaded when I tried to slow my breathing. Holding my side was awkward. The effort of running up the last hill corrected my overbreathing; the stitch disappeared.

When you get a stitch, analyze the situation. Keep track, mentally at least, of what helps relieve it. Proper breathing seems to help most to prevent and relieve stitches.

Cars

Vehicles pose a serious threat to runners using roadways and streets. Never assume that the driver sees you, or that he will yield the right of way. Wait to see if the car slows for the red light. Make sure the driver is looking your way before stepping into the street. Gesture (politely) your intentions to the driver.

On the road you should usually run facing traffic, staying as far to the left as possible. Cross, however, if you feel the shoulder or path on the other side is safer. I have gotten in the habit of crossing to avoid being on the inside of a blind curve. If you do get caught on a blind curve when a car is approaching, extending your arm will warn the driver of your presence.

Wear clothing that will make you more visible. Bright colors are easily seen during the day; white or reflective at night. Da-glo orange is effective at dawn or dusk.

DRIVE SLOWLY
RUNNERS
AHEAD
AVON
10
Marathon

7

Safety for Women Runners

Overcoming the dangers of running: cars, canines, pollution, and muggers

Richard Benyo

Nancy Rudolph, a 26-year-old San Franciscan, was taking a one-mile jog through Yellowstone National Park. As she crested a small hill she was attacked by a bear. In a rush, the bear threw her to the ground; as she fell she had the presence of mind to curl up and play dead. After a brief mauling, the bear wandered off.

Staggering to a road, Rudolph waved down a passing motorist and was given a ride to a nearby hospital. She was consequently transferred to Salt Lake City's University Hospital, where four surgeons worked on her for 5½ hours to repair damage to her face, arms, and body. The surgery was successful because of her good fortune in being able to flag down help along the road quickly enough.

Things did not turn out so well for a young woman on Hawaii's island of Oahu. The woman was out jogging along a road when she was hit by a car. Dazed by the impact, she was forced into the car by the driver; she was sodomized and raped.

When the case came to court, Wilbur Moyd, a 21-year-old Marine based on the island, was charged with sodomy, but the rape charge was dismissed by district judge Robert Richardson on the grounds of insufficient proof of force. The incident drew quick response from the women of Hawaii. Janice Arnold-Jones, chairperson of the Women Against Rape group, spoke before a rally of 700 men and women across from the courthouse, saying: "Judge Richardson has made a very dangerous decision. He's declared open season on all women joggers and he puts women in the position of having to fight, even if fighting could mean death or serious bodily injury."

These two incidents point up several things to joggers and runners:

Safety should be a full-time consideration of a woman who jogs or runs, and one's safety should never be taken for granted; threats to the safety of a jogger or runner come from two directions: nature and "civilization."

Before considering many of the elements that go into running safely, and before examining more closely the sources of threats to a runner, it should be pointed out that, as with material covered in other chapters in this book, what applies to women also applies, in most cases, to men. Also, many of the topics covered in this chapter will be at least touched upon in other chapters of this book, because matters of safety for runners cannot be overstated.

PUTTING THINGS IN PROPORTION

Now that you are frightened out of your wits about even venturing out the door, much less running several miles from your home, let me assure you that the dangers are not lurking around every tree—unless you are running in New York's Central Park at midnight on a dark night. Most of the injuries you will suffer as a runner will come from running itself, and not from the world you run through. The aches and pains of overstressing some part of the body by running beyond your current conditioning level will likely be the only injury most runners will ever suffer from running.

Pain and suffering from outside influences working adversely upon a runner are not especially common—primarily because most runners, by applying common sense and by running conservatively, manage to avoid situations that would otherwise endanger them.

Women, in that regard, are at a disadvantage, however. Until recently, young girls were discouraged from exploring the world around them from the same perspective as boys did. Girls were encouraged to play house or to stay in the yard; they were discouraged from engaging in sports or activities that might in some way expose them to skinned knees, getting dirty, or meeting the pratfalls of life. Boys, on the other hand, were pretty much allowed their due; and in most cases, they took it to the limit, gathering intimate knowledge of every swimming hole, construction site, drainage pipe system, and fenced lot within miles. They all came home with nicks, scratches, bloodied heads; they sampled the dangers of the landscape first-hand and survived.

When they take up running, women are venturing into a land beyond the streets on which their doll houses were constructed. Even tomboys are expected to turn into socially-acceptable girls somewhere along the way to maturity, and their ability to deal with the hostile little beasts of the world is short-circuited.

In a sense, though, the caution instilled in young girls may come in handy as they take up running because caution is the first rule in running through the world safely. (The male's cockiness in knowing the world and its traps might well be what leads him into trouble on a run.) Let's explore the wonderful world of Nature first, where we can meet bears and snakes and poison oak and getting lost and heat and cold and slippery leaves and probably the greatest danger to a runner: over-enthusiasm.

THE PITFALLS OF NATURE

Most woman runners, fortunately, will never see a bear outside a zoo. The mauling that Nancy Rudolph suffered is fairly uncommon because such a small percentage of runners do their roadwork in National Parks and because there are so few bears to go around. The lure of running in a beautiful natural setting, especially for someone who has been doing most of her training in an urban situation, is certainly strong.

When running in or near the woods, it is best to forget every Disney movie you've ever seen. Two rabbits sitting in a field are not conversing on your running style, and they are not demurely giggling about the passing of the world before their burrow.

Be cautious around wild animals. Avoid them if at all possible.

A cute, seemingly harmless male deer, looking so majestic and graceful with its antlers crowning its noble head, can easily attack a human if it is spooked or approached at the wrong time of the year. The antlers that are so attractive are put there for a purpose. Allow the deer to go on grazing and give it a wide berth; you really would be better off not finding out for what purpose Nature gave the deer antlers.

Returning to bears: They may look cute begging for food from car windows in the National Parks, and we all know what teddy bears are for. No matter how cute they may look, however, an adult bear could easily roll a car over to get at something that interests it underneath; its jaws are capable of cutting down young saplings. Bears are some of the moodiest creatures on earth, capable of quickly developing the disposition of an enraged mother-in-law. They are also very curious creatures, and seemingly almost always hungry. Some hikers and campers report that they've seen very positive evidence that bears are attracted by various types of perfumes and that they are almost always attracted by women who are in their menses cycle.

The best advice is to avoid running where the bear population is known to hang out looking for handouts. What they see as a handout may well be something you were planning on keeping.

It gets a little difficult following *this* advice, but while running in wooded areas, especially in the middle of summer, look up while you are running so you can be pre-warned of animals like deer and bears but try to look down, also. Most snakes you are likely to see are harmless; all snakes will be as frightened of you as you are of them. Snakes are naturally timid creatures. They don't go out looking for runners or hikers to bite. Snakes bite things they want to eat. What would they do with a 112 pound woman after they bit her? They don't chew their food, they sort of wrap their very mobile jaws around it and work it into their belly. They take a measure of the meal in advance by nosing around it to see if it's too big to eat and only a very gluttonous snake tries to swallow more than it's capable of handling.

I've had several pet boas, and while I can state that snakes (even of the same species) have very individual personalities, I wouldn't advise a woman runner to stop when she sees one to ask it about its eating habits or its religious beliefs. Luckily for most women, their playing in the yard with dolls ill-prepared them to be comfortable around snakes, and the reaction of most women when confronted by a snake is to turn from a jogger into a sprinter. If you spot the snake early enough, flight is the safest course. If you spot a snake when you are nearly upon it, running is the worst possible thing to do; the safe course is to freeze. Snakes have very bad eyesight, and they sense their prey or the clumsy person who's pushed them into an offensive stance by smell and by the vibrations from the quarry's feet being passed through the ground to the snake's sensitive underbelly.

Confronted by a rattlesnake as a nine-year-old while picking huckleberries in Pennsylvania, I'd had enough coaching from my father in advance so that I simply froze and called to him. The snake was quickly dispatched, but for the period of time it took for my father to arrive with a big rock, I had ample opportunity to study the snake. As soon as I froze, the snake's senses went into overdrive trying to pick up some indication of where I'd gotten to; its head turned slowly from side to side while it occasionally rattled its tail; as my father approached, the vibrations of his footsteps drew the snake's attention away from me. I'm sure that had I been alone (which is not a good way to go traipsing or running through the woods), the snake would have eventually calmed down and wandered off; it was ready to strike because I'd come upon it while it was sunning, and I was an unexpected intrusion and it did not have enough advanced warning to retreat.

Snakes know they're at a disadvantage in size when compared to human beings (unless they are full-grown pythons or boas or anacondas in the jungles), and they don't want any hassles. The primary poisonous snakes in the United States are copperheads, coral snakes, moccasins, and rattlesnakes; it is possible to find rattlesnakes in most parts of the country, while the rest are very regionalized. Instead of learning all the poisonous and nonpoisonous snakes in the country, and then forgetting which are which, it is safest to avoid all snakes. This can be done by glancing at the ground in front of you when you run, by avoiding rocky areas, by checking with a ranger or campers, and by avoiding running after dark; snakes like to lie on asphalt roadways and rocks after dark, soaking up the heat that the sun has beat into the road and rocks all day long.

Snakes, although not strictly social animals, are often found in the company of other snakes, so when (and if) you see one, don't jump blindly into another snake to escape the first. Again, the best advice is to run with a companion. If bitten by a poisonous snake, do not run hysterically away from it; such activity only speeds the poison through the body. Move away from it calmly and sit down; send your companion for help; or wait for the people from your campsite to come for you since you undoubtedly were smart enough to tell them in advance where you were going to be running and they'll be coming to look for you.

Attacks From the Air

Recently, on one of the courses I run frequently in Palo Alto, California, I have been "attacked" by a blackbird. The bird lives in a tree somewhere off Alma Street and although I've never done anything to it, whenever I come plodding through its territory it takes to the air like a jet interceptor and begins making dives at me, all the while making war-like sounds. It never quite comes close enough to strike me, but it does harass me until I pass through its territory. Although children and adults of all shapes and sizes walk and ride bikes and run through the same territory, they are not attacked. I have come to the conclusion that it may be the orange shirt I wear when I run. I'm planning on trying that course with different colored shirts to experiment with the belligerent little bird to see just what his gripe is.

I thought that perhaps my situation was unique until I read the report of a hawk back in my native Pennsylvania that is not just harassing runners, but actually attacking them. It clobbered five different runners from behind in a one-month period, hitting them hard enough to knock them to the ground. The hawk resides in Tyler State Park and although hawk experts say that this type of hawk behavior is unlikely, runners like Sam Petryszak and Steven Harnish have cuts on the back of their heads to prove otherwise. Hawk experts insist that the bird is a horned owl that is trying to protect its young; the numerous attacked runners insist that they know a hawk from an owl. To date, the hawk has not been found in the 1700-acre park. Park officials are warning runners and joggers of the danger.

Flora Fights Back

In addition to attacks from the air, a runner must be cautious of attacks from the ground by plants.

There are three plants that every runner who ventures near the woods, whether Central Park or Yellowstone Park, should know intimately: poison sumac, poison ivy, and poison oak.

Even if it involves sending for government pamphlets or buying books on plants, familiarize yourself with the itching three. Some runners are capable of getting poison oak just by thinking about it; others are capable of contracting all three; some runners seem to be immune to anything. Some people seem to have changes in their reaction to the poison leaves as they age. As a child I could roll in poison ivy all day and it had absolutely no effect on me. While running cross-country workouts in college, I wandered past a stand of poison ivy and was miserable for a week, finally needing shots to get rid of it.

Get to know the leaves and the areas in which each variety grows.

Poison ivy is a North American plant; poison oak is a variety of poison ivy that has leaves that look like oak leaves. Paradoxically, neither plant is of the ivy nor oak family. They belong to the same family with poison sumac, which causes fewer problems than the other two culprits.

An oily substance on the plants that adheres to the skin causes severe inflammation. The little buggers are especially virile during the spring and summer, and the oily substance can be passed from one person to the other by contact, and it can also be passed by coming in contact with clothes that have brushed against the plant. The clothes and bed linens should be washed in very hot water with a double dose of detergent to decompose the oily substance.

If you've brushed against poison oak (which is common in the southeast and the Pacific Coast) or poison ivy, you have roughly two hours to get home, find a bar of laundry soap, take a shower, and wash it off; don't take a bath, as the oily stuff just floats on the water and will get right back on you as you stand up.

Poison oak especially can ruin your running, because once infected, besides the discomfort of itching and rash, it gets into the blood stream and can cause listlessness. In extreme cases, it can cause blood poisoning. Don't expect it to go away without a good nudge. The best way to deal with the poison plants, however, is to get to know them and then avoid them entirely.

I should digress for a moment and tell you a story about poison oak and another possible threat on your nature jaunts.

Getting Lost in the Woods

Amby Burfoot and I wanted to go on a run with some hill-work thrown in one Monday afternoon after work. I'd gone on a run the previous Saturday with a group of runners through a wilderness area behind Hidden Villa Ranch, in Los Altos Hills. We'd skirted some poison oak plants, but we were being led by a runner who knew the area very well, and who kept us away from the real concentration areas of poison oak. It was a very good run through a narrow wooded path, with a stream running next to us, with a steep hill at the end of the valley that ended on an open grassy ridge with a great view of the area. Amby and I both enjoy cross-country so we felt it would be a great run.

We ran two miles to Hidden Villa Ranch, down the dirt road to the buildings, past the picnic area, and across a log onto a path next to a gentle tumbling stream. I kept looking for the second log we had crossed on Saturday, but it never came. I consoled myself by the fact that the valley in which we were running was exactly the same as the valley we'd run in Saturday. Unfortunately, it wasn't.

We clambered over fallen logs, crossed and recrossed the stream as the path wound this way and that. We kept climbing, occasionally walking a rough spot. The trail pretty much disappeared. We occasionally encountered a game trail which we followed until it petered out. "We're bound to intersect with the ridge up ahead if we keep going," I said foolishly. I was working under the assumption that we had taken a turn to the left of the valley I'd been up Saturday. In reality, we'd gone off to the right of it, and there was going to be no ridge path at the top of the mountain.

We struggled onward, going higher and higher. We were perspiring and the sweat on our shirts began to take on a chill as the sun fell lower in the sky. The huge trees and the stream kept the valley damp and chilly. We began to realize that at least half the reason we kept moving was to keep warm. After spending a half-hour crawling over, under, around and through twisted trees and brambles where a rabbit would have trouble moving, we made the top of the mountain—and looked out at other equally impressive mountains. The end of the San Francisco Bay and San Jose were visible about 15 miles away. Before us, in that direction, lay brambles and shrubbery that a fly would have had trouble negotiating. The air was turning cold, as it has a way of doing in northern California when the sun dips to the horizon. Behind us, in the valley, it was already getting dark. We heard a low-flying plane and joked that it was the search party looking for our remains.

Fortunately, the valley up which we'd come was a good guide to getting back to Hidden Villa Ranch. Unfortunately, when you've traveled so far in dense underbrush, it don't look the same goin' back as it did comin'. We had the valley to guide us back. We also had the sun; by keeping it to our left (it was on the right as we came out on our run), we could obviously return to the spot we'd left. "We should have left bread crumbs to follow back," Amby said, still trying to keep up our spirits as the sweat on our shirts began to feel icy.

We found that, at least on the top of the mountain, we could not get back to the valley the way we'd come because the brambles were too dense and we couldn't find the exact meandering path we'd made. We were forced through one patch after another of exotic-smelling wild herbs and bushes. Eventually, we faced a little patch of poison oak about the size of a child's swimming pool. It lay in a little clearing as though someone had cultivated it there. There was no other way into the valley without a quarter-mile detour. The sun was gone below the horizon. So we charged through the stuff. It took two weeks, a bottle of calamine lotion, a visit to the doctor and a bottle of pills to shake the stuff, despite the fact that we both washed as much as we could when we returned to civilization.

We opted for the poison oak, though, rather than be stuck on a mountaintop any longer than we had to with the failing light. Neither of us relished the thought of spending the night curled up next to a fallen log while our sweaty shirts turned to ice chests.

It is common sense for runners, whether they be male or female, to run in pairs in unfamiliar territory. It is also good advice to opt for repeating a short loop near your campsite or cabin or motor-home than for a long loop that will take you far afield from your home base. The woods can be a great place to run in, a great place to camp and hike in, but a frightening place in which to be lost. Take precautions. Let people back at camp know where you are going and how long you expect to be gone.

Common sense also dictates that you take several pair of shoes along on trips to the woods. Take a pair with herringbone soles or something similar for running roads through the woods that might be damp or that might have wet leaves; the herringbone pattern gives you much more surface area on the ground and makes it more difficult to slip and slide; waffle soles are terrible for running on wet leaves, consistently damp asphalt roads through wooded areas, and roads that have quite a bit of tar patching on them (the tar gets extremely slippery when wet). Waffle-soled shoes can be used on dirt trails and in grassy fields and on dry roads.

Extremes of Temperature

In most parts of the country, there is a large range of temperatures and weather conditions; nature can make the landscape 40 degrees below zero at one time of the year and 101 six months later. Living near San Francisco, we get spoiled, because it is conducive to running 365 days out of the year. There is a cooling trend from the ocean during the summer, and winters are extremely mild; it rains when it's scheduled to rain and the sun shines most of the summer. Few other places in America are that ideal.

Having been born and raised in Pennsylvania, I know the sub-zero winters near the Pocono Mountains; having spent nearly five years outside Washington, D.C., I also know the 95-degree, 95-percent-humidity, the-air-ain't-moved-for-two-weeks summers.

Each radical change in temperature produces its own problems.

The greatest threat in winter is not freezing to death (unless you run blithely into a blizzard and get lost), but falling down on the snow and ice and getting broken bones. Running in the winter, your last concern should be fashion. Wear several layers of loose-fitting clothes. This provides several advantages. The various layers trap body warmth (and running does produce a great deal of body warmth) and keep the runner snug and warm; by wearing several relatively light layers instead of one big, bulky layer, as your body temperature builds and you begin to get warm, you can easily remove one layer and tie it around your waist, thereby bringing your body temperature down to a more comfortable level. It is very easy to become overheated while running in sub-zero temperatures. Removable layers of clothing provide you with your own thermostat.

There are parts of your body that should be protected during winter running because they will not be snugly inside layers of clothing. You can cover your face with a ski mask; even though you'll look as though you are running away from a bank holdup, it will protect your ears, nose, cheeks, and throat from cold air and from possible frostbite. Mittens or socks over the hands are good because you can keep your hands warmed if your fingers are in contact with each other rather than in their own little sheaths as they are in gloves. Socks are a necessity; wool socks are best because even if they get wet in the cold, the little body heat that your feet is producing will warm the

USA
73

dampness and will cause it to work like insulation.

It is also good to get in the habit of wearing something bright as your outer layer of clothing (except in the extreme heat, where white is best, since it reflects rather than absorbs the sun's heat) because it makes you much more visible to snowplows and to hunters. Brightly-colored clothing also makes it easier for motorists to see you, which will be dealt with more thoroughly later in this chapter.

The main caution when running in the winter is to consider the fact that with a great deal of clothing on, your movements are going to be somewhat restricted, so don't try to run quite as far as you would if you were going for a run wearing only a T-shirt and shorts. Don't do an out-and-back run equal to what you do in the spring; the road back may become incredibly hard to travel, and once you stop running and begin walking the cold will really begin setting in on all those little damp pockets of your clothing. Run close to your house in the winter. A nice, warm place to return to makes the run feel good; a nice, warm place to return to that is still three miles off when you've run out of gas can be a very bad way to see the new snowfall.

Hot Stuff

On the opposite side of the calendar is the extreme heat of summer. In some areas, the extreme heat combines with the equally extreme humidity. There are obvious cautions involved in running in hot weather.

The first caution involves liquids. When running in hot weather, drink some water before going on the run. While on the run, if your mouth begins to feel like cotton (dry and puffy) either find some liquid within the next quarter-mile or walk until your mouth comes back to the point where your tongue works as it's supposed to work. Don't try to tough it through a run in the heat without liquids. Your body is sending you a message that it needs water or some other liquid, even if your brain doesn't have the sense to understand that running in extreme heat uses up body fluids at an incredible rate.

The second caution involves clothing. Women feel slighted running in hot weather because society demands that they wear a T-shirt or singlet or halter-top or some other form of clothing over their chest. Male runners, on the other hand, often remove their shirts and run bare-chested. There are actually several ways of looking at the matter of clothing in hot weather.

Running bare-chested *may* be more comfortable. Running while wearing a shirt may also be just as comfortable. A light-colored shirt (white, yellow, bright orange) will reflect the sun, while bare skin and dark-colored clothes absorb the sun's heat. A shirt absorbs perspiration from the body as the body machinery attempts to regulate its temperature; the perspiration soaking the shirt cools as it leaves the body, creating a sort of cool insulation around the chest of the runner. (This sensation is very readily noticeable when running from sunlight into the shade; the coolness in the shade emphasizes the coolness of the shirt's perspiration, sometimes even causing a slight chill.) So, wearing a shirt of some kind is not necessarily a disadvantage for women; it may be just the opposite. Consider, too, that the damp shirt allows the body to lose perspiration at a much slower rate than does a chest exposed to the hot sun, when the perspiration often evaporates as soon as it emerges from the skin, and the body must immediately replace it. This evaporation effect is further speeded up if there is a slight breeze.

The third caution involves overtraining. Heat puts great strain on even a resting body. Body functions are going at full tilt to keep the very critical temperature at a reasonable level. Exercise puts further strain on the body, especially on the heart. Reports of people dying of heart attacks while running have scared many people. Running is reputedly supposed to help build up the heart, and here people are dying. What gives?

What gives is often that inexperienced joggers or runners are overtaxing themselves, especially on unseasonably hot days in the spring with the urge to get out and run the roads. The older a new runner is the more gradually he or she should ease into running; the more adverse the conditions (and an unseasonably warm day is an adverse condition), the more cautious a runner should be.

Many deaths are due to overdoing it without a proper training base built up beforehand. Some are due to overtaxing the body on a particularly hot day. Others occur because the person was scheduled, by the Great Schedule, for termination and they happened to be out jogging at the time; they could just as easily have been sleeping or eating supper or watching television; people die all the time and with the incredible number of people in America jogging and running, some deaths are going to occur while the person is engaged in that activity.

There is a great body of evidence that regular running, done intelligently, can contribute to strengthening the heart; there is some evidence that a person running at the marathon level becomes almost immune to heart problems. Arthur Lydiard of New Zealand, one of the world's great running coaches, has had a program for a decade of turning heart-attack patients into marathon runners within one to two years after their heart attacks.

There is the mad-dogs-and-Englishmen syndrome in many runners, however. The syndrome is usually apparent in middle-aged business executives who take up running. They are impatient, highly competitive, and demanding of themselves; they rush on where angels would take a rest, and they end up dying from the very thing that could have helped them. They run like madmen no matter what the temperature or conditions. (There are some female runners who are equally obsessed, especially younger runners. Which is one reason younger people seldom make good marathon-runners; they do not have the patience to pace themselves properly.)

I've seen middle-aged men, who've switched from tennis to running, and who are, in fact, running in their very expensive and exclusive tennis clothes, with a spare tire still in evidence around their middles, huffing and puffing and turning blue on the hottest day of the year. It is painful just to watch them abusing themselves.

In the heat, the air is much thinner than when it is cold, and therefore more air is needed to satisfy the body's needs; consequently, the runner is going to be breathing harder, faster. There is obviously going to be more strain. When running in the heat becomes a strain, it's time to head home for the day. If the compulsion to run is extremely great, put running off until the evening, when it may be cooler, or when the sun is down so that it is not sapping you of vital body fluids.

After running in the heat, give in to your body's needs for fluids. Drink as much as the body wants; you won't be able to overdrink. You'll find that even when you fill yourself with liquids during the first hour after running, you'll still be thirsty three hours later. The body will be replacing the liquids it expended for many hours; give it what it needs; you've got mechanisms in your body that will stop you before you drown yourself and that will excrete any excess you might be able to ingest.

If you are a woman who has progressed to the racing stage, and if you arrive at a race and the heat is stifling, just turn around, walk back to your car, and go back home. Races run in extremely hot weather conditions are not good for the body. They put too much strain on it and they rob it of too much, both physically and psychologically. After a particularly hot race, it is possible to feel down for weeks because of what the body has suffered. Running is supposed to be fun, and although racing is expected to be a little bit of a strain and somewhat painful in parts, it should not be cruel and unusual punishment to your body. It calls for a philosophy not too unlike the one used by wise generals in times of war: When the opposition builds to an overwhelming amount, retreat so that you can run again on another day; to go down for the sake of pride and glory is a waste.

PUTTING NATURE IN PERSPECTIVE

I've taken great pains to make the dangers of Nature sound worse than they really are because I'd rather a woman runner were overcautious than flippant. Some of the dangers are minor (poison ivy) while others are rare but can be fatal (bear attacks). But they are all out there, waiting somewhere, waiting for someone who forgets that the best way to approach running in Nature is by keeping common sense running five steps in front of you.

Some of the most beautiful and fulfilling running you'll ever do will be away from civilization. Running among redwoods is an inspirational experience. Skirting a lively brook on a run through the woods gives running a whole new meaning. Running slowly, comfortably through any aesthetically pleasing patch of nature allows you to see the scenery with new eyes because running identifies you with the animals that inhabit the place. This sounds relatively hokey, perhaps, but it is true. There's a certain freedom for the runner when he or she runs through the woods. Maybe it's a part of the primitive "collective" memory that stays locked in the genes, or maybe it's a psychological high, the mind thanking the body for getting it away from the hassles of civilization for even an hour. But there is something very special about running in the wilderness. With the proper cautions it can be an exceptionally uplifting experience and one that almost every woman runner will want to repeat often.

THE WILDERNESS OF CIVILIZATION

Running with the bear and the snake is preferable to running with the mugger and rapist. For many women interested in running, however, there are no real choices. If you want to run, you must face—and overcome—the rigors of civilization. Or else you must move to a rural or woodland environment, which is not especially easy, because the people who are running most are the people who depend on the institutions of "civilization" for their livelihood. For highly civilized Americans, the run is, in a way, a return to primitive pleasures while they still function in the modern world.

There are obvious dangers lurking around corners for the female runner in a civilized environment, whether it be urban or suburban. Or, for that matter, even rural.

There are dangers from other people (in the form of muggers, rapists, perverts of all sizes and descriptions and tastes), from pollution (both man-made and canine-made), from cars and trucks and buses, from children and bicyclists and pedestrians and other runners, from cracks in the pavement and from even house-broken dogs.

Without belaboring the point, I much prefer to face the dangers of the wilderness when I run than face the dangers of civilization. Like most Americans, however, the choice is not mine. My daily runs are through heavily-populated suburban/ urban areas. As with running in the wilderness, common sense is the runner's best companion. Common sense and the First Commandment of Running Amidst Civilization, which each runner—male or female—should have branded on the inside of the brain or tattooed on the inside of the eyelids: Treat everything in civilization as though it is out to kill you. If you don't, it just might.

(Again, an admonition: The following litany of dangers and ways to avoid them is not made to discourage women from running in an urban or suburban environment. These dangers are *not* lurking around every corner every time you run; but having all the odds on your side is the best way to enjoy running for the rest of your life.)

Running in the Streets

Rape and muggings are not new to civilization. Most societies have had them since the advent of man-made structures behind which a rapist or mugger could hide.

- Never run alone after dark. Never run in remote areas (such as Central Park in New York City and Golden Gate Park in San Francisco), as there are just too many places a rapist could hide and there are too many convenient places a rapist could drag you once he jumps out of hiding. Know the neighborhood in which you are running and don't wander into unfamiliar areas by yourself; especially in urban areas, the texture of a neighborhood can change in a matter of two blocks.
- Do not run blithely, not paying attention to what is going on around you; it is often possible to spot a potentially dangerous situation long before it materializes if you're paying attention.
- Carry the price of a phone call in a little pocket sewn inside your running shorts in case you find yourself in a neighborhood you didn't intend to enter; then call a friend or the police to come and get you. Don't ever assume that because you may be a liberated woman you can handle any situation that comes up; the rapist might not know that you are going to be able to handle everything and go ahead with his plans anyway.
- Try not to run the same route every day; don't help a rapist know where and when he can expect you. Despite the benefits many of us get from running alone, forego running alone to running with a group if it is in a time or place where you feel you may need the protection that friends can offer.

There have been more and more reports coming in of female runners who have managed to outrun would-be attackers (rapists, muggers, and perverts are not always in the best of shape); don't rely on that as a possibility, however. The male is still faster in sprint events, and you're not likely to get the opportunity to make the chase a marathon, so don't count on your running ability to get you away from potentially bad situations. Avoid the situations in the first place.

It is not a bad idea to organize the female runners and joggers in your area into groups, for mutual protection and for mutual training benefits. If you can get such a group formed, contact the local police department and have them send a representative to talk to your group about the best ways of avoiding dangerous situations. Approached properly, the local police will be more than happy to help female runners enjoy their avocation in safety.

Also, if you are going running, *always* tell someone where you are planning to run and what time you expect to be back, even though this takes away the free spirit aspect of the run. The little time and trouble involved in doing so can save you a lot of grief later on. If you are single, make arrangements to tell your landlord or even the janitor or some person in your building where you're likely to be and what time you expect to be back.

The runner, because of the amount of territory he or she covers, is a second string of police officers. Runners have come across traffic accidents, mugging victims, robberies in progress, any number of things, because they happen to be at the right place at the right time. The runner should be prepared to run to the nearest phone to report accidents, strange doings, the presence of perverts, whatever.

Runners have frequently been able to contact fire departments in time to save office buildings and family dwellings, when they've run past and noticed smoke coming from places other than chimneys. Be alert when you run, for your own safety and for the safety of others.

Pollution Gets In Our Eyes

And on our feet. Running in New York City is becoming more a training ground for hurdlers than for distance runners. If you can negotiate the stool from New York's dogs, you can easily qualify for the low hurdles or the steeplechase. Even walking is becoming difficult. An acquaintance who went to Manhattan for a few weeks reports that one night he saw a woman with eight dogs on leashes; they were jointly fertilizing two blocks of pavements. (Maybe the fertilization is what makes concrete grow over all the grass in big cities.) The caution for running in New York and similar environments is to always run in the daylight, because you'll be able to see more easily where you are stepping and what you almost stepped into. Bear in mind that the soles of running shoes are usually built in such a way that they'll pick up and store anything soft for quite a long time.

The major problem with running in cities and along heavily traveled highways, of course, isn't the doggie diamonds, but the pollution that hangs in the air. The problem is not as radical if you can run near or along roads where the traffic is heavy *but moving constantly.* High concentrations of pollution come from idling cars, such as at city intersections, during rush hour traffic that backs up bumper-to-bumper, where people are double-parked waiting for someone to come out of a store while the engine is idling, while police cruisers sit waiting for a speeder with the car idling. Cars traveling at 55 or 60 or 65 mph are polluting less than cars that are going nowhere. Try to avoid running near such high concentrations of pollution. The crap in the air in cities is getting incredibly worse and it has a way of accumulating in your lungs and your bloodstream. Certain cities, of course, are worse for pollution than others. Washington, D.C. is terrible because it is situated in a natural depression, a sort of huge bowl, and the pollution, without a strong wind to blow it away, just sits there patiently and gets thicker; in Los Angeles the mountains hold it where it is and it takes a mighty strong wind off the ocean to move it. San Francisco, on the other hand, has almost constant ocean breezes, so pollution is blown inland as soon as it is manufactured.

It isn't necessary to desert the city you live in or near, of course. You can protect yourself by taking certain precautions. For instance, if you are near a high pollution area, you might want to modify your running habits so that you run in the early morning; the streets are a little more deserted and it's generally a bit cooler so that some of the day's pollution is wiped away and the air is fresher. There are also surgical masks available, but they filter out only part of the pollution.

Do not kid yourself into believing that if you run in a city park you are safe from pollution. Plants breathe in carbon dioxide, but cars produce carbon *monoxide*, and trees and bushes don't intake that; plants don't like it any more than people do. Bruce Dern used to run in a park, hoping to avoid the LA smog; as he found out, though, the park setting does nothing practical to help you if there's pollution in the air; the pollution formed nodules on his lungs and eventually they caused one of his lungs to collapse. He's still running, and doing very well in his daily training, but it was a long road back after the collapsed lung.

Take opportunities during the weekend at least to escape the city atmosphere to do some running in a country environment. Your lungs could use the vacation. Run in the morning when possible. Eat plenty of fruits, as they have a way of extracting the pollutants from your body.

YOUR ENEMY, THE CAR

The automobile is not bad by itself. But automobiles in numbers create pollution that the atmosphere cannot dissolve because the system is overloaded. And automobiles are bad when someone who is incompetent gets behind the wheel.

The automobile (coupled with a driver) is probably the runner's single most dangerous enemy.

My own rule of thumb, which I repeat over and over and over until it becomes monotonous, is simple: *Treat every automobile as though it is out to kill you.* That way, when the one out of 50,000 that is going to try to kill you makes its attempt, you'll be prepared for it.

Automobiles are from 18 to 45 times as heavy as the average female runner. Trucks and buses are even heavier. If you feel you are unable to stop a car that weighs two or three tons or a truck that weighs 10 tons, don't assume that you have the right of way at an intersection—even if you know that you do. Runners who argue with cars and trucks that are moving are taking leave of their senses.

Let the car go through the intersection even though you have the right-of-way. Just keep running in place or do a stretching exercise against a telephone pole to keep yourself loose. When it is safe to cross, cross. Don't assume that a car is going to stop automatically for you, even though some states insist that they must. Lose a few seconds rather than losing a few months hobbling around with a leg in a cast. Even if a driver waves you through, don't take the invitation; wave him through instead.

I've had instances when punks in cars have tried to see how close they could come to hitting me while I was running in bike lanes; a miscalculation in my step could have sent me to the hospital very easily. Being the untrusting soul that I am, though, I'm always ready to dive for the side of the road when I hear the car's tires crunching the debris that builds up in the bike lane or when I hear the tires hitting the little reflectors that are built into the roads here in California.

When a runner named Hank Austin was running in Michigan last winter, a motorist attempted to scare him by aiming his car at Hank. The motorist succeeded in doing what he had intended. Hank was duly scared. Hank wrote the license number down and recorded the exact sequence of events. What the motorist didn't know was that Hank Austin is a deputy sheriff who also happens to be a runner. The next day Hank presented his story to the prosecutor and told the prosecutor that he could identify the driver of the car. The prosecutor issued a warrant against the driver for felonious assault with an automobile. He was arrested the following day. (Although you have certain rights under the law, do not assume that the automobile driver knows what they are. The automobile driver usually doesn't know his air filter from his oil pump. And don't attempt to make a citizen's arrest when you're on foot and the offender is behind the wheel of a car.)

Before wandering off on a tangent, let's examine a few of the most common instances you'll likely encounter in your continual sharing of the roads with the automobiles of America:

The first rule is to take every precaution to make sure drivers *see* that you are sharing the road with them. Wear bright clothing, especially at dawn and dusk, when the natural light is especially uncertain. After dark, run with extreme caution; wear some sort of reflector material on or over your clothing or else stay off the roads. If you run after dark on little-traveled roads, don't let your mind wander so that you don't hear the approach of a car or see its headlights. The best practice for night running is to step off the roadway until the car safely passes; one never knows what a sedate old lady will do when she sees a figure in white coming at her out of the night; the usual response is to let the car get out of control, and when this happens, the car usually goes in the direction of whatever scared the driver. Night running demands very special safety precautions and should always be done with a companion and near home. Also get in the habit of carrying an identification card somewhere on your person so if there is an accident, your family can be contacted; the card should also contain your blood type and any information about medications to which you might be allergic; there are necklaces available that have the pertinent information printed on them.

Always run *facing* traffic; in other words, run the left side of the road. That way, you and the approaching cars theoretically have more of a chance to see—and avoid—each other. Unfortunately, the people who came up with that rule do not run some of the country roads the rest of us do; there are some tight two-lane country roads where it is suicide to follow that rule. Use common sense. If there is a blind curve coming up, run on the *outside* of the curve, and then cautiously, because if a driver loses control of his car, he's going to slide to the outside of the curve, because that's how centrifugal force works. You are safer out there, though, because he can see you in advance of reaching the curve and because you will have more room in which to maneuver your body out of the driver's way.

Never run on highways or freeways. Never. When I was in college, a portion of Interstate 80 in Pennsylvania was being completed and for months no cars knew anything about it. The stretch was eight miles long. I used to run it every Saturday morning as part of a long run. The shoulders were new asphalt, there was no litter, there was no traffic. It was like running in another world. Unfortunately, people soon found out about the stretch and only a looney would run it now. Traffic along large highways moves too fast; you have absolutely no time to react if something goes wrong, and things often do. You can just as easily be killed by a tractor-trailer's retread coming apart and bashing you upside the head as you can by being hit by the truck itself.

Run with automobiles as though your life depended on it. This is being repeated, yes, but it can't be repeated too often. Do not trust any driver. Nuts come in all shapes and sizes. Treat cars as though they're out to get you, because all it takes to do the job is the one you weren't paying attention to on that last run.

Whether or not you personally have any interest in cars, take some time to learn the sounds the car engine makes when the car is taking a turn, slowing down, when the driver quickly pulls his foot off the accelerator, or when the power is applied to the engine. The car is talking to you, and you should be listening. If a car is coming up behind you on a two-lane road (or if you happen to be running on the right side of the road at a spot where it's dangerous to run the left) and you can tell by the sound of the engine that the driver just pulled his foot off the accelerator, it probably indicates that the driver just realized you were there; this should indicate also that he may not be in full control of his car at that point, so a judicious move farther to your right would be in order in case he still isn't in complete control when he comes by you.

Also, try not to do extremely long runs on well-traveled roadways. You'll be getting very tired within the last few miles, your reactions will be sluggish, and your concentration will be less than acute; if you find yourself getting into that dazed state that occasionally happens when you run, head for safer roads where you're not likely to get yourself into trouble.

And lastly, give some indication of what you intend to do at intersections or when you find it necessary to cross lanes so that any cars in the vicinity are given ample warning. I've seen some runners dart out into a road without making any kind of indication that they were going to do anything but keep running in the direction they were headed; if a driver is confused at that point, it isn't his fault.

Most drivers aren't out to kill or maim runners; many of the drivers are runners themselves. It is still best, though, to avoid drivers when possible. When it's not possible, take great care not to do anything foolish. It only takes one mistake to put you out of running for a long time.

THE CANINE CONNECTION

Runners may be put into a lot of categories: fast and slow, morning and evening, young and old, serious and recreational...appetizing and unappetizing. Get a roomful of runners and it's almost possible to divide them in half between those who have had problems with dogs and those who have not. There is, naturally, no middle ground; you've either been attacked by a dog or you haven't.

Some runners seem to send off an aroma that draws dogs faster than the newest dog food being huckstered on television commercials. It has to be something like aroma, because it seems impossible to explain otherwise how some runners who've been running for 20 years have never been attacked by a dog while others who have been running less than six months have been attacked several times.

There is strong feeling between the two groups of runners about what should be done to protect runners against dogs. The unattacked find it terrible that some runners should have elaborate plots hatched against man's best friend, while those who have been attacked become tired of hearing those who haven't defending the canines and admonishing the scar-bearers that they must have provoked the dog.

Whatever your stand on the matter, it is wise to have a plan to defend yourself. Some male runners shout the dog down or make threatening sounds and gestures that often confuse and disorient the dog. Others carry defensive weapons (the most workable being an automobile antenna, which is light and can be telescoped down to almost no size at all, but which can be used as an effective whip at the first advance of a lip-licking doggie).

Some women have found that a dog can be talked down when it proposes an attack, although you've got to be a fast talker if he's already made up his mind to do you in. Other women contend that ignoring the dog will discourage it. And others claim that the best way to avoid dog attacks is to set up courses that do not match territory frequented by dogs.

Whatever your planned approach to the dog problem, bear in mind that dogs are usually "civilized" and "domesticated" animals, if not in every habit, at least in the fact that they live in conjunction with man's civilization. Consequently, they have at some point in their lives been accustomed to accepting orders from people. Therefore, be prepared to command the dog, in no uncertain terms, to get the hell away from you or you'll make life miserable for him. The direct approach works with most dogs, especially if it is made with a threatening gesture (as long as you aren't dealing with a trained attack dog, for whom threatening gestures are an invitation to take off your arm). For the small percentage of those dogs who do not cower at the voice of mankind, any auto supply store sells antennas.

LOST IN THE WILDS OF CIVILIZATION

One of the most confusing creations of mankind is the typical suburb. Oh, there are some that are laid out like a piece of graph paper. But most of them are, from the air, like the convolutions of the human brain.

Anyone who's tried to follow directions through a suburban labyrinth very quickly feels like a rat in a maze. It is almost as easy to get lost in some cities, where the city was laid out according to the lay of the land rather than by some geometrical design.

Women have a tendency to be less Lewis & Clarkish than men. This, like everything else, is not an across-the-board generalization. (Again, it may be due to boys being allowed to wander far afield as youngsters while girls were often confined to playing house in the yard.) As you become stronger and more ambitious as a runner, the day will come when the urge will surface to go farther than you ever have before. You'll attempt to hold yourself back, but the urge is very strong because it is joined firmly with a feeling of joy with the world, and once this happens, there's virtually no holding that person back. The old courses will seem woefully inadequate, stale, and boring. The wanderlust will overcome you and you'll find your feet taking you into new areas of the city or the suburbs.

Much like you would in the wilderness, tell someone when you are going running, what direction you are going in, and how long you expect to be gone. If this is not possible (and even if it is), begin to carry some change (at least the price of a phone call) in a little pouch you can sew inside your shorts so that, should you get lost or need help in strange territory, you will not be without resources.

Several runners have suggested window decals, so that other runners who are in some sort of distress can identify a friendly house to run to for assistance. The idea has merit if it can be standardized, but in the meantime a runner is pretty much on his or her own. Getting lost can become frustrating, distressing and—in cold weather especially—downright dangerous as the runner wearies and the body temperature can no longer ward off the cold. The best solution is not to run more than a block or two into new territory at any one time. Also remember that when you turn around to come back from a new portion of your running course, the streets will look entirely different because you are seeing them from the opposite direction, and this can very easily disorient you—especially if you are tired or moving faster than the mind can sort out the proper turns.
can sort out the proper turns.

Neighborhoods in both cities and suburbs can change radically within the space of a few blocks; the street you felt perfectly safe on before may look like juvenile delinquent haven four blocks farther along, so be very cautious in adding new and unexplored streets to your run.

IN SUMMARY

It is very easy to look back over this chapter and feel depressed about the many potential dangers waiting for runners. The word that makes the subject positive, however, is *potential.* As long as dangers are kept as potentials rather than as actuals, running can be beneficial both physically and mentally. Although it can be safely stated that not every run brings on the fabled "runner's high," it can just as safely be stated that no run needs to bring tragedy.

The obstacles and dangers that nature and civilization put in the way of the runner are likewise there for the walker, the cyclist, for virtually anyone. Life is something of a course through the obstacles. A person who is careful can negotiate the obstacles successfully at whatever speed is comfortable for that person's life. Running merely intensifies what other human beings meet along the road of life.

The intensity, however, is what makes life all the sweeter. It is certainly what brings on the "runner's high" and it is what leaves a runner flushed after a particularly satisfying run that may have taken the runner to new accomplishments even on the seemingly mundane mid-week training run. It is the way the foot falls so surely, so firmly on the curve of the local bridle-path. It is the sweet morning spring air following a hard winter that rushes through the mouth and into lungs expanding as the runner moves up a hill that four weeks before required a rest halfway to the top.

The dangers runners face often are from their own running. The injury most often comes from overtraining, from upping mileage too rapidly, from becoming so enthusiastic that common sense has no room in the runner's castle of dreams. Shin splints and runner's knee and black toenails and sore ankles and tired muscles are the female runner's greatest threat to safety.

The other dangers are there, certainly, to a degree proportionate with the area the woman runs in. But the majority of the dangers can be avoided by dredging up cautions we all heard over and over and over as children: *Look before you cross the street; Don't go out by yourself after dark; Stay away from those woods over there; Don't fool with strange dogs; Get back here when you're supposed to or we'll send the cops after you; Don't play by the freeway,* etc.

All the messages are there, much like the grooves on a phonograph record; all we need do is play it back every once in a while. And there's lots of time in which to play it back on the run.

Part 2

The Vehicle: Body and Mind of the Woman Runner

74
CHEPSTOW-WALES

8

Inner Workings

Anatomical, cardiorespiratory, and psychological aspects of running

Dr. Gerald Besson

The title of this chapter implies that there is something unusual about the female runner that needs elucidation, but the female runner needs neither explanation nor justification. There is a persistence of a wide variety of myths about female runners, however, that should be dispelled. Similarities between male and female so far outweigh the differences that to emphasize the latter would be inappropriate. Yet this book is written for a wide audience: for women just beginning to run to world-class female marathoners. It would be helpful to review, therefore, the basic biological functions involved in running, and to discuss those differences between male and female that may have an impact on running for women. Most of them are of no importance unless we want to compare peak speeds between male and female, which really have no practical meaning.

Rather, the emphasis in this chapter will be on the fact that we are all endowed with certain biological characteristics that are innate. There have been many myths and some purported research that have implied that women are somehow too fragile to engage in sports, let alone endurance activities. The male ego has often created restrictions against women in sports and has so perpetuated so many sociocultural myths that women have all but given up trying. But some souls have persisted; not only have they survived but they have excelled, and by doing so have broken through some significant barriers to women in sports. This chapter will review the biological foundations of running and separate fact from fancy.

A review of some basic bodily functions which are called into play for the runner would include the cardiorespiratory, the anatomic, the musculoskeletal, and the psychological.

All of these systems are subject to adaptation. The body, stressed by running, adapts to the stress to handle it better in the future. Indeed, one of the most fundamental biological traits of living things is the ability to adapt. Our capacity to do so is awesome and is shared equally by all living matter.

This adaptability is the basis for the "training effect": to demand slightly more from each active organ system than is demanded in its resting state. The body accommodates where it can; and this gearing up process makes the same demands easier the next time. Or, if one would rather keep the demands at the same level, more work can be accomplished with that effort.

Anyone with the proper adaptation can not only run but do so safely and naturally with existing abilities. The enjoyment and the benefits are identical for both sexes.

The beginning female runner should not be intimidated about running and should accept it as a fundamental human ability. It takes much encouragement and reassurance for the beginning woman runner to take the first few steps. Because of her sociocultural brainwashing she may feel out of her natural setting; she will feel embarrassed, she will find reasons to justify not running because she doesn't know how or has never done it, etc.

I can recall my married daughter's first fun-run when she started out like a bolt at the word "Go," leaping away from the pack, only to fold in 50 yards, gasping and telling me she couldn't run. See how out of breath she was, and so forth. My wife was fortunately along and we both stayed with her as she alternately walked and ran the quarter-mile.

Having done that and progressing in the same vein for the half-mile and the mile run, she trained for our annual 7.6-mile spring madness in San Francisco: the Bay-To-Breakers run. But the same brainwashed state kept returning to overwhelm her. It was too far to go; she was not ready yet; perhaps next year; she wasn't a runner, only a jogger.

When she found she couldn't back out gracefully, we all went and had a marvelous time with thousands of other irrepressible beginning runners. Women, children, young athletes—magnificent people having a great Sunday morning. As we ran together, the endless row of smiles on the sidelines seemed to agree that we were all mad but they wished that they could be in there with us.

When we finished and ran back to meet our girl still chugging along, we ran the last of the 7.6 miles hand-in-hand to the applause of the crowd—for her it was like an Olympic finish. She now had no doubt but that she was a runner. Having come that far, she could do anything. She had finally buried the myth for herself about a woman's role in sports. She became one of us without the slightest intimidation that must plague all beginning women runners.

THE MATTER OF SPECIAL ALLOWANCES

Another myth about the female runner is that special allowances need be made because of her reproductive functions. It has been demonstrated that menses interferes not in the least with running. Many women have run during their pregnancies without any significant interference. Postpartum women seem to return even stronger to a competitive level.

Another idea is that running is not for all women; nothing could be farther from the truth. Running is not for the elite alone nor for any special group. It is for all ages: for the obese as well as the slim, the active as well as the passive, the solitary as well as the gregarious. For entirely too long in our occidental culture and particularly in our sports, we have reserved a special place for the participants with the highest scores, the fastest and best performances. The also-rans, the second-bests, are all considered as being not quite up to what they should be and are therefore diminished in comparison. What choice, therefore, but to sit on the sidelines as spectators.

All of that changes with running. We are all winners. The true athlete becomes ourselves.

So the emphasis shall be to run; not competitively but for self. There will be time enough to run competitively if that spirit moves one. The basis for running enjoyment is the act itself, however, with no reference to winning or losing.

Racing represents another level undertaken in the spirit of play. Then there are additional rewards if unusual talents are found. However, studies have shown that elite runners rank internal rewards far greater than the visible ones. That represents the basic approach of the average runner—male or female. The winning of self-esteem that accompanies running is a large enough victory.

Let us examine some of the biological parameters involved in running, and some of the similarities and differences between male and female runners.

The central biological male/female difference is the reproductive function. There are basic hormonal differences associated with reproduction that produce changes in a variety of bodily functions and structures such as muscle mass, body composition, bio-mechanical differences, stature, and organ size. These can not be viewed as more or less than, or better or worse; only as different.

The male hormone is testosterone. The female hormone is estrogen. These hormones have differing effects on the body which not only involve the various secondary sex characteristics but a variety of more subtle differences. Hormonal production, therefore, is a genetic endowment and is not easily altered. Studies have shown that female competitive runners do not change their hormonal composition; any body changes that occur with running represent a training effect alone. Consequences of hormonal endowment produce differences in stature, in body composition, in weight, and in organ size. These have no impact on the average or elite female runner's ability. The impact is of importance only when comparing male and female performance.

Musculoskeletal

The female is shorter and weighs less than her male counterpart. Her legs are consequently shorter so she necessarily has a shorter stride. She compensates by a faster running tempo. These characteristics are no different than might be seen with a tall female runner and a short male runner. The shorter stride produces a slower speed in the woman compared with the man not quite made up by the faster tempo. Indeed, the energy expenditure seems to be slightly higher for the female runner at the same speed. In a well trained female runner, on the other hand, there is a lower body weight per unit of muscle mass that serves as a distinct advantage. Bone and joint functions are identical in both sexes. Because bones and joint-supporting structures increase in strength with stress, the fact that they are lighter in the female does not make them any more fragile than in the male, considering the stress she imposes on them.

Yet women do seem to have more injuries than men. This may be a response, not so much to greater fragility, but to the socioculturally-induced sedentary role of the female. Involvement in sports is not usual for a woman; her musculoskeletal system, therefore, has probably over the years been subject to lower stresses than necessary to adapt her to avoid injury. But this is also as true for the sedentary male. Bones, tendons, and ligaments are biologically indistinguishable between sexes. If the injury rate is greater among women runners it can be avoided by more prudent conditioning and avoidance of the overuse syndrome, but the suggestion is just as applicable to males.

The term "overuse syndrome" may be a new one and may need definition. The condition may occur in any organ system but primarily refers to the musculoskeletal system where there may be a small anatomical defect or be caused by the way a shoe fits or with a joint position which we can normally handle without discomfort. But with repetitive use, as with high-mileage running, continued excessive use eventually leads to breakdown without sufficient periods for tissue adjustment, repair, or adaptation.

One additional point that might be mentioned here is the need for conditioning the major organ systems at the same pace. If the cardiorespiratory improvement is faster than the musculoskeletal adaptation, we run the risk—almost a certainty—of overstressing our musculoskeletal system and incurring an injury.

I have become aware of a particular hazard in laying off running for periods when our family is skiing in the winter. If the layoff is for a week or 10 days, muscle adaptation is lost faster than cardiorespiratory adaptation. When returning to running, because my aerobic capacity hasn't changed significantly, I may run listening to that distant drummer and overstress my musculoskeletal system even though both were adapted equally before the layoff.

While we have some guides to our aerobic state of exercise, such as our respiratory and cardiac rates, the only guides to our musculoskeletal nearness to capacity, and therefore injury, is discomfort; often not even that. A stress fracture occurs suddenly with no warning when the bone reaches a breaking point. A pulled muscle or torn ligament does the same. Male and female runners must equally observe the warning, therefore, of allowing the body enough time to adapt its organ systems at the same pace when faced with the increased demands that running entails.

Muscle function is identical in male and female runners. Muscles are anatomically indistinguishable except for the greater muscle mass in the male, both in the entire muscle as well as in the individual fiber. This is in response to the influence of the male hormone testosterone. Muscle conditioning seems to be the same in each sex, although there is a greater gain for the larger male muscle mass than the female. Individual muscle fibers are of several types but basically there are fast-twitch fibers, used by the body for sudden, explosive needs; and slow-twitch fibers, used for the long, steady, slow use as in running. There are no male-female differences in the percentages of each group of fibers.

Muscle enzymes that create energy from foodstuffs and oxygen seem to be slightly more numerous in the male but studies have cautioned again that this may be a reflection more of the activity level of the subjects used in the study, with boys generally being more active than girls and, therefore, not completely comparable so far as muscle enzyme studies are concerned.

In summary: while there are differences in the musculoskeletal system between male and female runners, they have no bearing on the ability of the woman to run any distance, remain free of injury, train to a competitive level, and thrive on every moment of it. She has all the natural endowments and no impediments whatsoever.

BODY COMPOSITION

A second major area where male and female differ is in body composition. There is a greater amount of relative body fat in the female under the influence of the female hormone estrogen in contrast to the greater muscle mass in the male. As with stature and limb length, these differences produce no significant impediment for the average female runner. They do produce advantages and disadvantages for the male peak-performance runners.

An increase in body fat is a disadvantage because it represents increased body weight that must be carried for each step. Elite long-distance male runners have a body fat of less than five percent. Frank Shorter, Olympic marathon runner, has two percent body fat. He would be considered underweight on our usual height-weight charts.

L'eggs
8003
L'eggs
MINI
5464

Our ideas for biological normals are based on the bell-shaped curve that has a mean that is by definition the norm. Runners are giving the health professionals new ideas about the great variation between the norm and the desirable. A male does not have to have a cholesterol level of 250-300 milligrams percent* because that is average. He is better at 150. His high-density lipoprotein level need not be 35 milligrams percent. It is better at 70. The height-weight charts are not used by the alert physician. He uses skin-fold thickness or other methods to determine body fat.

In all of these measurements and in others he will find his runners are not average. His findings begin to suggest that runners represent a new class that casts doubts on what we consider to be healthy because it is in the "average" range. Many parameters of health and illness will undergo further close scrutiny when the runner's makeup is more extensively understood as a more healthy model than is the average.

Fat stores are there for most of us. The average sedentary female who is not obese has a 25-30 percent body fat compared with the average male's 15-20 percent. Even the leanest long-distance runners show this relative difference. Although such excess body fat in the female is a normal characteristic it can be effectively trimmed by the running female to the advantage of her ease of running as well as her appearance. There is ample evidence that this occurs in women as well as in men.

The lighter female weight seems to compensate for the relatively greater fat percentage. Women also seem to have these fat stores somewhat more readily available for energy. Fat stores represent the body's design that guarantees nourishment when there is no food intake for prolonged periods. This rarely happens in our affluent societies; these stores are carried in vain waiting for an emergency that never occurs.

Energy for muscle contraction is derived from carbohydrates, fats, and proteins. Sustained muscle work seems to be based primarily on fat utilization. Therefore, for a female runner there is a tradeoff between having the extra relative weight to carry versus having energy available for prolonged sustained action. Such fat utilization produces a decrease in fat stores. A long-distance runner uses glycogen stores and fat for energy. It

---

* The percentage of a substance in 100 milliliters of blood.

is reported that a marathon runner operating at 75 percent of his aerobic capacity will deplete his glycogen stores at about 18 miles. He will then use fat stores for energy. Women seem to be better adapted to this and don't have any symptoms associated with the shift in metabolism. Men often do unless they have specifically trained their intermediary metabolic pathways to make this shift with ease.

Perhaps, in our Grand Design, women were equipped to metabolize fats readily as a way of providing available energy stores during pregnancy when metabolic energy priorities are under rapidly changing states. Perhaps they have the mechanisms to repeat the process easily in contrast to the male. All runners develop a decrease in fat stores and there are also adaptive increases in muscle mass and muscle strength. Muscle fiber contraction and therefore strength are identical in an equal weight of muscle, male or female. The innately greater muscle mass in the male allows for greater strength, but the female can increase her muscle mass identically with training. Incidentally, the paradoxical finding of weight not changing in the well conditioned female may be based on this exchange of fat weight for muscle weight. The specter of the musclebound female, of course, never materializes. Witness the physically fit well conditioned runners whose lean, lithe, and ideally proportioned appearance would be the envy of any woman and attractive to any man.

For the beginning woman runner, if one of her motivating forces is a desire to lose weight, there is no doubt that a continued program of running will accomplish that and allow her to feel great while doing it.

In any event, women have higher fat stores and metabolize them readily, which proves to be an advantage in endurance running. Body composition imposes no handicaps for the average female runner. For the competitive female runner compared with the male, there are some characteristics of body composition that are beneficial and some that are a relative handicap.

Anatomical

There are no significant female anatomical characteristics that affect her running. All internal and external organs are adequately supported so that a woman can run without concern about jarring anything loose. Use of the bra for comfort is completely optional. There is ample evidence that the menstrual cycle has no bearing on a female runner's performance. On the contrary, running seems to affect dysmenorrhea and premenstrual tension beneficially. An active and heavy running schedule may also shorten menses or even produce times of amenorrhea.

Some women who have had children are plagued with an annoying problem of slight urinary incontinence with stress. They generally have learned to avoid a full bladder at times of anticipated stress, which adequately controls the problem.

The wider childbearing pelvis of the female runner tends to produce a slightly different foot plant and running gait from the male runner, but this is of absolutely no concern for either the average or the competitive runner as it affects running performance.

Shorter stature and lighter weight produce smaller internal organs which decrease a female runner's oxygen delivery capacity. But these internal organs are otherwise identical with the male and function in an identical fashion. So while there are some uniquely female anatomical features, they have no bearing on the ability to run comfortably and efficiently.

Cardiorespiratory

A brief review of the role of the heart, lungs, and circulatory system is appropriate. Running involves a rhythmic repetitive contraction of certain large muscle groups of the legs with associated arm movement. Muscles contract on demand by utilizing complex high-energy chemical bonds. These energy bonds can be used in one of two ways, either with oxygen or without. The word *aerobic* literally means to take place where oxygen is present. *Anaerobic* then means without oxygen. To allow for muscle contraction in a hurry, we are designed to work either way, without adequate oxygen but for limited times; or to allow for muscle contraction indefinitely with adequate oxygen and, of course, with the basic energy sources themselves in the form of food.

All of us have a threshold where we shift from aerobic to anaerobic function. That threshold is limited only by the amount of oxygen we can deliver to the muscle. In turn, that maximum amount of oxygen delivery is based on how much air we can move in and out of our lungs, how readily we can move oxygen to the bloodstream, how fast and how much blood we can deliver to the muscles, and how readily and fully we can extract oxygen from the blood and deliver it to the muscle cell.

All of these acting together produce a maximum aerobic capacity, the ultimate fitness measure that varies from less than 20cc per minute per kilogram of body weight in the sedentary to over 80cc per minute per kilogram of body weight in the long-distance runner.

We increase the muscles' demand for oxygen when we exercise. The body adapts itself to this increased demand by a number of changes, all of which improve the efficiency of the body to deliver ultimately a greater amount of oxygen per unit of time. This adaptation is an identical biological trait in males and females and represents the cardiorespiratory training effect. Except for some minor anatomical differences, all of the parts are identical in both sexes. Therefore, the physiological effects of running on the cardiorespiratory systems of men and women are identical.

The minor differences referred to are based on organ size. The female lungs are slightly smaller and therefore have a smaller vital capacity and smaller maximum breathing capacity. The heart is slightly smaller and ejects a smaller volume of blood with each stroke. As a result of menstruation, hemoglobin levels are lower in females; the blood therefore has a lower oxygen-carrying capacity. The net effect of these differences is that the maximum oxygen capacity is less in women than in men. As with our previous comparisons this would have no bearing on a woman's effectiveness as a runner. The technicalities of maximizing the training effect to enhance the body's ability to deliver oxygen are of concern only to someone interested in peak performance in male or female.

There are studies that show the training effect increases oxygen capacity by increasing cardiac output and by increasing the ability of tissues to extract more oxygen.

There is the additional psychological training effect, for a beginning runner particularly, of recognizing that shortness of breath is normal, that one can tolerate it and can learn precisely how to train at from 75 percent to maximum aerobic capacity for a long time and recover quite nicely. Studies have shown that long-distance runners, both elite as well as postmyocardial infarction runners, do so at the same general percentage of their maximum aerobic capacity, which is somewhere between 75 and 80 percent. The female runner operates in an identical fashion after she learns, as any beginning runner must learn, how to feel for that level and use it effectively.

It must be reassuring to any beginning runner to know that patients who have had heart attacks participate in marathons regularly. Any woman who has had any qualms about the safety of running for herself or her male friends need not be put off by sensationalized accounts of joggers' deaths. A cardiorespiratory system that adapts itself slowly to increased demands is functioning far more efficiently after conditioning than before. With treadmill tests to determine safe peak levels for beginner middle-aged males and with an understanding of how to avoid overstressing the body at any time, running is safer than any other sport that demands peak bursts of effort.

The marvel of our bodies, which are so anxious to please us and accommodate our wishes, is that they will improve conditioning at only 50 percent of our aerobic capacity. The hazard for some lies in being highly competitive souls who believe that if a pulse rate of 120 is good a pulse rate of 180 must be better. The not-so-secret methods of various cardiac rehabilitation centers around the country is to avoid that philosophy like the plague. They exercise their post-heart attack patients in slow, graded fashion and get them to a point where marathons are handled with ease.

Gentle running is equally safe for male and female; both have all the natural equipment to improve fitness to a high level with the attendant benefits and enjoyment.

Psychological

Any discussion of the inner workings of the female runner would not be complete without mentioning the psychological. There is not much question that *pleasure of running* is the primary motivating force that keeps a runner going. While running's tremendous growth in the past few years largely had its impetus through the protection it seemed to offer men against the ravages of coronary artery disease, that has taken a back seat to other benefits of running that seem suddenly to have been discovered and assumed pre-eminence. Those other benefits are primarily psychological. As in each of the previous sections it has been helpful to look over the features of running that impact equally on males and females, then look for the unique impact of running on the female.

WHEN RUNNING IS JOY

There have been many attempts to articulate elusive psychological benefits of running; all seem to fall short. Every major treatise on running attempts to deal with the subject but has difficulty explaining the phenomenon. Yet every runner has experienced the good feeling that running produces. It has been described as taking us back to our childhood, or to a more primitive state, or discovering the way we would have lived thousands of years ago.

As a physician constantly in touch with biological bases for illness and health, I believe the answers to the joy of running are on a more fundamental level. As humans we are the current product of nature's almost infinite variety of experimental designs. We are not the last word in design for even now we have an endless variety of arrangements among the human species, ranging from variations in enzyme function to color and to size. All of these bodily functions that characterize us as humans have been the result of chance, but their perseverance has been through necessity. If a chance mutation served a useful function that improved the recipient's chance of survival in a hostile world, it persevered and the progeny of that mutant also persevered until the mutation became predominant, only to be replaced in turn by one that offered a still better chance of survival.

The process has been a slow one, with each change taking thousands and millions of years to develop. Human history and our perception of present time must be viewed in biological terms to see that it represents a brief stop-action view of what is really a constantly-changing panorama.

But here we are: with calf muscles that are designed just so, with an ankle joint that is universally put together in one way; with a heart that has certain capabilities and limitations; with hemoglobin that varies in its affinity for oxygen, depending on who we are; with mitochondrial enzymes that have an exclusively refined function.

All of this magnificent creation, this endlessly perfected and constantly redesigned thing of beauty, is at our complete command, awaiting only the signal for it to perform. The muscle waits patiently for its signal. The enzyme that converts fat to energy waits for its signal. The emergency pathways of metabolism that provide us with energy when there is none left, the entire magnificent effort is endlessly at the ready for the moment we will it to begin.

I believe the joy of running lies here. It is the sum total of all these parts doing what they were designed to do that translates itself into physiochemical signals decoded in the brain as the thought "that was good, do it again."

How can one try to pinpoint the source of gratification in instinctual behavior? It is implanted too deeply in us, and cuts across all biological systems. The sociobiologist would have us believe that DNA rules our lives. We are only now beginning to understand that much of what we think, feel, and do are the results of the endless physical and chemical reactions in our body that add up to a signal that makes us hungry, thirsty, happy, restless, maternal, sexy, or sleepy. Many of these signals are understood by modern man but most are not. Most seem to arise seemingly out of nowhere.

The runner is taking a giant step when he learns to listen to his body and discovers for the first time something that we have lost in the millenia of our acculturation: that the body, the sum total of all those exquisite acts that orchestrate in this primitive act of running, is telling us all kinds of things and that these unified biological functions say "my human worked hard and he rested and it was good."

These are human psychological benefits that apply to all of us. While fundamental, they are part of a larger series of psychological events that seem to occur in runners. It is as if this awareness of body and its language at a cellular level provide us with new insights into living in harmony with our inner and outer worlds. There are endless paths to this awareness and running is only one of them. It combines several unique features, however, that give it such effectiveness. Physical effort puts us in touch with ourselves.

The procedure of running is simplicity itself. There are no lessons, no gurus, no equipment, no right way, no wrong way. There is no one to exhort you and no one else affected but you. Goals are simple or need not be set. Change is evident from the beginning. One learns where self begins and ends; and one is free to choose how that self will relate to its universe.

Nowhere is this more evident than in the female runner, for it is the female that bears an age-old burden of the subservient role in our culture. Not only has acculturation led them to lose the ability to listen to their bodies, for many women it has led to a true loss of identity. Who does she see when she looks in the mirror but a reflection, not of self but of someone who is easily recognized by how well she plays the role she has accepted. She is someone's wife or sweetheart. Someone's mother. Someone's cook. Someone other than an individual in her own right.

Running strips away all these sociocultural impositions and leaves the female runner quiet and alone with her true self. It is *her* breathlessness alone. *Her* pounding heart. *Her* tired legs, *her* weariness, *her* own determination that tells *her* she *will go on this one lap or this one mile or ten* and then proceed to do it. All of us must be able to say to ourselves "I can do it," and on doing it thrill in the joy of accomplishment, no matter how small. To be able to do so daily is a privilege, doubly so for the woman. There is nothing in the way but her own thoughts, her own body, her own determination, and a precious few moments in her life when she has the opportunity to become aware of herself and her uniqueness. Once seen, nothing else is quite the same again.

She has touched a fountainhead of self-esteem and confidence that carries through the days, the weeks, the years. Running gives her the opportunity to know precisely who she is and how she fits in to the larger order of things.

In summary, we have discussed the various biological functions that affect running and have described the male-female similarities and differences. The differences carry no value judgment. That one parameter is less-than or more-than has no relevance to the overriding consideration that the human is admirably designed to run. All of us have natural endowments that allow us equally to run naturally and comfortably, to condition ourselves, and to improve our fitness to run competitively and excel.

The female runner has been subject to a variety of sociocultural and psychological handicaps that are finally being overcome. The biological myths are being dispelled. She now has an opportunity to secure her wider awareness and freedom through running.

There is nothing to stop her once she begins.

9

The Incredible Machine

The world's foremost authority analyzes the woman athlete's "secret" weapon

Dr. Ernst van Aaken

In a textbook of sports medicine published in West Germany in 1976, women's athletic potential is evaluated on the basis of muscle strength alone, then compared with men's. Women are judged inferior in their potential for certain types of athletic events. Where strength is a major factor—as in short sprints and other running events up to 600 meters, the shot-put, discus, boxing, wrestling, weightlifting, etc.—this is a perfectly valid judgment. What is completely overlooked, however, is that women have been running the 800 meters since 1954; 1500 meters since 1966; and 3000 meters, the marathon, 100 kilometers, and even 100 miles since 1973.

Since official international women's marathon racing began in 1973, we see an increasing trend for women to move into training for and racing 100 kilometers. At the 100-kilometer race at Unna, Germany in September 1976, for example, Christa Vahlensieck finished fourth among 800 men in the fantastic time of 7:50:37. Natalie Cullimore of California ran 100 miles in 16:11 in a 1971 race that none of the male entrants managed to finish.

Mary Etta Boitano, 11, ran 3:01 at the first U.S. Women's Marathon Championships in 1974, finishing fourth. (Mary Etta's time was almost 28 times faster than the 1904 Olympic Games marathon gold medalist: Hicks of the U.S.) Both of the world women's marathon records in 1975, by Jacki Hansen of the U.S. and Christa Vahlensieck of West Germany, were faster than Alben Stenroos's winning race at the 1924 Games in Paris.

Neither of these women had ever raced the marathon until three years before their record-breaking runs.

All of these feats prove that negative claims, and the barring of women and children from official endurance events have been completely uncalled-for. Decades will probably pass before such prejudices are erased. The effect of labeling high-level sports competition a matter of pure muscle strength has been to exclude women even from sports that do not require muscle strength.

What counts in endurance events is not muscle strength, primarily, but low body weight and faultless functioning of the body's enzyme systems.

WOMEN ARE METABOLIC ATHLETES

The adult male "muscleman" is by no means the exemplar of sports excellence he has been made out to be; he represents the rare exception among males. Women and children of normal health are biologically stronger than the average stereotypical male Adonis. The internal biochemistry of women and children gives them an excellent prognosis for long and healthy life: much better than that of the strong man.

Statistics tell us that women are biologically tougher than men. The average life expectancy for women is now around 73 years, that of men barely 70. Statistics from England show that each year only 20 men celebrate birthdays of 100 or over in that country, while there are 100 women in that category. To put it in other terms: for every 100,000 girls, 7818 will reach the age of 90; of every 100,000 boys, only 3460 will live to see a 90th birthday.

Let us compare the ideal body types for men and women, and their corresponding metabolic advantages and disadvantages. We will follow the example of U.S. researcher John H. Bland, choosing ideal weight for men of 70 kilograms (154 pounds) and, for women, 55 kilograms (121 pounds).

The male body is composed of up to 60 percent water by weight, the female body about 52 percent. In a man's body, 45 percent of the water is stored in the cells. Women have a more concentrated solution in their cells, on the other hand, with only 40 percent of their fluids being stored there. A man's body contains 30-35 percent solid substance by weight, woman's up to 40 percent. Of these solids, in the male organism about 35 percent are organic substances; for women the figure is 45 percent or higher—mainly accounted for by protein. A woman's body contains more vital substances by weight than does a man's, in other words, with enzyme proteins most likely predominant.

The most important difference between men and women from a biochemical and sports-physiological standpoint is that men's bodies are 40-50 percent muscle tissue by weight, while muscle tissue accounts for only 20-30 percent of a woman's weight (the average being 23 percent). Muscle is 32-52 percent water. This means that a man's body binds more water. The critical factor here is that more water means more hydrogen.

Women have less muscle tissue than men, and this usually puts them at a disadvantage in athletic events calling for strength. But women have more subcutaneous fat which represents a reserve source of energy for endurance exercise and protection against cold. Women also float higher in water because of their subcutaneous fat, and this partly accounts for women holding all the world records in endurance swimming, including the absolute world's best timed ultradistance record: a distance of 90 kilometers (55.8 miles).

A woman's muscle and connective tissues give her a superior starting point for endurance exercise. She also has more protoplasm, which means that her muscle fibers are better adapted to long exercise. Woman's musculature is made to order for middle distances but not for sprinting.

Muscle tissue in humans and in many test animals reveals a mixture of "fast-twitch" and "slow-twitch" fibers. Fast-twitch fibers are white to pale pink; slow-twitch fibers are red. The red comes from myoglobin, an oxygen-bearing protein richly present in the slow-twitch fibers, but almost completely lacking in fast-twitch fibers.

A woman's skeletal muscles are designed for endurance, too. They stand somewhere between skeletal muscle and heart muscle in their functions and biochemical makeup, and in this they resemble muscles of the uterus. These female skeletal muscles, again and with very few exceptions, are not designed for sprinting; but they are capable of performing at high efficiency levels for very long periods. This is apparent in women's superior ability to handle the 100-kilometer distance without great muscle trauma or exhaustion. The skeletal muscles depend on a continuous supply of energy from aerobic metabolism, as is also the case with other endurance muscles: the heart muscle, the diaphragm, the flight muscles of birds and insects. All these endurance muscles are especially rich in enzymes and other components of the respiratory cycle found in the mitochondria; the count of their mitochondria depending on their specific endurance function.

Even in women who are not athletic in the sense of muscle-strength, the muscle fibers are very thin, so that oxygen passes easily into their fibers from the bloodstream—an extremely favorable factor for endurance.

Men have an advantage at racing distances under 400 meters, because of a high content of ATP (adenosintriphosphoric acid) in their skeletal muscles, consisting of about 5 mMol/kg of muscle. Women have less serum ATP in their skeletal muscles than men—at most 25 milligrams percent, compared with Olympic-class male athletes such as Harald Norpoth (5000-meter 1968 silver medalist at Mexico City), with 31 milligrams percent.

Creatine, a nitrogenous acid acting in muscle contraction, accounts for more than half of the nonprotein nitrogen in muscle tissue. Creatine is present mostly in the form of creatine phosphate, in amounts of up to 20 mMol/kg. The heart muscle, the supreme endurance muscle in the human body, contains very little creatine—only 1 g mMol of ATP and 2 mMol of creatine phosphate. Women's muscle tissue contains only small amounts of creatine phosphate, too. The muscles change creatine into creatinine which is eliminated in the urine; this gives us a way of measuring the muscle's consumption of creatine and phosphate. Sprinters and middle-distance runners burn up huge amounts of these substances, but women eliminate only a third as much creatinine in the urine as men, even after strenuous endurance performances.

It is still widely stated that endurance performance depends on the glycogen in the liver and muscles. Research by Bing in the U.S. in 1956, however, showed that this is not true of the heart muscle—the body's best endurance muscle. Bing found that the human heart prefers to metabolize noncarbohydrates, in particular the fatty acids. His figures for the fuel of the heart muscle were: 67 percent fatty acids, 17.9 percent glucose, 16.46 percent lactic acid, 5.6 percent amino acids, 4.3 percent ketone bodies, and 0.54 percent pyruvic acid.

My own measurements showed that endurance is *not* increased by a high-carbohydrate diet. A 2:30 marathon runner will burn 2600 calories during his race, corresponding to 650 grams of glycogen. But this much glycogen is not found in the muscles or liver of even the best trained human body. A runner could not use it all for running even if this much glycogen were available, because the body also takes carbohydrate (along with fat and protein) to rebuild its own tissues. During emergency conditions (when the body's carbohydrate reserves are exhausted, corresponding to about a half-day of walking), the body can continue to work by using other fuel reserves such as the fatty acids. This was proved in 1897 by Asia explorer Sven Hedin, who walked 500 kilometers (310 miles) across the Takla Makan desert in 13 days without food or water.

The following values, derived from original data published by Dr. Howald of Magglingen, W. Germany, were obtained for a group of 14 runners in a 100-kilometer race.

Average weight: 65.7 kg
Total body fluids: 40 liters
Fat-free solids: 18 kg
Total fat: 7.7 kg
Total muscle mass by weight: 26.3 kg
Total muscle solids by weight, without water: 9.2 kg
Fuel fats in muscle: 22.3% (4014 g)
Highest value obtained for total liver glycogen: 340 g
Highest estimated muscle glycogen content (assuming 4 percent by weight: 368 g
Total glycogen (maximal): 708 g
Energy equivalent of total: glycogen, 2832 calories (equivalent to 40-kilometer run)
Energy equivalent of total free fuel fats: 37,731 calories (equivalent to 539-kilometer run)

The greatest endurance feats are not fueled by carbohydrate alone, but by a mixture of fatty acids, amino acids, and carbohydrate. In the long distances and ultradistances, carbohydrate is the "small change" of energy metabolism; the true "capital assets" are the fatty acids. Racewalkers in the 500-kilometer (310-mile) Paris-to-Strasbourg event lose nine pounds of body weight in 69 hours, when the body relies primarily on fatty acids for its fuel. For a trained female marathon runner who weighs 97 pounds, this racewalking performance is equivalent to a run of about 180 kilometers (112 miles) relying on fat reserves for power. The total carbohydrate reserves in our hypothetical woman runner's body—about 368 grams—would carry her no further than about 21 kilometers (13 miles).

The body's glycogen reserves can be maximized by years of training to about 700 grams. But does it make any sense to rely cntirely on stored carbohydrate for energy, when the well trained (not well-padded!) body's fat reserves are sufficient for 201 to 500 kilometers (125 to 310 miles) of continuous running? As I've written elsewhere, this ability to run on the body's fat reserves can be learned by frequently running very long in training on an empty stomach.

During his brief muscle-power exercise, the stereotypical male athlete burns carbohydrate, creatine phosphate, and ATP. His muscles have a high water content, but women athletes have less intramuscular water, more fatty acids, and less carbohydrate to give them biochemical talents for endurance rather than strength.

A woman's connective tissue counts in her favor when it comes to the endurance events, giving her special protection from muscle tears and tendonitis. Compare the male decathlete, whose body structure condemns him to constant injury, with 100-kilometer specialist Eva Westphal who almost never is injured.

Important reasons for woman's organic toughness are found in the metabolisms of water and minerals. The exercise capacity of human beings depends strongly on economical water metabolism. The reason for this is that hydrogen, the more abundant component of water, is an acid that can cause all kinds of mischief when too much of it is in our bodies. A woman will have, on the average, less hydrogen in her body than a man. Cell respiration (biological oxidation) has the single function of removing great quantities of hydrogen from the body.

This process is complex—more than 200 separate enzymes are involved in taking hydrogen through the respiratory cycle to combine with oxygen and form energy-rich ATP, plus water and carbon dioxide as waste products. Having stored less hydrogen, a woman needs less oxygen; a reduced oxygen requirement, combined with woman's lower body weight, allows her to keep running longer.

Men who carry too much weight in muscle and fat are at a disadvantage in competition at long distances. The heavy male will have to burn a greater amount of hydrogen to match a woman's endurance, but he may not be able to process enough oxygen to do so. A male decathlete is in fact far inferior to a good woman runner in the endurance required for racing at

1500 meters, for example.

Another reason for woman's greater relative endurance is evident from the following table, which shows how much water is formed during exercise from 100 grams of each of the three main fuel substances:

Fuel	Water Formed (per 100 grams)
fatty acids	107 cc
carbohydrates	55 cc
protein	41 cc

A slender woman who weighs 100 pounds has more protein in her blood than a man, which means that she is superior to a man in pure endurance. It is well-known that the typical male runner loses extraordinary amounts of perspiration on long, hot runs (losing valuable mineral salts), while women run "dry" and are better able to tolerate exercise in hot weather.

In the 98-degree heat of the 1976 Boston marathon, top woman finisher Kim Merritt ran a personal best time of 2:47:10, while fully 1,000 of the 2,000 male entrants dropped out. Only 8 of the 70 women failed to finish. With few exceptions, each of the men who finished was exhausted at the end; but I saw every one of the 62 women finishers looking quite fresh, many of them even managing a finish-line sprint.

In the urine of men who've run to exhaustion in the marathon, potassium values have been measured at 400 milligrams percent and higher, while among women in exhausted condition, potassium values have never been higher than 250 milligrams percent. Urine pH in exhausted male runners was frequently near the critical 4.4, while for women the pH was generally between 6.0 and 5.3. Titratable acid for the urine samples taken from males was 1,000 out of 1,000, meaning that total acidification was just barely being checked by elimination through the kidneys.

SULFUR: WOMAN'S SECRET WEAPON

As much as 30 percent of the body's total protein is located in connective tissue, the cells of which are organized in three distinctive patterns: (1) collagenous fibers, (2) reticulate (net-like fibers), and (3) elastic fibers.

All these fibers are bedded in a kind of basic binding substance that also serves as a water storage depot.

The male body stores water mostly in muscle; the female in

connective tissue. Connective tissue is also a storage depot for electrically charged mineral particles (the so-called ions) that regulate the acidity and electrical charge of the body's fluids. Substances passing between the bloodstream and tissues move through this binding tissue.

Connective tissue is made up of a number of mucus-like carbohydrates in combination with sulfur and protein. Research by professor Max Burger has shown that all women's bodies contain more sulfur than men's.

There are many enzymes in the body that contain at least one sulfur-hydrogen group (SH-group), the presence of which is essential for the effective function of the enzyme. Among these are an enzyme catalyst, called dehydrogenase, essential to the process of breaking down hydrogen in the respiratory cycle. Women's bodies, with more SH-enzymes, are given yet another advantage in endurance metabolism: the female organism seems particularly adapted to break down hydrogen. This may account for women seeming to require less oxygen than men for running a long distance.

It is well known that some women are less severely affected by metal poisoning than men. Sulfur, in compounds of the sulfate group, combines with phenols and detoxifies them. This is important in exercise, because the toxic heavy metals block SH-enzymes, thus inhibiting chemical reactions of the respiratory cycle. The female organism, containing a greater concentration of SH-substances, uses sulfate compounds to remove heavy metal from its enzyme bonds.

Exercise stretches and contracts the connective tissue, improving its ability to bind water and hold electrically charged mineral solutions. The plasticity of the connective tissue is increased with regular exercise. Cartilage, tendons, and spinal discs are thus given a measure of resistance to injury. This is evident in gymnastics, where the great stability of women's bodies against twisting stresses is visibly proved. The more that connective tissue is trained, the less is the risk of injury—regardless of general opinion in academic medicine.

In taut connective tissues—the tendons, for example—X-rays reveal an almost crystalline pattern along both cross-sectional and longitudinal axes. This crystalline pattern develops with age, especially with consistent exercise; where exercise is lacking, in paralysis or in old age, the pattern degenerates and becomes disorderly and knotted.

L'eggs
7006

A woman's spinal discs will deform less than a man's even under long-continued stresses. The spinal connective tissue will deflect and slide out of position, to the point of rupture, only under extreme loads.

Electrically charged mineral ions such as potassium, sodium, chlorine, phosphoric acid, and sulfur are stored in connective tissue; these play an important role in the exercise characteristics of a woman's tendons and spinal column. A dry tendon is brittle, fragile; water makes connective tissue soft and pliable.

We know that most well-trained men store more water and minerals in their muscles, predisposing them to perform well in sprint and strength events; and women store more water and mineral ions in connective tissue, giving them better endurance and stress resistance. There is scarcely a male runner alive who can finish a 100-kilometer (62.14 miles) run without pain; but among women freedom from pain and muscle ache is the rule, not the exception.

Connective tissue is affected in many ways by hormones. The mineralocorticoid hormones promote growth, sulfur storage in connective tissues, aid in regeneration of tissue in wounds and the formation of calluses after fractures; in fact, we see these calluses more often in cases of fractures involving trained women. Estrogens enrich fluids of the connective tissue by increasing the amount of mucopolysaccharides.

Contrary to views held by earlier researchers, the heart muscle appears to be equally trainable in men and women. Two West German national-champion runners, Antje Gleichfeld and Anni Pede, each had a heart volume of 1,040 cc. Triple gold medalist Emil Zatopek had a heart volume of only 1,060 cc. It's reasonable to assume that future women runners in the marathon and 100 kilometers will have larger heart volumes than international-class male distance runners and racing cyclists. Having more protoplasm, a woman probably has an advantage in maximal trainability of the heart muscle. Plasma in males accounts for 4 percent of body weight, on the average, while for women the figure is 4.5 percent.

WOMEN'S BODIES BIND MORE IRON

Women runners commonly reveal subnormal hemoglobin, leading physicians to diagnose anemia—the blame for which is then laid to distance running. This is a prime example of medical judgment prejudicial to the patient. The "normal" hemoglobin count has been arbitrarily set at 16 grams; but no one has yet established a true norm for women, given the common knowledge that women tolerate blood losses better than men.

A woman I was coaching became German national trail-running champion with a hemoglobin count of 58 percent. Dozens of similar cases could be cited, and we cannot assume that such women are ill, if only because their running performances are convincing proof of the contrary.

I believe that women can get along well on less hemoglobin because they have a better capacity for binding iron in the bloodstream.

The main vehicle for the transport of iron in the body is siderophiline, a protein with complex iron bonds. We know that siderophiline accounts for 3 percent of serum protein on the average, and that one siderophiline molecule can carry at most two iron atoms. Because trained female distance runners show total serum protein values higher than men's (7.4 to 9 grams percent), this means that *women have a greater general iron-binding capacity than men. They compensate for lower hemoglobin by a higher iron content in the blood.*

This explains why women marathoners weighing less than 100 pounds have better iron-binding capacity than many male athletes, surpassing even the weightlifters with their mountains of powerful muscle. Lydia Ritter, a West German marathon-runner, weighed 93 pounds at the time of laboratory testing and had 325 milligrams percent cholesterol, 82 milligrams percent hemoglobin, 9.0 grams percent total protein, and an iron-binding capacity of 142 gamma percent. These figures exceed those obtained for three international-class male runners: Harald Norpoth (110 gamma percent), Firedhelm Bongartz (116 gamma percent), and Herbert Schade (119 gamma percent). Analyses conducted by the University of Cologne Sports Institute at the world's first women's marathon on October 28, 1973 showed that gamma globulin values in these runners were above average.

Traditional medicine has apparently diagnosed anemia in cases where in fact none existed. Lower hemoglobin is simply compensated in trained female runners by increased iron-binding capacity. The female body seems also to have a higher concentration of iron-containing enzymes—specifically cytochrome and catalase.

Myoglobin, a muscle pigment generally given less attention

than hemoglobin, has an oxygen-binding capacity many times greater than that of hemoglobin. Myoglobin becomes saturated with oxygen at a mercury pressure of only 3.26mm compared to 20mm for hemoglobin. The white fast-twitch fibers in a male sprinter's muscles contain great amounts of ATP and creatine phosphate; the red endurance fibers that predominate in the skeletal muscles of women contain more myoglobin than does white muscle. Myoglobin's oxygen-binding capacity accounts for the ability of seals and whales to remain under water as long as two hours. These ocean mammals store oxygen in the myoglobin of their heart muscle. While the myoglobin count for the heart muscles of seals and whales is 7.7 grams percent, a hunting dog that can run well has only 0.5 grams percent myoglobin. English scientists working in the Andes have trained llamas for endurance at 4000-meter altitude. They found that with endurance training the hemoglobin in these animals increased by 25 percent, but that myoglobin had risen by 71 percent.

Lasse Viren seems to have built up his body's myoglobin in preparation for his gold-medal races at Montreal. Viren spent more than a year, at state expense, training at altitude in Mexico, running five days a week and about 25 slow miles a day at a pulse rate for optimal respiratory efficiency of 130 beats per minute.

CHOLESTEROL: MOTHER LODE OF PERFORMANCE HORMONES

The high water content of a man's body will remain high after puberty, because of the development of heavy muscles. It may increase further with rising body weight during the years past 30. But in women, water content falls after puberty, because hormonal conditions cause an increase in subcutaneous fat, and this fat has a low water content of only 2.3 percent. As we saw earlier, low water content is an advantage in endurance exercise, because it means less need for oxygen.

Cholesterol is referred to in academic medicine as the eternal enemy of the organism, but this is true only insofar as too much cholesterol in the diet may be harmful; and the same could be said of all dietary substances. The body can actually manufacture its own cholesterol, though a rich diet will bring in large additional amounts. The body makes about 1.5 grams of cholesterol every 24 hours, but it also processes about 5 grams of cholesterol daily in the liver. Cholesterol formation increases in cases of obesity. All 60 billion cells of the human body synthesize cholesterol, which is used in the construction and repair of cell membranes.

Cholesterol is a product of animal metabolism and is found in large amounts in animal foods such as meat, liver, and especially egg yolk. No cholesterol is made in plants. Through fasting and distance running, the cholesterol level can be greatly lowered, a fact that should be considered in the treatment of persons suffering from high cholesterol with attendant risk of coronary illness.

From cholesterol come the sex hormones, adrenal cortical hormone, and the gallic acids. Adrenal cortical hormones could be called the body's performance hormones. More than 40 adrenal cortical hormones have been analyzed, a deficiency of any of which (from disturbances in the adrenal cortex) produces death by loss of energy, known as Addison's disease.

We get a hint at the physiological role of cholesterol in exercise from the fact that skeletal muscle contains 250 milligrams percent of cholesterol, the uterine muscle 1,000 milligrams percent, and the heart muscle 2,000 milligrams percent.

High cholesterol in the blood and serum does not always signal disease as proven by my own tests on female age-group runners. These schoolgirls very often had 300 milligrams percent cholesterol in their blood; weighed only 90-100 pounds; had long, thin muscles, and were far from overweight. Their cholesterol and total-cholesterol values typically fell below 200 milligrams percent after a long run. A German age-group champion in the 3,000-meter trail run weighed 97 pounds and had 320 milligrams percent cholesterol. Following a 5,000-meter training run in 21 minutes her cholesterol was 195 milligrams percent. Lydia Ritter, who stood high in the world women's marathon lists in 1974 with a time of 3:05, weighed 93 pounds and had 325 milligrams percent blood cholesterol at rest, which fell to 176 milligrams percent after a time trial.

The adrenal glands of a woman weigh 10 percent more than a man's. The metabolic type of the trained woman as an "enzyme athlete" is equally expressed by her larger liver. Remarkably, as measured at rest and after exercise, some liver activities of certain enzymes are higher in female runners. The enzyme SGPT, normal at 12 mU for example, rises as high as 25 mU.

Women runners, as well as men for whom similar values are obtained, are definitely not suffering from liver ailments, though they may be in danger of being diagnosed that way even by specialists.

Cholesterol eaten in food requires several days — even weeks—to be assimilated and balanced with the cholesterol of the blood plasma and tissues. Processing in the liver, on the other hand, occurs in a matter of hours.

The adrenal cortical hormones derived from cholesterol have the closest possible relationship to the sex hormones. Male and female sex hormones are found in close proximity in both the male and female organisms. Progesterone, the "pregnancy hormone," is a key in the formation of the steroid hormones. Estrogens, the female hormones, are manufactured especially in the female body but also, in smaller quantities, in the male. The most effective form of estrogen is estradiol. Estradiol causes increased protein synthesis and improves respiration; and in fact, the best women marathoners have high protein values in their blood serum.

Of great interest is an estrogen-dependent hydrogen transfer between the pyridine coenzymes in the respiratory cycle. Estrogen and two other substances (NADPH2 and NADH2) are formed in greater amounts than in the male. What this means for the endurance abilities of women is that, due to higher estrogen content, the respiratory cycle runs more smoothly from the very start of exercise than it does in the male organism with its more specific sex hormones.

As I emphasized long ago in a paper delivered at the Sports Medicine Congress at Weimar in 1955, the endurance ability of women derives primarily from favorable metabolic conditions relative to the steroid derivatives.

The most important method of converting sugar into energy in the liver is not glycolisis (fermentation), as it is in the muscles, but a process involving oxygen. The oxidative function of a woman's liver is stronger than a man's (*Handbuch der physiologischen Chemie* von Flaschentrager—Lehnartz, Band II/2, 67). This means that women convert liver glycogen into energy more efficiently than do men.

The greater weight of women's adrenals (by 10 percent) likewise signifies better metabolic performance and endurance. In the male, the hormones adrenaline and noradrenaline are found in greater concentration in the adrenal core, providing short term energy for emergency situations as all-out sprints of 100-400 meters. On the basis of the predominant function of his adrenal core, man is once again just a sprinter.

Woman is an endurance performer because the functions of the adrenal cortex predominate in her metabolism, and the role of the cortex in energy metabolism is primarily to control the functional capacity of all the tissues and organs (Sayer, G. 1950 *Physiol.* rev. 30, 285).

Every special load on the organism, every so-called stress, brings about an increased need for adrenal cortical hormones. In short- and middle-distance racing there is acute depletion of the adrenal cortex, but moderate endurance exercise leads to a gradual hypertrophy (growth beyond normal size) of the adrenal cortex (Creutzfeld, Husten, Hager, 1953, cited by Buchner in *Allgemeine Pathologie*, p. 401).

More evidence of the biochemical basis for superior endurance in women, of the superior activity of her adrenal cortex, is that estrogens also promote hypertrophy of the adrenal cortex (Kimmelsdorf, D. J., and A. L. Soderwall: 1947. Changes induced in the adrenal cortical zones by ovarian hormones. *Endooxinologie* 41/21). The male sex hormones, on the other hand, reduce the size and function of the adrenal cortex (Greep, R. V., and I. C. Jones, *Rev. Proger. Hormones* Res 5/197).

My own laboratory tests involving isolation of 17-ketosteroid in the urine of seven of the best female 800-meter runners in West Germany from 1953 to 1955 resulted in single test values during training that averaged 13 milligrams percent compared with 9 milligrams percent in men. This chemical is one of the mineralocorticoids of the adrenal cortex that store potassium and thus favorably influence the endurance of the cells and cause increased glycogen formation in the liver and muscle. And so here we have yet another explanation for favorable metabolism in women. Men are influenced more strongly from the sympathetic nervous system, i.e., from the adrenal core; women from the parasympathetic nervous system, or the adrenal cortex.

PERSPECTIVES IN ENDURANCE DEVELOPMENT IN WOMEN'S ATHLETICS

All that I've said so far supports the general principle that woman has no special gift of speed or strength, but that she compensates for this during exercise by her superior metabolic resources. This is why I have been saying for years that women are more enduring than men.

In terms of absolute, timed performances this is certainly not yet a true statement; thus it would be a flight of fancy to cite the present records at 800, 1,500, 3,000 and 10,000 meters as proof of women's inferior endurance. (The women's national middle-distance coach in West Germany actually did just this in 1959. In my rebuttal, I wrote: "What woman has not yet attained, *she definitely will attain one day* as the result of training methods specifically suited to her.")

Women's track-and-field records will, to be sure, never surpass those of men unless it happens in the longest distances. Sex-specific differences in strength and speed are subject to little change through training. An 11-second 100-meter time is an extremely rare exception, found only in certain women who combine light weight with strong legs. But the endurance processes of biological oxidation can be improved to an unsuspected extent. Knowing this, it was clear to me as early as 1954 just where the emphasis should be placed in thinking about performance opportunities for women athletes.

Women who are now running 800 meters in under two minutes acquired their speed by training for endurance. The slowest 400-meter runner at Montreal won the 800-meter in 1:55, based on her superior endurance at 1,500 and 3,000 meters. Incidentally, I predicted in 1959 that a woman would one day run this time to the second. My reasoning at the time is still valid, and I reproduce it here:

Russia's Itkina had just run 400 meters in 53.8, and I compared her performance with the endurance of a schoolgirl whom I was coaching in Waldniel, who'd run 600 meters in 1:39.8 and 3,000 meters in 10:25. If Itkina had been capable of running 3,000 meters in around 10 minutes, her 400-meter speed would have given her a time for 600 meters of 1:22 or 1:23, by analogy with the Waldniel schoolgirl's times. This would indicate an 800-meter potential of 1:55 or 1:56. Trainers and runners alike laughed at me for making such a prediction. But now a 1:54.96 has been run at Montreal—by the world record-holder at 1,500 meters.

We can estimate that the winner of the women's 800 at Montreal, Kazankina of the USSR, could run the 1,500 in about 3:52.6, equalling the proud world record set by Paavo Nurmi in 1924. That this is neither a dream nor deserving of laughter we can derive from the fact that the fifth-place finisher in the 1,500 at Montreal, Ludmilla Bragina (gold medalist at Munich) ran a women's world record for 3,000 meters of 8:27.4 a few weeks later, a time that Nurmi didn't match until 1925 at Berlin with an 8:25.0. Nurmi, with an 800-meter best time of 1:54.8, was no faster than the winner of the women's 800-meter race at the 1976 Games. The legendary runner of the twenties has been equalled by women, at both the 3,000 meters and the 800. Still, this is very far from the probable limits on women's running records.

No progress worth mentioning has been made in the men's 800 meters since Harbig sped through the 800 in 1:46.6 in 1939. Harbig was a good sprinter, with best times of 10.6 for 100 meters and 21.5 for the 200; but his 1,500-meter best was a slow 4:01. His ability in the sprints deceived everyone including his coach, Gerschler, into believing that the 800-meter specialist should be very fast, and that his training should concentrate on further developing his gift of speed. But as long ago as 1947 I realized, and wrote, that the sub-1:40 runner of the future will have to do marathon-style training.

We are still a long way from 1:40 and under, though such times are clearly quite possible. The most recent world records at 800 meters, 1:43.7 and 1:43.5, were set by 400-meter runners who had no unusual endurance. Everyone believed these times were the *ne plus ultra* of Olympic attainment; but even Peter Snell, whose best time for the 400 was only 48 seconds, came very close to reaching his ultimate potential in the 800, which a valid predictive formula tells us would have been 1:44. Snell ran 1:44.3 to set a new world record, and I estimated his absolute potential as 48 plus 48 plus 8 seconds, or 1:44. The reason Snell was able to realize his full potential was that he did marathon training which gave him the endurance to run equal 400-meter splits in the 800.

Snell confirmed this to me in a long conversation in San Francisco in 1975, and his coach, Arthur Lydiard, also told me in August 1975 that Snell was capable of running 10,000 meters in under 30 minutes just before his 800-meter gold medal at Rome—this, despite his heavy, broad build and an unspectacular 400-meter best time of 48.6.

Alberto Juantorena, having already run the 800-meter heats and final and the 400-meter heats at Montreal, ran the 400 final in 44.26. Given the endurance of a Peter Snell, he'd have the potential of running the 800 in 44.3 plus 44.3 plus 8 seconds, or 1:36.6. But in view of the present-day training methods for 800-meter runners, such a time will long remain a mere utopian dream.

Lydiard never flinched at sending his proteges out on the roads to run 30 miles, just as Australia's extraordinary Percy Cerutty did with Herb Elliot. Meanwhile, our West German trainers encourage their 400- and 200-meter runners to race at 800 meters, still thinking of the 800 as a matter of pure speed.

The women's 800- and 1,500-meter races at Montreal, on the other hand, were a revelation—especially for those who 20 years ago couldn't imagine that a *woman* was capable of running 800 meters. Kazankina, surely the slowest at 400 meters of all the 800-meter finalists, came into the final turn in seventh place, 150 meters from the finish line then easily moved out into the third lane and passed the others to win. To win in the final sprint—a miler! She had more endurance when it really counted—she was still the freshest in the final sprint.

Szewinska of Poland ran the 400 meters at Montreal in 49.3. It is not unrealistic to say that a runner of similar tall, slender build and low weight could be endurance trained to run 1,500 and 3,000 meters in world-record times. (*Any* human being can increase his or her endurance to tremendous levels by running slowly in training for very high mileages.)

Let's assume that a female runner of the future has the basic speed to run 400 meters in 49.3, 1,500 meters in 3:50, and 3,000 meters in 8:10. Judging from the present world records this is quite possible. The speed and endurance hinted at in these times could then realistically be synthesized for an 800-meter race in accordance with the formula: 49.3 plus 49.3 plus 8 seconds, equals 1:46.6.

The endurance of women has long since been proved in swimming. Petra Thumer, an East German Olympic team alternate, swam the 400 meter freestyle at Montreal in 4:09.9. The Olympic freestyle 400 was won in 1924 by Johnny Weissmueller of the U.S. in 5:04.2. Though this was 54 seconds slower than the 1976 women's winning time, Weissmueller was so exhausted at the finish that he would have drowned if someone hadn't quickly fished him out of the pool. These strong men of an earlier day had no endurance in swimming; they exceeded their endurance limits in the first 100 meters and never trained at distances longer than 1000 meters a day.

I hope that this brief summary of theoretical and biological principles will bring about recognition of women as superior endurance athletes, and that the authorities will accept my recommendations that women be allowed to run 10,000 meters on the track and a marathon on the roads at future Olympic Games. A uniform long freestyle racing distance should be inaugurated in Olympic swimming in which men and women will compete against each other. It is by no means predictable which sex would win a race of, say, 10 kilometers.

East German trainers have reported that women have more endurance in training than most men. Based on my own experiences and the findings from East Germany, women are more tireless in training, more intent on performing well, and more capable of training long distances without complaint. Their male counterparts are more prone to take time off, including days of doing absolutely nothing. With few exceptions men are not consistent enough in their training, whereas women who become strongly motivated toward good performance do not let anything deter them from consistent application of training toward their goals. I saw a number of examples of this in Waldniel as early as 1953-59, when for perhaps the first time ever women like Marianne Weiss, Margret Bach, Josefine Bongartz and Anni Erdkamp were consistently running 12-18 miles a day.

Endurance training like this was the basis for Anni Erdkamp's first official women's world marathon record in 1967 at Waldniel. Though she'd been training specifically for the 800 meters at the time, endurance training paid off at all the racing distances from 800 meters to the marathon.

NEW MEXICO

10

Limits of Performance

A different viewpoint: critique of the van Aaken-Ullyot theories of women's running

Nick Marshall

The readers of this book know the story.

Once upon a time, not too long ago, it was assumed women were incapable of withstanding the rigors of stamina sports like distance running. Even men who ran the roads of the nation were scarce. They were looked upon as oddities and a breed apart in their endurance pursuits. Naturally, fragile females, so dainty by nature, had nothing in common with such masochistic eccentrics.

Of course, this conventional wisdom overlooked some of our own past history, such as the endurance feats performed by women pedestrians in the six-day races of a century ago. Societies can have short memories when such thoughts conflict with cultural stereotypes.

Myths change. At an accelerating pace over the last ten years, females have shed the shackles of that particular fiction. Now, though some recalcitrant sorts still grumble about the change that has taken place, most people will concede that women are much tougher than they'd thought, and are capable of participating fully in endurance sports once imagined too difficult for them.

We can all issue a "Bravo!" over this healthy change in affairs.

Unfortunately, while one pervasive myth dies, another is born. The pendulum has swung drastically. Now, instead of everyone thinking that women are frail creatures ready to collapse at the first physical stress they encounter, a new myth is winning a place in the public consciousness.

Women were exposed for the weaklings they weren't. Awareness of their athletic potential sprang to the fore. Time was right for a shift in public opinion. And along came Joan Ullyot, well-known doctor, marathoner and author on running topics, to revolutionize our thought with the bold proposition that women may in fact be superior to men in activities requiring extended periods of exertion. The subsequent spread of her ideas has been impressive, with the result that statements which once would have been considered absurd are now being voiced by many respected runners:

> *"One thing is undeniable. As Dr. van Aaken claimed over 20 years ago, women are relatively better adapted by nature for running the long distances than men are."* (Manfred Steffny, West German Olympian)
>
> *"I have no doubt that the best person on this planet would be a woman. They are built for stamina, while men are built for speed."* (Kenny Moore, US Olympian)
>
> *"I'm totally convinced that, if there were as many women marathoners as there are men, the women would be running as fast as the men."* (Penny DeMoss, 50-kilometer recordholder)

Statements such as these indicate a dramatic switch in the climate. It is a complete reversal from what was once acknowledged as fact. What happened to trigger this turnaround in opinion?

WHERE IT STARTED

Joan Ullyot wrote an article. And in a time when women were flowing into the sport in rapidly increasing numbers, many enthusiastic supporters of this movement eagerly accepted her tentative theories as gospel. It was like striking a blow for the oppressed.

The article by Ullyot that started the ball rolling appeared in *Runner's World* in 1974. It was titled "Women's Secret Weapon: Fat." In it, Ullyot speculated women may in fact be better suited than men to running long distances for the simple reason that their bodies have larger supplies of fat to draw upon for energy use once their carbohydrate-based stores of muscle glycogen have been consumed. The theory was an intriguing and provocative one, but there was not enough data to either prove or disprove it conclusively. Though interested by the idea,

I was skeptical of it. A wait-and-see attitude seemed most reasonable, as I figured it would quietly fade away after a while, like many other questionable ideas have done.

However, since then a strange thing has happened. Although little additional info, pro or con, has been forthcoming, the once-novel theory itself has taken firm hold. When I queried Jack Bristol, a fine New England ultramarathoner, before a 100-kilometer race whether or not he thought women would eventually be better than men at such long events, his reply was a casual, "Of course." And in that barometer of American opinion, *Time*, in an article on the jogging boom, agrees in principle, saying, "Probably the sex gap is uncloseable in the marathon, but in the ultramarathon distances of 50 and 100 miles, women's lightness and endurance may be a commanding advantage. . . ."

Hold it!

What we have here is the solid beginning of a new conventional wisdom, but one with a dubious foundation in fact. While the possibility of women's superiority in this realm cannot be dismissed entirely, the idea is purely hypothetical for the present. It certainly doesn't merit the widespread currency it seems to be gaining. What is clear so far is that the shreds of evidence to support it are indeed skimpy and tenuous.

The "fat conversion" theory sounds reasonable. In her 1974 article Ullyot suggested the crucial factor contributing to a woman's superior endurance potential is the larger amount of active, trained-on, body fat she has in comparison to a male runner. In this view, men's physiology will permit them to run faster only as long as they have glycogen stores available to call upon. However, under conditions requiring a sustained high level of oxygen uptake, even if one has carbohydrate-loaded in order to super-saturate one's cells, a runner's muscles will largely deplete their glycogen deposits in two hours. As these carbohydrate supplies become exhausted, the human organism is forced to utilize correspondingly higher levels of fatty acids for effective energy production. At this point, the biological advantage begins swinging over to favor women. In the shorter muscle-dependent runs, Ullyot says women will not overhaul men's performances. But, theoretically, where fat is a factor, she sees triumph in the offing for her sex. While men will falter, women's reserves of fat will give them the energy to keep going.

WHERE IT GREW

It is a plausible notion at least, and in the years subsequent to her *RW* article on the topic, Joan Ullyot has continued to peddle it. In 1978 she reaffirmed her belief in the idea, saying on television that, "It's becoming quite clear women have a certain natural advantage in endurance races, distances like the marathon, or even longer. In these races, the women's greater staying power and probably their ability to burn fat better seems to enable them to carry on at a fairly fast pace longer than the men."

Ullyot popularized the idea after first being introduced to it in conversations with another doctor, the West German Ernst van Aaken. Dr. van Aaken is justly noted for his longtime advocacy of endurance training and pioneering work in opening up running to women. However, as with some other famous foreign guru-coaches like Cerutty and Lydiard, he is an individual of strong opinions, and many of these fall into the realm of unsubstantiated hypotheses. The fact that Ullyot and van Aaken are both doctors shouldn't carry undue weight when we realize that in such an inexact science like running it is tough to be an expert. Too often the "M.D." attached to a name is merely a smokescreen concealing thinking that is only pure guesswork. In this case, as an ardent supporter of the rights and powers of women, it seems Dr. Ullyot is indulging in simplistic wish-fulfillment in espousing her position that women will excel beyond men in extreme endurance activities because they possess a superior fat metabolism.

Ullyot supports her own argument mainly on subjective personal observations. It is her impression that as distances increase, there is a relative narrowing of the gap between men's and women's performances. She also contends women adapt better to the stresses involved in such experiences, being quoted in the *New York Times* as saying, "In long races, there's less chance of women hurting themselves than men. Women have the endurance and better metabolism. After 20 miles, women utilize their fat better. By then, all the carbohydrates have been burned up." In another *Times* article, she amplified this thought by commenting, "After 20 miles or so, when the glycogen is used up, men tend to 'hit the wall.' They have to go the last few miles on sheer guts. Women don't seem to hit the wall, because they convert from glycogen to fat more easily, more naturally." What she sees is a divergence of abilities past a certain biological breaking point. Thus, in a marathon, while the men are dying in the final six miles, the women are ideally cruising to a comfortable finish. Not only do they have more fuel available in the form of fat deposits, but their bodies supposedly burn it more efficiently. It is all attributable to an endurance-oriented anatomy that permits women to convert from glycogen-burning to fat-burning without suffering the consequent deteriorations in strength or pace that plague men in the same circumstances.

HOW IT WAS WRONG

These are Ullyot's perceptions. Undoubtedly, they are shared by many other runners these days. People look at something which surprises them. It may shatter preconceptions they once accepted as truths. In the resultant euphoria of discovery, rough impressions may be extrapolated wildly. New-found abilities are frequently overrated. Although the person involved may feel freed from ignorance, this doesn't guarantee intelligence. Joan Ullyot herself was once a self-admitted creampuff with no awareness of her strong athletic abilities. Both her own transformation and that of other women to outstanding marathoners has been an extraordinary revelation to her. What appeared impossible has happened, and so straws must be grasped at to explain the miracle.

Women as a sex are still new to distance running. The dynamics at work here are much the same as with any new individual in the sport. Improvement at first is dramatic. Soon the person can "logically" dream about being a world recordsetter, through a process of extravagant extrapolation: "Why, all I have to do is keep improving at this rate for a few more years and I'll win at the Olympics for sure!" Thus we get statements like this from an AAU chairwoman watching the 1978 Boston Marathon: "The times are still not close to what the men are doing, but what's really significant is comparing the rates of improvement. The women are getting much better much faster, and I think that trend will continue because, physiologically, they're better able to handle a marathon than men are." It is all part of the new wives' tale. Clearly, there is less disparity between men's and women's times, but in the very long runs, from my own personal observations as an ultramarathon specialist, any growing equality stems in no way from mysterious body chemistry that tips the scale toward women past, say, 20 miles. Or 30, or 40, for that matter. Rather, it is attributable to psychological factors and less reliance on speed as opposed to stamina at longer distances.

Being dependent upon training volume and methods available to all runners as it is, stamina is simply less sex-related than is speed. Unlike natural speed, stamina is an acquired gift built up through hard work. In long runs, this and the individual factor are paramount, instead of any hocus-pocus about "fat conversion" or other extraneous matters. Of course, body composition is important, but fat content is onlv one of a myriad of facets present in forming running ability, pace, endurance, etc. To single out one facet and conveniently exclaim, "Aha, here's the key!" is sheer sophistry. Although fat is obviously part of the running picture, and women do test higher in it, that should not lead to any quick conclusions, inas nuch as so far it has not been a determining factor in performances in any way that can be clearly ascertained. In other words, I've seen no indication to date that female fat supplies negate the male advantage in muscle strength at *any* distance.

Of course, the ultimate outcome of the argument will depend on actual performances. Potential is always theoretical. And theory can be fine and fun, but performance is what gets you on the victory stand. So far in this instance, theory is substituting almost entirely for performance. Primarily this is due to a lack of hard facts, as opposed to rough impressions, supporting the view that women are better adapted to handle long distances.

The men's world record for the marathon has been stalled for over nine years at Derek Clayton's 2:08:33. In this same period, the women's record has been lowered precipitously, from Anni Erdkamp's 3:07:26 to Christa Vahlensieck's 2:34:48. This has been the result of the rapid expansion of racing opportunities for women and the consequent growth in female participation. However, 26.2 miles is still a distance primarily dependent upon glycogen-based speed. Joan Ullyot suggests women's true potential will surface in the ultramarathon events lasting well past the two-hour point of normal carbohydrate depletion. It is in these superlong contests where women's superior endurance capacities will be demonstrated.

Unfortunately, we don't have a lot of data to go on, as few women have stepped up from the marathon. When Ullyot's article first appeared, it was expected to spark feminine interest in the ultradistances. However, while male participation grows slowly but steadily, women remain a relative rarity in such events.

SOME COMPARISONS

Nevertheless, some veteran women marathoners have taken the step up, and their experiences offer us some preliminary hints. The empirical evidence they provide us doesn't lend any support to the claim of feminine supremacy in events beyond the marathon.

To date, the most popular ultramarathon length in the U.S. has been 50 miles. The five fastest American women at 50 miles have been Nina Kuscsik, Judy Ikenberry, Eileen Waters, Donna Gookin and Natalie Cullimore. Waters and Cullimore are two examples cited frequently by Dr. Ullyot to prove her thesis. However, when we examine the 50-mile runs of these women in relation to their marathon abilities and then contrast this relationship with the corresponding ratios demonstrated by the top five male 50-milers in this country, we come up with some interesting statistics.

The raw times are irrelevant to this discussion. What is important is the runners' individual differences in pace between the two events. If women can actually take advantage of a superior endurance physiology once glycogen stores are exhausted, the percentage difference between their marathon and 50-mile paces should surely be less than the men's. Yet in fact this is not the case at all. While the men's pace difference is between 12.3 percent and 16.4 percent, the women go 17.8 per-

COMPARISON OF TOP U.S. MALE AND FEMALE 50-MILERS

Runner	Best Marathon	Pace Per Mile	Best 50-Mile	Pace Per Mile	Difference in Pace (in secs.)	Percent Slower
Men:						
1. Jim Pearson	2:22:32	5:26.18	5:12:41	6:15.22	–49.04	15.03%
2. Frank Bozanich	2:25:26	5:32.80	5:14:36	6:17.52	–44.72	13.44%
3. Bob Deines	2:22:04	5:25.11	5:15:20	6:18.40	–53.29	16.39%
4. Skip Houk	2:22:05	5:25.15	5:15:22	6:18.44	–53.29	16.39%
5. Darryl Beardall	2:28:53	5:40.71	5:18:55	6:22.70	–41.99	12.32%
Women:						
1. Nina Kuscsik	2:50:22	6:29.86	6:35:54	7:55.08	–85.22	21.88%
2. Judy Ikenberry	2:54:28	6:39.24	6:44:43	8:05.66	–86.42	21.65%
3. Eileen Waters	3:01:49	6:56.08	6:55:27	8:18.54	–82.46	19.82%
4. Donna Gookin	3:08:26	7:11.22	7:12.51	8:39.42	–88.20	20.45%
5. Natalie Cullimore	3:18:00	7:33.11	7:24:50	8:53.80	–80.69	17.81%

cent and 21.9 percent slower when running the ultramarathon. Contrary to Ullyot's theory, the gap widens. A negative rather than positive correlation exists.

The most outstanding super-long run by a woman was the 7:50 for 100 kilometers by West Germany's Christa Vahlensieck, a van Aaken protege. Her time was fast enough to earn her fourth place out of 800 contestants in that race. Such an unusually high place would appear to support the thesis of women's superiority over the long haul. However, it doesn't do this any more than the rare case of Marian May's beating all the men in the 1975 Midnight Sun Marathon in Alaska. Examining Vahlensieck's performances in other events, we discover that she is a superbly conditioned athlete. More notably: she is the women's world recordholder in the marathon. She has enough speed to beat the large majority of men across a whole spectrum of shorter distances as well.

In this country, only a few hundred individuals have tackled 100 kilometers. Thus, so far only seven U.S. men have done better than Vahlensieck's 7:50 for 62.1 miles—Park Barner, Frank Bozanich, Roger Welch, Don Choi, Jack Bristol, Brian Jones, and myself. Curiously, comparing our marathon PRs to Christa's, we find in each instance (except for Bozanich), they are slower than Vahlensieck's best. Further delving into statistics fails to uncover any secrets showing that her superiority to most male runners at long distances is related to sex rather than individual characteristics. That is, she doesn't necessarily excel more as the distance increases. For example, her best 10,000-meter time is 85 seconds faster than mine and her marathon PR is 6½ minutes quicker, yet at 100 kilometers her time is 33 minutes slower. This pattern is the exact reverse of what we should see if a sex-based advantage is at work to the benefit of women at distances beyond which men's glycogen edge is negated.

Looking at 100-mile performances, the longest standard distance run any U.S. women have completed, we find that only a dozen American men have gone faster than Natalie Cullimore's 16:11:00. While at first glance this too seems to support the Ullyot theory, there is a different explanation available. One hundred miles is a rarefied atmosphere. Simply put, gender becomes irrelevant as the distance involved increases so drastically and the pace slows accordingly. Except for a few elite athletes, a 100-mile race is a survival struggle. Anyone able to

AYMOND
TRY

maintain a semblance of a jog over such a long distance will end up with a respectable time. The object is merely to finish and this is best achieved through a sheer gritty determination equally available to members of both sexes. As John Hill, for several years an organizer of the Camellia Festival 100-Miler near Sacramento, commented in a letter to me, "Our past Camellia 100s indicate that motivation and luck are both more important than condition and ability."

PERSONAL EXPERIENCES

In the first 100-mile event I ever attempted, I had some hopes of lasting the distance but was dubious about my prospects. I came through the halfway mark in second place in a fairly comfortable 6:48. However, fatigue was setting in rapidly and with 50 more miles to go, I knew the test would soon turn into a grim ordeal. I couldn't have continued to run it nonstop and feared the idea of having to jog/walk for hours in a gross state of deterioriation. Sudden dread gripped me and I pulled off the course without warning a half-mile further on. Physically, I was not yet spent but mentally I couldn't hack it any more.

Three years later, I attempted the distance again. I wasn't in peak physical condition but had a lot more experience behind me and was well prepared mentally for the attempt. Where before I'd panicked and quit, this time my mind stayed in firm control and let my body come through the 100 miles in 14:37:05. It was the same way Natalie Cullimore managed the same length run.

The irrelevance of gender in these long runs can be seen by examining the ages of top ultramarathoners. For example, not a single one of the 100 fastest American marathoners is over 40 years old. Yet of the 40 fastest men in U.S. history at 50 miles through 1977, six were masters. And of 18 men under 18 hours for 100 miles, only one was younger than 25 and six of them—Ted Corbitt, Cahit Yeter, Ralph Paffenbarger, Paul Reese, Lu Dosti and Gordon Dugan—achieved their performances while ranging in age from 42 to 54!

If older men seem to excel in these long runs more than young men, can sex be the reason? Of course not. Similarly, if women also seem to excel in them, should we thus conclude this is due to anatomy? No.

Youth by itself is not a detriment in these longer runs, but it is readily apparent that it gives one less of an edge. As it is with age, so it is with sex. Women are less handicapped by their bodies at longer distances not because they have a more suitable sex-related physiology than men, but simply because the importance of any specific physiology is diminished so tremendously. As Sherry Horner, a clubmate of mine, observed after setting a national 100-kilometer record, it's an individual matter. Sex matters less than personality.

Strong performances in ultramarathons can best be obtained by a combination of extreme stamina and a tenacious spirit. Each of these aspects can be developed on an individual basis, with neither age nor sex being an inhibiting factor. Individual training and psychology is paramount; female fat conversion is not.

One thing contributing to distorted perceptions is the limited popularity of long races. a *Time* cover story on women in sports recently noted with satisfaction that women "...have run men into the ground during ultramarathon races 50 miles long." It followed up that statement by quoting Joan Ullyot to the effect that, "The evidence suggests that women are tougher than men."
tougher than men."

Bosh! Some are. Some aren't.

Sweeping arguments like that overlook a few basic facts. Most people cannot or will not run 50 miles. The distance defeats them. Any woman who does so, will therefore naturally run many men "into the ground." Thereby proving little. In one 50-mile race, ten-year-old Greg Hill placed fifth out of 28 starters. Does this mean young kids make the best ultramarathoners? Hardly. It only shows they can handle very long distances, just like everyone else.

Consider a 3:30 woman marathoner. Match her in a 26-mile run with the members of an average high school boys' track team and she'll likely whip them all, finishing strongly while the young men's bodies are strewn alongside the roadway behind her. Watching this, an observer could easily conclude that women are naturally better in such endurance contests. They might even figure this was due to a difference in the respective fat compositions of the sexes. Of course, this would be absurd. Train those same boys specifically for endurance running and soon many, if not most, of them would be outlegging the 3:30 woman. It is not particularly fair. But it is a fact.

MORE SIMILAR THAN NOT

The similarities between male runners and female runners

are more profound than the differences. And distance is a great equalizer. If proportionately more women excel in ultramarathons, this is due to individual factors rather than ones based on gender.

Men and women can both be tough. There should be nothing startling about that. Yet people, in their continuing sexist preconceptions, expect little of women. So when they do difficult things like competently running marathons and further, onlookers go ga-ga over the spectacle and unrealistic leaps of fantasy result.

What impresses some people is the observation, in Joan Ullyot's words in *WomenSports*, that "...women tend to be less physically exhausted than men after long-distance runs." Two of her favorite examples are the runs of Natalie Cullimore and Eileen Waters when they set ultradistance records in 1971 and 1974. While the men around them were allegedly collapsing in the throes of agony, these women remained outwardly serene and finished strongly. Again, the suggestion is that they were operating on a longer-lasting fuel supply which spared them the tragic fates suffered by the depleted males they faced in the race.

This is pretty flimsy evidence on which to base any conclusions at all. By contrast, Sherry Horner was wrecked after her record run, and I've seen many men finish ultradistance events in lively condition. Mainly, though, subjective appearances can be deceiving. They are in the eye of the beholder. Furthermore, facial expressions don't mean much. They can be entirely extraneous to performance, as any spectator who watched Ted Corbitt in his heyday well knows. Corbitt is the greatest ultramarathoner yet produced by this country, but you would never have guessed it from looking at him in the early miles of some of his races. More often than not throughout his career, he wore a deceptive mask of agony, all the while usually destroying his competition and setting numerous records.

In race accounts of women's marathons, Ullyot herself has described retching competitors and the usual tales of distress suffered by many runners after hard distance efforts. It is not your sex, it's how you prepare for a run and go through it. Undoubtedly, had Waters or Cullimore been less well-trained prior to their finest races, or run too fast in the beginning, they too could have experienced gross deterioration before the finish.

It's just the disconcerting phenomenon of people who run

good races often completing them in apparent better shape than those who ostensibly haven't run as hard. Typically, a marathon winner will start quietly discussing his run with reporters as soon as he breaks the tape, seemingly unwinded, while miles back on the course many others have been reduced to walking wrecks alongside the road.

It all ties in with pace and psychology. If women have any plus over men, I definitely believe this is where it lies. A couple years back in a *Parade* article, Christa Vahlensieck hit the nail on the head when she said derisively of men: "They are vain creatures. They would rather sprint than be passed by a woman. As a result, they waste their reserve energy, and after six or seven miles, I pass them anyway." Ah, there's the rub. Men are generally faster and stronger than women, but quite frequently not as smart.

MISPLACED EMPHASIS

In the 1975 New York City Marathon, Kim Merritt won the National AAU women's title while placing 26th out of 535 runners overall. In a newspaper story afterward, a big fuss was made over how many men she'd passed in the closing miles. By coincidence, Neil Weygandt and I finished in the next two spots behind her after being in Merritt's vicinity throughout the race. We, too, passed many other guys at the end but saw nothing unusual about Merritt's performance, beyond its being an example of how a good runner should do a marathon. She put together a fine, intelligently-paced effort, and this is precisely what many men fail to do.

The fast-finishing women of the world, like Eileen Waters, have benefitted from a culturally-induced conservatism with which they were raised. Although this is in the process of changing now, as long as women were an exotic minority in running, there was little pressure on them to perform to their top capacity. Merely participating was enough to impress people, because in the past discrimination had prevented even that. Only now, as women approach full acceptance in the sport, is the competition heating up for them. Although women's records will continue to fall, the coming years will also bring a corresponding rise in the number of women who drive themselves to exhaustion in races.

It's like a race with one trophy in the 50-and-over age group. If only one runner shows up in that category, he has the luxury of running easy and yet gaining some recognition. Stick several more guys his age in the race, though, and some tongues may be hanging out.

Because of the past low expectations of women, they have been able to approach long distances more sensibly. While the men who were nurtured on dreams of athletic glory start out chasing it, only to die frequently in pursuit of it, the women have not been tricked by delusions of grandeur. While serious about the sport, they have tended to ease into it with a less manic attitude. Thus, in race situations, we've seen them generally maintaining better control of their abilities while many overly ambitious men are swept away to their doom. This noticeable contrast in approaches has been mainly responsible for giving observers the idea that women tend to finish marathons and ultras in better shape than men, hence the notion they are more suited to endurance running. Actually, it is just patience which is rewarded in long runs, and there is a positive correlation between women and patient, conservative pacing.

Finally, talk about "the wall" clouds the issue. Though cherished as a fact, it's another convenient myth. Oh, of course, the longer a race is, the more likely you are to reach a fatigue zone. But there is nothing magical about either two hours of exertion or twenty miles of running. A properly-trained runner of either sex should not hit any collapse point in a marathon if they pace it wisely. And if one has the necessary stamina either through nature or training, one cannot only pass those legendary breaking points but go much further without crashing. Men, women, young and old can do it. Feminine fat composition is not required but an intelligent pace is. In that sense, it might be wise for anyone to "run like a woman." But it is better psychology, not physiology, that is required for success.

This entire topic has been a tough one for me to tackle. I originally tried writing on the subject two years ago but wound up junking the article. I'm afraid my comments will be read by some as an attack on women, and mistaken for the sour-grapes protestations of a die-hard male chauvinist. That would be a faulty, kneejerk reaction which is blind to the heart of this piece.

As noted previously, I think the similarities between male and female runners are considerably more profound than their differences. It is an overlapping spectrum. And as an authority on the ultradistance scene, I am well aware that women are fully capable of running very long distances.

Women distance runners deserve praise for their achievements but it isn't necessary to "explain" these achivements with shaky scientific buttresses. These women are runners. Praise them as such. To be amazed, like Joan Ullyot and many others have been, that women can run good marathons and even go fifty miles or further, is subtly sexist. Of course they can. What else would you expect?

TOMMY'S
NURSE
AMERICAN MEDICAL

11

Injury Prevention

An investigation into biomechanics, orthopedics, and proper shoe fit

Dr. John Pagliano

One of the most common questions I am asked is: Do women suffer different running injuries than men? The answer is that they do suffer the same running related injuries; the main difference is that they suffer a higher percentage of *certain* injuries as compared to men.

From a general anatomical standpoint, we know that women are usually smaller, smaller boned, and lighter in weight than men. They have a greater percentage of body fat and conversely less muscle tissue. These factors will all have significance as we discuss individual foot and leg injuries.

In general, the muscles, tendons, ligaments, and other soft tissue structures of the foot are smaller and more delicate than those of men. Therefore overuse syndromes and overstress injuries such as tendonitis, fascitis, etc., are more common in women runners.

In previous studies (Malina, R.M., "Physique of Female Track and Field Athletes," *Med. Sci. Sports* 3 (1): 32-38), it has been pointed out that female distance runners are lighter in weight, shorter in stature and shorter in leg length than their male counterparts. It is interesting to note, however, that a woman's relative stride length was longer than their comparison male models. It would appear that these women may be overstriding, which can lead to anterior and posterior compartment injuries; these will be discussed later.

Nelson, Brooks and Pike, in a study grant from the U.S. Olympic Development Sub-Committee for Women's Athletics, came to the conclusion that there are significant differences in running technique between men and women long-distance runners. Briefly, the females had shorter strides, longer relative strides, lesser times of support, higher stride rates, and longer times of non-support.

It was interesting to note that during the gait cycle, the women were in flight 4 percent longer than men but covered 4 percent less distance during this period. This would be accounted for by the greater takeoff angle, which could be due to several factors, including the anatomical position of the lower leg (known as "genu valgum") or a tighter gastro soleus complex compared to men.

Fat percentage, which plays an important role in foot injuries, is higher in women and is sex-linked. In other words, estrogen promotes fatty deposits in women while the male hormone, testosterone, promotes growth of lean tissue or increased muscle mass. However, in comparison to the general public, the woman runner is definitely classed as an ectomorph and is much leaner.

Getting to the subject at hand, the foot is a very complex organ. It consists of twenty-six bones and over 100 muscles, ligaments, tendons, and other soft tissue components. It is designed to absorb the stresses and strains of walking and the severe forces exerted by running. We can divide the foot into three sections:

The *forefoot* consists of the five metatarsal bones and the fourteen phalangeal bones. This makes up the toes, ball of the foot, the transverse arch and part of the longitudinal arch.

The *mid-foot* consists of the five tarsal bones.

The *rear foot* is composed of the talus and the calcaneus. It is in this segment that most of the foot pathology in women runners originates. The talus is likened to the keystone of the foot.

The ligaments of the foot and leg lend stability to the foot. The ankle joint receives its support from the medial and lateral collateral ligaments. Due to the angulation of the leg upon the foot in the female runner, these ligaments are the ones that are most often sprained. We discussed the smaller ligaments in women, and in many cases these ligaments are not enough to withstand the strain of running. Therefore, inversion ankle sprains become very common.

The ligaments are also important in the movement of the subtalar joint, which governs the motion of the foot during the running cycle. Those with very lax ligaments have a very "mobile" foot while those with extremely tight ligaments suffer from lack of foot motion.

Another important joint in the foot is the mid-tarsal joint, which governs the position of the forefoot during the running cycle. I have found that most women have a positional formation known as forefoot varus or a foot the bottom surface of which looks toward the inside. These can be pathological in some cases.

The foot muscles can be divided into intrinsic muscles (which originate and terminate in the foot itself) and extrinsic muscles (which originate away from the foot and act upon the foot).

The most common muscles are the gastrocnemius, which runs down the back of the leg and terminates in the Achilles tendon, the anterior tibial and posterior tibial, which balance the medial side of the foot, and peroneals, which act on the lateral side of the foot.

Other important anatomical structures of note are the plantar fascia, or bowstring of the foot which runs along the plantar surface from the heel bone to the toes.

THE LOWER LEG

Let us now discuss the entire lower leg structure to get a better picture of the female foot.

It is obvious that women have a much broader pelvic span than men. As a result, the femur, or thigh bone, is at a greater angle than the thigh bones of men. Thus, there is a greater frontal plane deformity, and this is known as coxa varum (fig. 1). Also related to this is a genu valgum (fig. 1), which results in an overall condition that we affectionately call knock knees. Men develop just the opposite configuration (fig. 2) which involves a tibia varum or bow legs. Each of these biomechanical arrangements results in a specific set of foot and lower leg injuries.

Due to this particular angulation, there are usually more cases of knee pathology in women runners than in men. Dr. Robert L. Larson, M.D., reporting in *The Medical Aspects of Sports* (16) states that subluxation of the patella is frequently seen in the female. Anatomic factors common to females predispose to an unstable extensor mechanism and may produce increased wear for the articular surfaces of the patellofemoral groove.

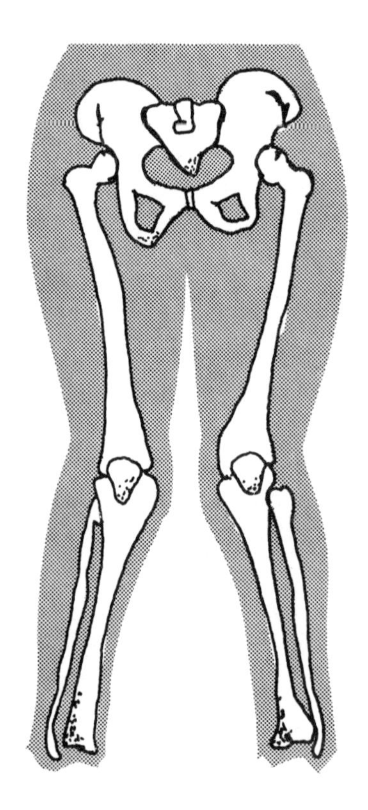

Figure 1

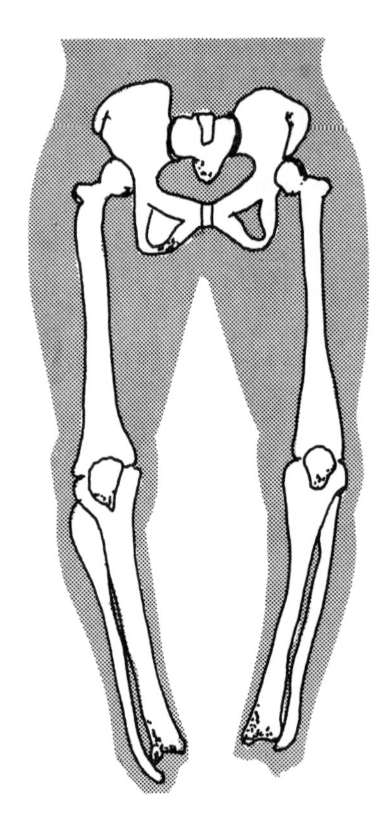

Figure 2

Figure 3 gives a simple picture of this condition. The patella or knee cap tends to ride out of its normal groove on the femur or thigh bone and there is an increased chance of chondromalacia, or runner's knee. This can be corrected through realignment of the knee apparatus by strengthening of the quadriceps and realignment of the foot with functional orthotics.

This leg torsion also puts the lateral knee ligaments at a greater stretch, and as a result we see more lateral collateral ligament strains as well as iliotibial band syndromes (strains on the outer side of the knee).

The iliotibial band syndrome is a generalized pain along the outside of the knee area, specifically at the insertion of the band on the lateral-distal aspect of the femur and the lateral aspect of the head of the fibula.

The iliotibial band tends to sublux somewhat and rubs on the bones on the outside of the knee. It can become very painful and limit movement of the knee.

Treatment includes stretching, ultrasound and rest.

As we all know, "shin splints" can be a very painful and disabling entity. It strikes women more frequently than men. It is a musculo-tendinous inflammation of the posterior compartment musculature and tendons, and is better termed posterior compartment syndrome.

In many cases, this condition is due to a sociopathological origin. Young girls are not given the chance to run and play as boys are. As a result, their anterior lower leg musculature is extremely underdeveloped by the time they become teenagers and young women. By this time they become interested in sports and start rigorous training programs that emulate those of the men. This weakened or underdeveloped anterior musculature is put under a great stress and usually becomes inflamed and injury occurs. I have seen some of the most swollen and painful "shin splint" syndromes in middle-aged women who decide to run after thirty years of inactivity. They assume they can perform the same training programs as the Jacquelin Hansens, the Nina Kuscsiks, and the Miki Gormans. They then jump into accelerated programs and tear this musculature.

In a recent survey I took among the U.S. Olympic women's volleyball team, 18 out of 24 women had shin splint pain of one degree or another. Some were extremely severe, others mild. I was very surprised at the high number of these pathologies in what one would assume to be a very high level fitness group.

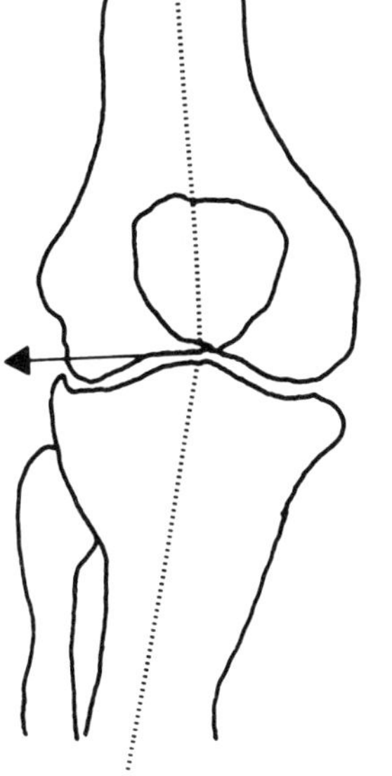

Figure 3

Related to this is the distal posterior medial stress syndrome, an actual fracture of the medial-posterior aspect of the tibia, which is the bone in the shin splint area. The worst cases of this syndrome, which is essentially a fracture, are in young high school women sprinters. They undertake fast-interval type workouts with spikes without proper background preparation, and this injury occurs.

Achilles tendonitis is another injury frequently seen in women runners, especially in those women over the age of thirty. Many have worn high-heel and platform shoes for many years to keep in fashion. As a result, the gastro-soleus complex (Achilles tendon) assumes a functional shortening.

The would-be athlete now changes from her high-heeled shoes to a low-heeled running shoe and the Achilles is stretched beyond its normal physiological length. This extra one- or two-inch stretch causes tendonitis and para-tendonitis around the Achilles tendon. There is extreme swelling and loss of motion around the ankle joint. I have yet to see a rupture or partial rupture of the Achilles tendon in a woman athlete.

Inversion sprains of the ankle are more common to the beginning woman runner due to the laxity and weakness of the collateral ligaments of the ankle. I recommend stretching exercises for the foot and ankle. *Runner's World* has appropriate pamphlet handouts available.

FAT IN THE FEET

Earlier, we had discussed the fat content of the woman runner and its importance in injury prevention. As a rule, we said that women have a higher fat content than men. This also rings true for the foot. While most men have very little natural fat padding under the heel, women have a nice protective cushioning. As a result, we do not see as many heel pathologies in women. This natural padding absorbs shock and prevents injury. There is a very low incidence of calcaneal fractures in women and also an extremely low incidence of heel spurs. I would take a guess that men outnumber women in heel spur injuries ten to one. Most heel injuries in women come from those who are engaged in high jumping, long jumping, basketball, and volleyball.

Fractures are becoming more of a commonplace injury among women runners as they increase their mileage and speed. As was discussed earlier, the bones of the foot are much lighter and more fragile than in a man. As a result, women are more prone to fracture pathology.

The most common sites (fig. 4) are the second, third, and fourth metatarsals. These are marked on the foot outline. Fracture of the second is the most common of the "march" fractures, especially in those with a Morton's toe or long second metatarsal. This long second metatarsal is in conjunction with a short first metatarsal, a deviation of the seamoids and a hypermobile first ray (see *Sports Medicine* '78, Richard S. Gilbert; "Stress Fracture in the Athlete and Morton's Foot," *Track Technique*, March 1975, John W. Pagliano—"Foot Notes"). This condition places the second metatarsal under a great deal of pressure when running and as a result, is the one prone to become fractured.

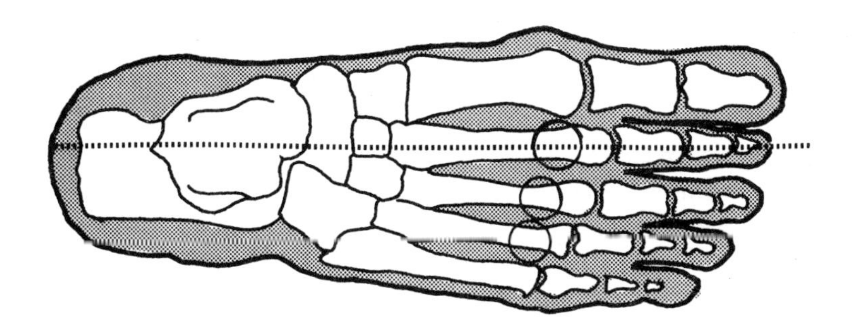

Figure 4

I have rarely seen severe stress fractures of the ankle or lower leg in women athletes. However, I do expect to see a higher degree of lower leg and foot fractures among women runners as they increase their mileage and their speed. This will all be due to simple overuse and over-training syndromes in relation to the lighter and more fragile osseous system.

The lighter weight "women's running shoes" on the market today also aggravate this condition. If a woman is going to train over the 10,000-meter level, she must wear a heavier type of training shoe. She will need the added cushioning and protection afforded her by a heavier training shoe (see "Effect of Footwear Upon Runners" later in this chapter).

All should be fitted with a Spenco Insole to absorb shock and prevent blistering.

The number of strains, tendonitis, hamstring injuries and blister problems are common to both men and women. Blisters can be a debilitating problem, especially to the novicc woman who usually has her shoes fitted improperly.

Blisters can be and should be treated as such (see the blister section included in this chapter).

The use of ice in the prevention of injuries should not be overlooked, either. (See ice section of this chapter.)

The incidence of hallux valgus deformities (bunions) seems to run the same in men and women. It is a hereditary condition which becomes aggravated by running and ill-fitting shoes.

Hammertoes are toes that buckle up and rub against the tops of the running shoes, forming black toenails and corns. These are more predominant in women, as women are or were forced to wear fashionable shoes. This crowded the toes and forced them into a contracted position. These can be corrected surgically, with very little downtime from running.

I have tried to present the particular problems that the woman runner must be aware of before setting her mileage goals. Most of them can be avoided by good stretching and training programs, good shoes, and a little caution. We should encourage more women to run. It is still mainly a male-oriented sport, but with the advent of the Bonne Bell races and women's road-running groups, they need not fear being isolated. We are seeing an increase in young women smokers among our population, and this is alarming. We have to reverse this trend and running is a very viable answer.

EFFECT OF FOOTWEAR ON RUNNERS

The most important and difficult decision facing a runner during his athletic career is the choice of a running shoe. The majority of athletes will choose the incorrect shoe, the incorrect fit, and as a result, the incidence of injury will be increased.

There are hundreds of athletic shoes on the market today manufactured by both American and foreign shoe firms. There is a multiplicity of styles, shapes, and types from which to choose. Most shoes are not worth the price of the shoe box and the runner would be just as well off running in a pair of bedroom slippers.

However, with a little intelligent study and foresight, the athlete can make a proper choice and minimize the margin of error.

It is difficult to dictate the type of shoe each individual should wear, but parameters can be established under which each individual runner can make a better decision. Feet are as different as fingerprints; ideally, there should be individual footgear for the individual foot. This is virtually impossible, but with an intelligent choice and the use of shoe modifications, the difficulties are minimized and can nearly obtain the proper shoe. To make the proper decision in obtaining the running shoe, the athlete must know the basic components of the shoe. The following definitions correspond to the cutaway view of the running shoe in figure 5.

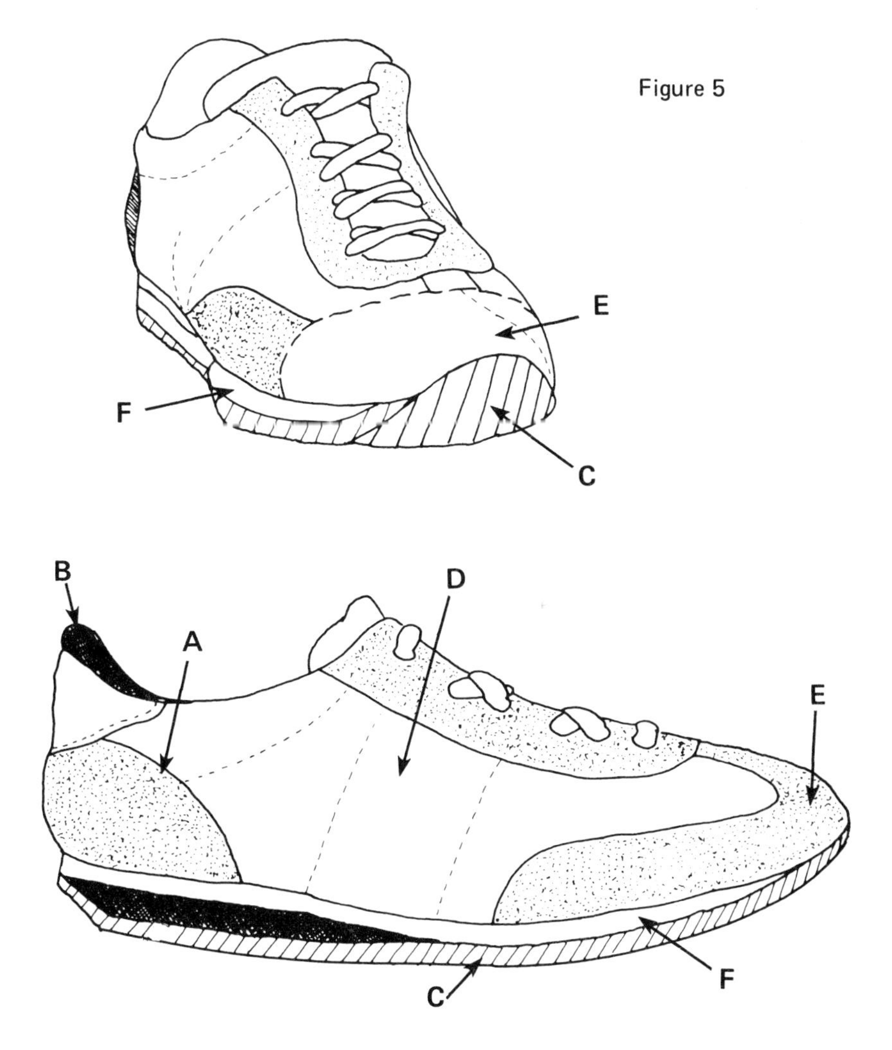

Figure 5

ANATOMY OF THE RUNNING SHOE

Last: The basic mold around which a shoe is fashioned. In most cases it is hand-carved wood, but later-model shoes are constructed around a plastic mold.

Sole: The bottom of the shoe and can be made of different materials of various thicknesses and layers.

Outer Sole (C): The portion of the shoe that makes contact with the ground. It provides protection from the running surface and improves traction. Most common types are the waffle, ripple, and transverse ridge.

Midsole (F): The portion of the shoe between the outer and inner soles. Its purpose is to provide added cushioning.

Insole: The inner portion of the sole that makes contact with the foot. Materials used in its construction can be either leather, rubber, or preferably, Spenco.

Toe Cap (E): The larger foxing that radiates into the toe area, originally designed to prevent scuffing, lifting the upper material away from the top of the foot.

Heel Counter (A): The inflexible material surrounding the heel area which adds stability to the heel and reduces the pronatory forces entering the heel area during heel contact.

Pull Tab (B): Small tab on heel area which allows the shoe to be pulled on the foot.

Upper (D): The material covering the upper part of the shoe. Nylon is the preferred material.

Foxing: The material portion of the shoe giving medial and lateral support to the sides of the shoes.

Shank Support: The small arch pad of very little use. In walking shoes it is a metal piece which runs through the middle of the shoe.

Spike Plate: A plate material placed under the ball of the foot providing a base for the spikes, when applicable.

The following two categories should be considerations of every runner in regard to shoe fit and have been listed according to primary and secondary importance.

Primary Considerations

1. Outer sole composition (flexibility)
2. Midsole composition (cushioning)
3. Heel counter (support/cushioning)
4. Box toe (height/composition)
5. Nylon upper
6. Heel lift

Secondary Considerations

1. Flared outsole
2. Outer sole tread
3. Ankle padding
4. Arch support
5. Inner sole
6. Heel height
7. Shoe weight
8. Color

To explain the above terms:

First, sole composition and flexibility refer to stiffness. The sole should allow a great amount of flexibility for foot motion and be constructed of appropriate materials that are tough enough to withstand shock but soft enough to provide cushioning.

The midsole should be constructed of a rather flexible material that absorbs shock and allows flexibility. Extreme stiffness should be avoided. Too much thickness in the outer and midsole gives the platform-effect and detracts from the efficiency of the shoe. Look for a good relationship between flexibility and cushioning. This minimizes the risk of lower leg injuries such as shin splints and tendonitis.

The heel counter is one of the most important aspects of the shoe. It should be constructed of rigid material and extend as far distal as possible to minimize the pronatory and supinatory forces in the heel area. A soft heel counter leads to rotational injuries of the lower leg, knee, and hip.

The toe box is essential for a long distance running shoe. This keeps the upper material away from contact with the top of the toes. Those who have had to drop out of races because of toe blisters will appreciate this point. Always allow for at least ¼ inch extra toe length in all shoes. During your runs, the foot will swell by a size to a size-and-a-half. This will be covered more fully later in this chapter.

Nylon upper composition is a necessity for all running shoes. It decreases the abrasion forces placed on the foot in comparison to the leather uppers and also does not take on the shape of the foot. Leather molds to the shape of the foot and runners with pronated feet are habitually subjected to excess shoe force which aggravates the problem. Nylon retains less moisture and is a more comfortable material.

The proper height and material for the heel is essential. The heel takes the brunt of the force during gait contact and must provide good shock absorption. Beware of bias cut heels as they tend to put excess strain on the Achilles tendon.

The secondary considerations are self-explanatory. The value of the flared outsole is questionable. Those of us who have an extremely abducted gait tend to get calf cuts from the outflare of the opposite shoe.

Outer sole tread is the choice of the individual runner, and should be selected according to comfort. The waffle tread and ripple sole appear to be better for dirt-grass running while the transverse treads are more desirable for street running.

The arch supports built into shoes seem to be of minimal value. If they are comfortable, wear them, although they should be removed if you plan to wear orthotics in your training shoes.

The inner sole should be made of Spenco material, the best shock absorber available. It limits the blistering that occurs while running. Cloth inner soles tend to irritate.

It is wise to use cotton socks for running. Cotton absorbs perspiration and adds cushioning; nylon retains more heat and moisture.

Heel height does not seem to be of significant importance unless you have a tight Achilles tendon. If so, then you should wear a higher heel and avoid the bias cut heel shoe (fig. 14).

The weight of the shoe depends on the preference of the runner. The lighter the shoe, the greater the chance of injury. The heavier the shoe, the more protection. You must determine priorities, more speed or more protection.

Figure 6 gives the basic diagram for shoe fit:

A. Proper length.

B. Heel to ball of foot at widest point.

C. Forefoot width.

The athlete should choose her own shoes according to preference and comfort. Remember that many shoe salespeople are more concerned with sales than with proper fit.

When being measured for shoes, always take the measurements standing and near the end of the day when your feet are slightly larger. The shoe will then accommodate for foot swelling when you run.

Figure 6

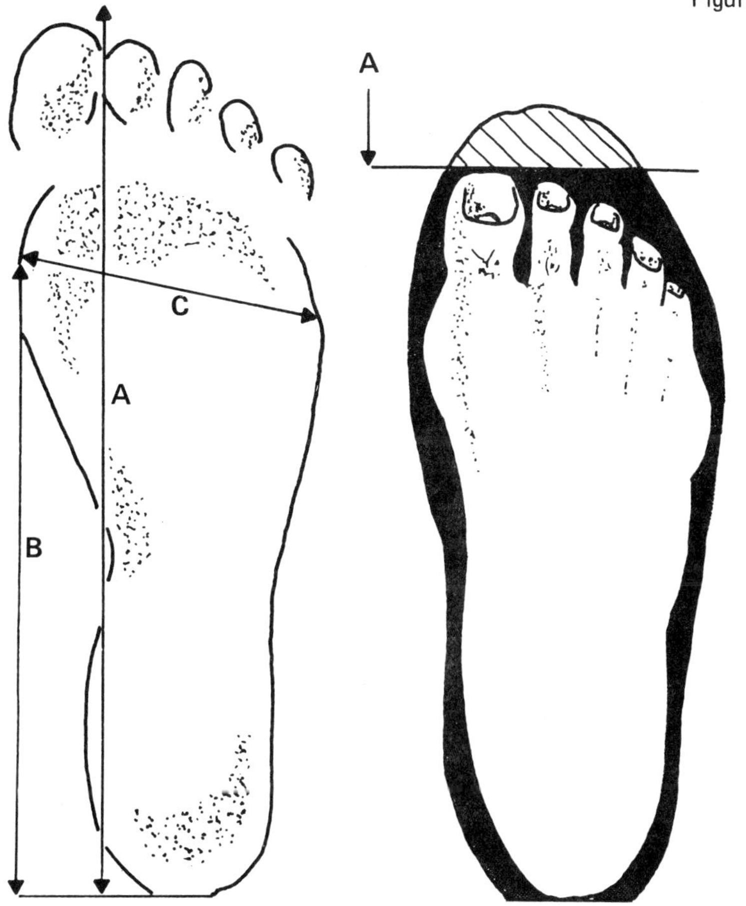

Shoe sizes vary from brand to brand and even within the brands themselves. The Brooks, New Balance, Puma, Etonic, and Adidas Runner tend to be a D-width or wider. The Adidas SL 72 and SL 76, Nike Road Runner, and Tiger (except for the Montreal II) run narrower. If you wear an E-width you will probably wear a larger shoe such as an EE or EEE New Balance 320.

Fit the shoe from heel to toe length first. For those with a Morton's foot or a long second toe, measure from the end of that toe. The width should be measured at the ball of the foot at the widest point (fig. 6). The heel counter or space around the heel should fit snugly. The heel may ride up slightly if there are no blisters.

The toe box should allow free movement of the toes with little friction. A tight toe box may cause corns, black toenails, cramping, or hammertoe deformities. The toes should not touch the end of the shoe.

These are the shoes I recommend after professional evaluation and personal experience. We have worn each shoe for at least 1,000 miles, some for over 5,000 running miles. The shoes were tested by individual long distance runners who average between 70-160 miles per week. No mechanical testing was performed; the runner is the most perfect testing machine available. If the shoe has proved to be improper because of discomfort, poor quality, or high incidence of injuries to the runner, it has been left off the list.

The following is a brief listing. The detailed shoe information charts are listed on following pages.

Recommended Training Shoe List
Extended Running = 6 Miles + A Day

New Balance 320	Puma 9190/9190 S
Puma Mercury II	Tiger Montreal II
Adidas SL 72/76	Adidas Runner*

Limited Running = 1-6 Miles A Day

Nike Road Runner	Nike Waffle Trainer**

Economy Shoes

Penneys Sport Oxford	$ 8.00
Penneys 400-78	$12.00
Penneys Suede Top	$13.00
Foot Locker MBA	$15.00
Pony (Foot Locker)	$18.00
Sears 81-85 Training Flat	$ 8.00
Brooks	$24.00

The lower priced shoes mentioned above are a good cosmetic match for the higher priced brand name shoes. These can be used for those who wish only to jog or walk short mileage and who do not wish to compete.

---

*The Adidas Runner is the better shoe type for the heavier weight runner. It has a stiff "star" type sole. These can be cut transversely across the sole for more flexibility. The LD 1000 has been improved and is now labeled LDV and is still under study.

**The Nike Waffle Trainer was designed with a waffle bottom for running on dirt and grass. It is not a good cement and hard surface shoe as it wears down rapidly.

POSITIVE FEATURES	NEGATIVE FEATURES	INDICATIONS COMMENTS
New Balance 320		
Heel counter good Heel cushioning good Heel fit snug Outer sole tread good Midsole cushioning good Inner sole good Nylon upper Fit: comes in widths	Quality control poor Narrow toe box	Good for runners with fit problems Comes with Spenco insole Comes in widths Long distance/road work
Puma 9190		
Heel counter good Heel cushioning good Heel fit medium Outer sole tread good Nylon upper Fit: wide Quality control good Wide toe box	Lack of cushioning midsole in forefoot area Needs Spenco	Good for runners with wide feet Long distance/road work
Adidas SL 72/76		
Heel counter good Heel cushioning good Heel fit narrow Outer sole tread good Nylon upper Fit: narrow Quality control good	Lack of cushioning midsole in forefoot area Needs Spenco	Good for runners with narrow feet Needs Spenco Long distance/road work
Tiger Montreal II		
Heel counter good Heel cushioning good Heel fit snug Outer sole tread good Midsole cushioning good Innersole fair Fit: medium Nylon upper Good toe box	Outer sole slightly stiff Mild bias cut heel	Good for medium road work Needs Spenco in-sole

POSITIVE FEATURES	NEGATIVE FEATURES	INDICATIONS COMMENTS
	Adidas Runner	
Heel counter good Heel fit medium Heel cushioning good Midsole cushioning good Nylon perforated upper Fit: medium Good toe box	Star outer sole too stiff	For runners of the 170 lb. range Too stiff for lighter weight runners Good quality control
	Nike Waffle Trainer	
Heel counter good Heel fit snug Heel cushioning good Nylon upper Fit: narrow Midsole cushioning fair	Narrow toe box Light weight	Probably better used as racing shoe Good for interval work on grass or dirt
	Nike Road Runner	
Heel counter good Heel cushioning good Heel fit snug Innersole good Fit: narrow/medium Nylon upper	Outer sole tread fair Midsole cushioning poor Light weight Fair toe box Waffle tread wears fast on hard surfaces Curved outer sole Mild bias cut heel	Good for medium and light grass and dirt running Not for use on cement/asphalt Good for racing Use in snow good
	Puma Mercury II	
Heel counter good Heel cushioning good Heel fit medium Outer sole tread good Nylon upper Fit: wide/medium Quality control good	Lack of cushioning in midsole Needs Spenco	Good for runners with wide feet Long distance/road work Successor to Puma 9190

SHOE MODIFICATIONS

In discussing modifications for running shoes, we must realize that shoes are usually poorly made. Many are made over valgus or varus lasts. Others are made for the European foot or the Oriental foot. Some are made just for looks and not for function, whereas others are made with materials that appear sturdy but break down after a few miles. Many American-made shoes have an inner sole made of cardboard! A major athletic shoe company is inventing a throw-away shoe! So, in many cases, the athlete must make his own shoe modifications.

Many problems come from the toe of the shoe. Most runners have a difficult time finding a shoe with a large enough toe box. If the toe is rubbing against the lining, the area may be stretched with a ring-ball stretcher, or one can simply make a slit in the shoe to allow more room for the toe. This may have to be stitched to prevent further tearing. To avoid these problems, a simpler approach would be to push a sock full of sand down into the toe of the shoe and leave it for two or three days. This will open up the front of the shoe.

Possible modifications to the outer or midsole are varied. Many types of outer soles can be added to your present shoe, independent of make or type.

For those of you who have excessive heel wear, the hot glue gun or shoe glue is recommended. The sole area should be scrubbed first before application. Add the material to the heel area and while it is cooling, take a warm iron and flatten out the material. It must be applied flat. Any excess buildup will add improper angulation to the foot and shoe.

Another running tip: Take old inner tube material and cut into the shape of your heel. Use Barge Cement to glue them on. They are good for about a week and are an inexpensive "heel saver." Or, try using regular bathtub caulking cement which can be easily applied with a spatula.

If the foot needs to be balanced, the preferable way is inside the shoe; however, outer shoe modifications are also available. Also, all distance runners should wear Spenco Insoles for blister protection and shock absorption.

Dr. Richard Schuster has had success with metatarsal bars and recommends the use of "add on" material behind the metatarsal heads. He states that during heel lift, twenty-five percent of the body weight passes through the ball of the foot. This can produce painful areas under the metatarsal heads and

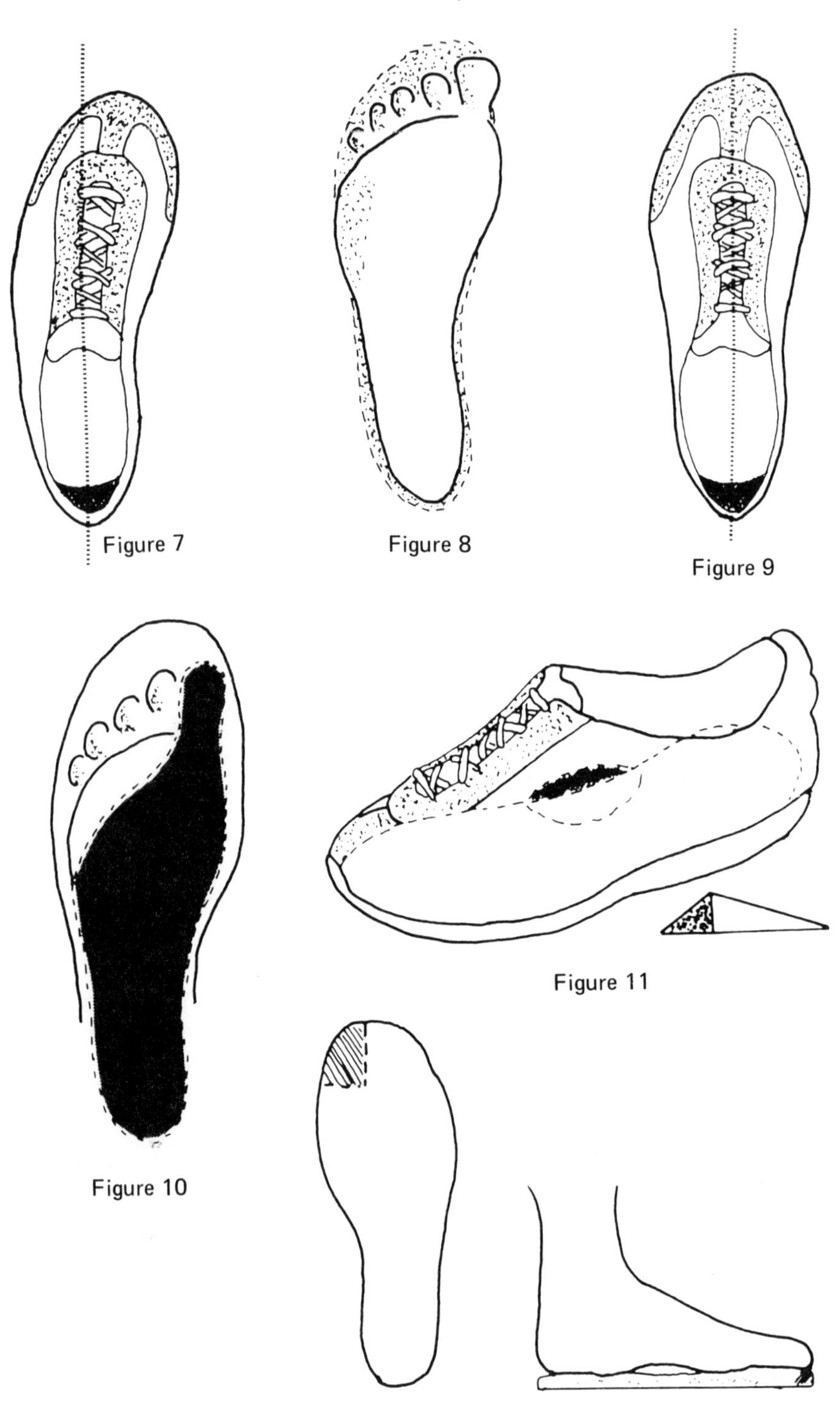

Figure 7

Figure 8

Figure 9

Figure 10

Figure 11

Figure 12

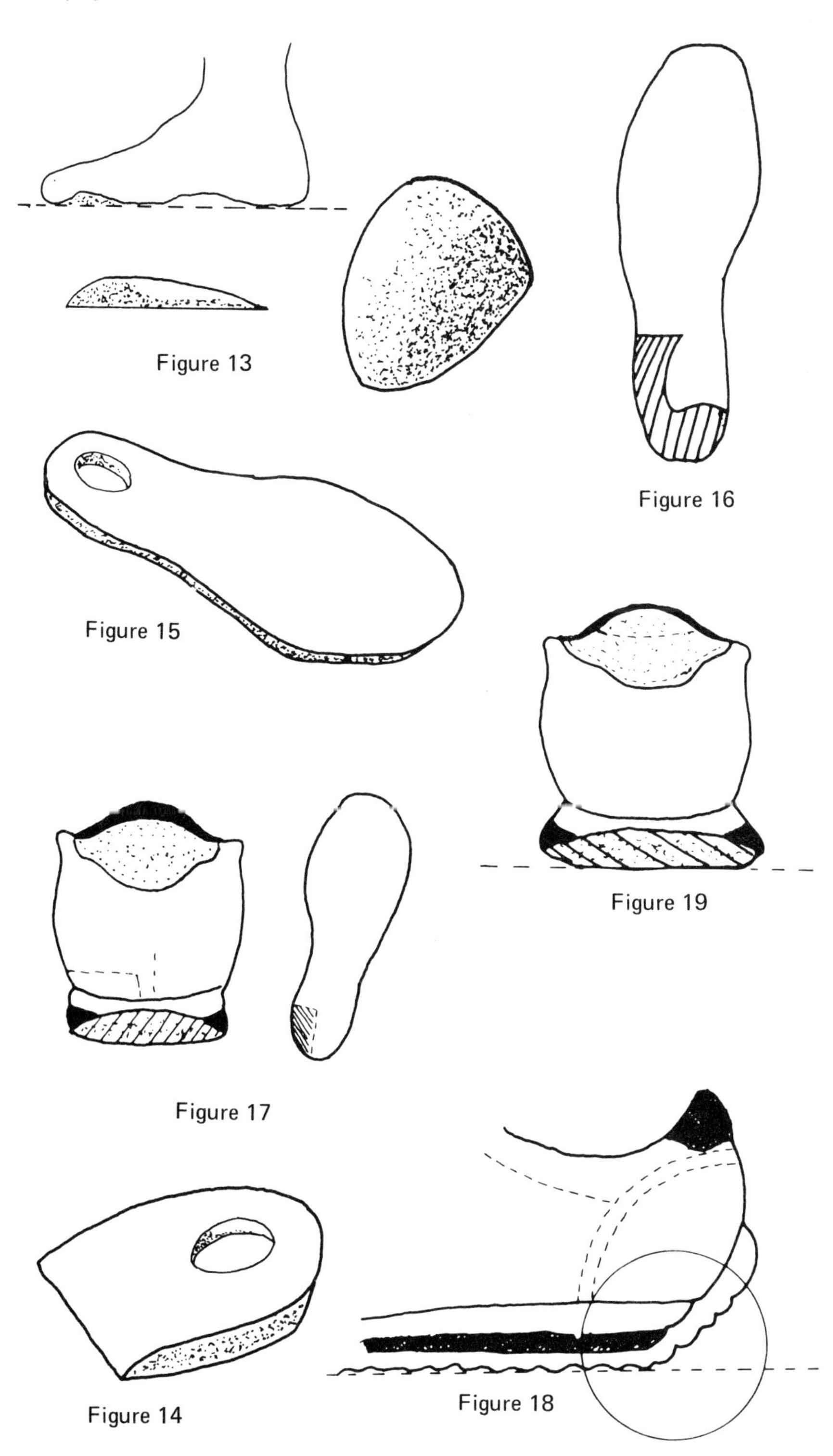

Figure 13

Figure 16

Figure 15

Figure 19

Figure 17

Figure 14

Figure 18

on the big toe joint. Many podiatrists recommend the use of a cuboid wedge pad for strain in the outer areas of the foot.

Many running shoes are now featuring a "bias cut" or rolled heel. These tend to cause heel instability and lead to excess stress on the Achilles tendon. I strongly recommend that you not use shoes with an excessive bias heel cut feature (fig. 18).

Another feature that should be avoided is the transverse rounding of the outer sole which can be found in some of the more popular racing flats. This is shown in figure 19. This promotes additional supinatory and pronatory foot motion and adds to the instability of the foot. The outer sole should sit flat on the running surface.

As explained previously, the "last" is the mold, either wood or plastic, over which the shoe is fabricated. From the mold, the shape, size, and contour of the shoe is determined. Ideally, each athlete should have an individual last of his or her feet to insure ideal fit.

The majority of today's training shoes are made around an inflare last. This means the shoe curves inward and is referred to as a supinated last. This is a poorly-contoured shoe, as it tends to constrict the forefoot and the toe area (figs. 7, 8).

An outflare last is a corrective type of shoe mold and is not normally seen in training shoes. This is the opposite of the inflare last, and the forefoot is swung laterally or to the outside.

Ideally, a shoe should be made from a straight last. It is neither outflare nor inflare. The straight last provides more forefoot room and is more comfortable for long-distance running. A shoe should be fitted on a straight last as indicated in figure 9.

Internal shoe modifications are probably the most misunderstood and misused of all shoe modifications.

Ideally, internal shoe modifications are flexible or rigid foot orthoses which are constructed from plaster casts of the individual foot. But, these orthotics should only be used in specific cases of foot deformities and imbalance. They should never be dispensed for general running wear. Always undergo a complete biomechanical evaluation before the use of foot orthotics.

The second most valuable shoe modifications are those which consist of simple pads which can be installed directly in the running shoe.

A *Morton's extension* is a device used to correct a condition which plagues many runners and has been dubiously termed

"Morton's toe" or "Morton's foot" (*Track Technique*, Volume 59, March, 1975, pp. 1891). This condition is described as a hypermobile, short, first metatarsal with a corresponding long second metatarsal (note: long metatarsal, not necessarily a long second toe). The hypermobile large toe becomes very painful while running and can lead to lower leg and knee problems. In more severe cases, I recommend a rigid or semi-rigid orthotic with a Morton's extension. In mild cases, a simple 1/8-3/16 inch pad extending under the large toe (first metatarsal-phalangeal articulation) can be used (figure 10). This can be placed between the insole and the midsole of the shoe in conjunction with a longitudinal arch pad or can be molded out of a Spenco insole (figure 11). The pad can also be placed on top of the inner sole.

A steel shank bar is a spring steel sole that runs from the heel of the shoe to the toe area. Shoes many years ago were built with a steel shank. These are helpful in hallux rigidus conditions to provide a more efficient toe-off during the gait cycle.

Longitudinal metatarsal pads are usually included in today's training shoes. They are simple pieces of rubber placed in the arch area. Their use is questionable as most are too soft to provide any sufficient support (fig. 12). They should be made of firm rubber or orthopedic felt, which allows some type of inner arch support. Many shoemakers or leather goods stores carry longitudinal arch pads of all shapes, and these should be tested in the individual training shoe. The pad is placed in the midtarsal area to prevent excessive eversion of the calcaneus (heel bone) and breakdown of the inner arch area.

Transverse metatarsal pads are small, teardrop-shaped items that can be placed under the metatarsal shaft area to elevate the transverse metatarsal arch. They can be made of firm grinding rubber or cut from orthopedic felt with beveled edges. It can be glued to the innersole or Spenco lining (fig. 13).

These are of great value for those with forefoot pain or metatarsalgia.

Many runners suffer from sore heels, the majority of which come from the formation of a spur on the bottom surface of the heel bone.

Calcaneal spur doughnuts are simple pads cut from orthopedic felt or sponge rubber (fig. 14). The purpose is to cushion the heel area and provide relief from pressure on the calcaneal spur. For training shoes, a minimum of 1/8 to 1/4 inch is recommended along with a highly cushioned training shoe.

A small aperture is cut into the felt or rubber piece, and this is fitted snugly into the heel of the training shoe.

In many cases, I have lifted up the inner sole and actually cut a hole into the midsole to provide relief. This is lined with a 1/8 inch grinding rubber or cork-rubber combination and thus eliminates the need to recut the doughnut for each pair of shoes.

M-F heel protectors may be of some use in mild cases, but I have not had much success. Ideally, a semi-rigid or flexible orthotic should be provided with a built-in aperture (fig. 15).

A modification of this device is the Egeers calcaneal spur pad. This is a ½ inch thick pad made of sponge rubber which is cut in an elliptical shape to relieve pressure on the medial aspect of the calcaneus at the attachment of the plantar fascia (fig. 16).

There are as many insoles on the market today as there are shoes. Most are made of cheap materials and cannot stand the stress during running. I recommend Spenco Insoles.

Shoe fit should be adjusted accordingly to the extra room the Spenco will occupy in the shoe. They should be broken in immediately with the shoe. The insole provides cushioning from the hard running surfaces and also reduces the chance of blister formation. Some types of running shoes, such as Nike and New Balance, build the Spenco directly into the shoe. I recommend that it be placed directly on top of the existing inner liner.

I have been using foamed polyethylene, plastazote and cork-rubber-fiberglass combinations with the United States Women's Olympic Volleyball Team this year. We have had amazing success and will try to adapt these features into the running insoles.

Wedging is probably the most dramatic and misused shoe adjustment in the running community today. Theoretically, a shoe wedge is a device that alters the stress entering the foot and can influence the direction of the foot during the gait cycle. The most common is the medial or varus heel wedge. This is a 1/8-1/4 inch wedge placed on the inner side of the heel (fig. 17). It is used to control excessive pronation in the rearfoot. Very few runners need a varus heel wedge and its addition may aggravate existing biomechanical deformities. Always consult with your podiatrist, orthopedist or orthotist before installing a heel wedge. Do not buy any make of shoe with this type of shoe wedge or built in arch support. They may aggravate an existing condition. We have left any type of shoe with this addition off our shoe list until further studies can be made.

The medial or varus heel wedge can be placed outside the shoe in the heel area or simply applied as a wedge from orthopedic felt or cork and placed in the shoe on top of the inner sole.

The outer sole wedge is used to control supination of the foot but is rarely used in running shoes.

A lateral sole wedge is used for correction of pigeon toe gait syndrome in children. In adults it can be placed on the lateral aspect of the outer sole and elevate this portion of the foot.

A medial sole wedge is placed along the inner border of the shoe under the first toe joint and creates an inversion of the forefoot.

RUNNING TIPS

- For long runs or marathon type of racing, Vaseline the feet and toes well. Use at least one-half handful for each foot. This is also applicable for other body areas that sustain chafing such as armpits, nipple areas, and groin. As Dr. George Sheehan so aptly put it, you can always tell an experienced marathoner; he is the one that slips off the bus seat.
- Use adequate liquid replacement. Test your drinks before using in a race. The best replacements are Body Punch, ERG, water, or Coke. Tea can also be used, and Jack Foster advocates several cups of warm tea with honey after a marathon. A newer approach that I have found satisfying is Perrier water on the rocks with a large squeeze from a fresh lemon. It replaces fluid and also cleans out the excessive mucous in the mouth.
- The use of a cap with a broad bill is helpful. It serves to provide shade to the face and can hold ice during very hot races.
- Add a pocket to your running trunks. You can carry a Band-Aid and extra Vaseline for emergencies during the run. Also, a dime in the pocket for emergency calls is a must.
- Wear light-colored mesh jersey and trunks. They reflect the sun. Darker colored garments absorb heat.
- Wear cotton socks or socks with as much cotton as possible. Reverse the sock to allow the smoother part of the sock against your skin if you are susceptible to blistering.

Blisters

Blisters, despite their lowly status, are truly the bane of all athletes. They occur in all sports and every athlete has experienced them many times during his athletic career.

In a recent study, ***Lancet***, a British medical journal, states that blisters are an epidermal type of fatigue caused by injury to the skin. The same fatigue in engineering material can be seen

PRIMARY INJURIES

Foot Injury	Description	Early Treatment
BLISTER	Separation of skin layers by serous fluid; caused by shearing forces.	1. Cool compress 2. Domboro, epsom salt soaks
CALLUS, CORN	Thickening of skin for protection from stress or friction	1. Light trim of thick skin 2. Accommodative padding 3. Vaseline
CONTUSION, BRUISE, HEMATOMA, BURSITIS	Damage to vessel area	1. Ice pack or heat to area first 24 hours 2. Anti-inflam-matories, enzymes, analgesics 3. Rest
SPRAIN	Joint injury with fibers of ligaments ruptured or torn, but intact; joint very unstable and can dislocate; edema.	1. Ice first 24 hours 2. Immobilize, elevate 3. Steroids, enzymes 4. Unna Boot 5. Tape
STRAIN	Overstretching of ligaments; integrity intact; joint stable.	1. Ice first 24 hours 2. Enzymes 3. Unna Boot
CRAMPS	Cramping of foot and leg muscles.	1. Moist heat 2. Enzymes, minerals 3. Massage

in experiments on friction blisters in the human skin. It is suggested that fatigue, rather than wear, heat, enzymes, pressure, stretching, or ischemia is the chief cause of blister formation. This fatigue is usually caused by some type of biomechanical disorder of the foot.

We can safely say that a foot that undergoes some type of abnormal pronatory forces during the gait cycle is susceptible to blister formation.

Extended Treatment	Location	Healing Time
1. *Sterile* drainage, compress, topical antibiotics 2. Spenco Insole	Toes, ball of foot, heel	Brief
1. Excision of irritant 2. Functional orthotic 3. Spenco Insole	Toes, ball of foot, heel	Brief
1. Moist heat 2. Orthotics 3. Rest 4. Elastic bandage	Plantar surface of foot	1–6 Weeks
1. Professional care 2. Plaster cast 3. Steroids, enzymes 4. Moist heat 5. Elastic bandage	Ankle	1–6 Weeks
1. Immobilize 2. Enzymes, steroids 3. Orthotic evaluation 4. Elastic bandage	Top of foot, arch, ankle, Achilles tendon	1–6 Weeks
1. Diet 2. Orthotics	Bottom of foot, calf	1–4 Weeks

Whatever the theory behind the cause, relief is an absolute necessity and immediately treatment must be initiated. This painful distention must be relieved so that infection and disability do not take place.

I recommend sterile laceration of the blister as soon as possible. The blister should not be touched at all and the outer layer of skin be left as a barrier against possible infection.

The skin should be scrubbed with an alcohol solution; Betadine or Phisohex products are recommended. Sterile aspiration at the edge of the blister should be undertaken. This should be done carefully so as not to introduce a pathway for bacteria under the skin layers.

Mild, local pressure should be used to drain the resultant

SECONDARY INJURIES

Foot Injury	Description	Early Treatment
DISLOCATION	Separation of bones at joint; rare in runners.	1. Ice 2. Immobilization
TENDONITIS TENOSYNOVITIS	Inflammation of tendon sheath and surrounding soft tissue.	1. Ice, first 24 hours 2. Enzymes, steroids 3. Unna Boot immobilization 4. Tape
SUBLUXATION	A partial dislocation	1. Treat as a dislocation
SHIN SPLINTS	Pain in lower, front part of leg; may swell.	1. Ice, first 24 hours 2. Ace Bandage 3. Dr. Jackson type strapping, lower leg
PERIOSTITIS (Bone Bruise)	Elevation of covering of bone.	1. Immobilization 2. Moist heat 3. Anti-inflammatories
NEURITIS (Nerve Irritation)	Irritation of nerve.	1. Moist heat 2. Injection

fluid from the distal aspect to the small opening. The outer flap should be left in place for protection. If the blister is small, the external flap may be carefully removed and the deep tissue exposed. However, if the outer layer is removed, the tender, thin inner layer becomes susceptible to trauma and infection similar to third degree burns. Sterile aspiration relieves the pressure and also allows for continuous draining and at the same time afford protection to the deeper layers.

The inner layers thicken within two or three days, and the excess skin will usually fall off. If secondary infection sets in, the blister has to be redrained and antibiotic therapy initiated.

After the initial draining, moist compresses with saline solution should be used. This should be followed by application of

Extended Treatment	Location	Healing Time
1. Professional care 2. Cast 3. Enzymes	Ankle, metatarsal area	2–8 Weeks
1. Professional care 2. Enzymes, anti-inflammatories 3. Vitamin C therapy 4. Rigid cast, orthotics	Various areas of foot	1–6 Weeks
1. Orthotics 2. Strapping 3. Ice after running, moist heat later 4. Enzymes, analgesics, steroids	Front of leg	4–8 Weeks
1. Professional care 2. Immobilization	Heel, metatarsals	2–8 Weeks
1. Immobilization 2. Enzymes, anti-inflammatories 3. Injection	Metatarsal area	1–6 Weeks

two-percent gentian violet solution or antibiotics with a covering of sterile Adaptic or gauze. This ritual should be performed twice daily.

Prevention is even more important than the treatment of blisters. As stated earlier, athletes with pronatory foot imbalance are most likely to develop blister problems. These biomechanical problems cause the foot to undergo excessive stresses while running, and this epidermal stress leads to tissue breakdown and blister formation.

Those who suffer from excessive blister formation should undergo a complete foot evaluation. Most problems can be relieved through a simple shoe change or some type of shoe wedging.

A warning sign for blister formation is the "hot spot"; all athletes should recognize these hot spots. Aside from biomechanical deformities, blisters may be caused by improper shoe fit, poor socks that wrinkle or roll up, improper insoles, poor foot preparation, etc.

If the blister is caught in the early stages, a protective layer of Vaseline and gauze can be applied. Wear a comfortable cotton sock (avoid seams—turn the sock inside out) and use a nylon top shoe with a Spenco insole. This provides a nearly perfect friction-free running surface. The Vaseline will ooze through the sock

COMPOUND INJURIES

Foot Injuries	Description	Early Treatment
STRESS FRACTURE	Sharp pain in foot; swelling.	1. Ice, first 24 hours 2. Immobilize 3. Unna Boot
COMPLETE FRACTURE	Complete break in bone; pain, swelling.	1. Immobilize 2. Ice, first 24 hours
SEVERE APOPHYSITIS	Separation or irritation of heel; Children, ages 9–12.	1. Immobilize 2. Enzymes 3. Elevate
PLANTAR FASCIA TEAR	Pain on the inside of the heel; localized.	1. Immobilize 2. Ice, first 24 hours 3. Moist heat

into the shoe; although unsightly, it will be appreciated at the 20-mile mark.

I do not recommend moleskin, Tuff skin, or any type of powder to relieve blisters. They clog skin pores and actually hasten blister formation. In severe conditions, thin nylon tape may be used.

Shoe fit should be carefully watched.

Many times, blisters form under the callus area of the foot, most commonly under the balls of the feet and in the heel area. This callus is built up under areas of stress and irritation. If not treated, a large, keratinized plaque forms and gives rise to deeper irritation that can become a hard, fluid-filled blister. Again, this can be treated by lancing the blister under sterile conditions. The callus itself should be kept trimmed and smooth. The pumice stone or callus file comes in handy for this.

Subungual hematomas and ungual deformities are the polite terms for those black, ugly runners' toes. They distinguish us from all other sport participants. They are more aesthetically distasteful than painful.

In the more severe cases, the nail becomes partially abulsed and ultimately the entire nail has to be removed to prevent further damage or infection. This should be done carefully and under supervised care.

Extended Treatment	Location	Healing Time
1. Professional care 2. Cast 3. Steroids, enzymes	Metatarsal area	4–12 Weeks
1. Professional care 2. Cast 3. Enzymes 4. Surgical	Metatarsal-tarsal area	6–18 Weeks
1. Orthotics 2. Rest 3. Cast	Heel	6–24 Weeks
1. Professional care 2. Steroids 3. Immobilize, strapping, Unna Boot 4. Orthotics	Heel	6–52 Weeks

Nail injuries should not be taken lightly; however, persistent or diffuse bleeding from the nail bed may be the result of a fracture or other deeper injury. Therefore, the mechanism of injury must be investigated and if there is a history of trauma such as running on hard surfaces or a fall, the possibility of fracture is high. In those cases, consult a doctor.

THE USE OF ICE IN ATHLETIC INJURIES

The use of ice in the treatment of foot injuries has been common practice for many years. Some physicians use it for the first 24 hours after an injury, others use it for the entire duration of the injury. Before ice application, the sports physician should understand the physiological effects involved in ice therapy.

The primary effect of cold takes place in the first few minutes of application and its physiological effect is vasoconstriction. Vasoconstriction is strictly a reflex reaction with an accompanying decrease in the capillary blood pressure and an increase in the arterial blood pressure. This is used for the first 24-48 hours for acute musculoskeletal injuries such as inversion sprain, fracture and tendonitis.

The secondary effects are vasodilation and an increase in the rate of blood flow to the area. A massive hyperemia is being produced due to the increase in blood flow to the area with the peripheral vessels being constricted and the deeper vessels being dilated. In heat application, one gets a dilation with stagnation of blood in the area. This is an important point to note. One wishes to influx the area with a quantity of blood to rid the injury area of waste products. With heat alone, you bring in a greater quantity of blood the body cannot use. It therefore has to dispose of the excess blood as well as the waste products.

Cold also produces an anesthetic effect to the area, a decrease in spasticity of the muscles, and in increase in the blood flow rate, rather than a gross increase in circulation.

There are several methods of cold application. Crushed or shaved ice works best by providing a greater surface area, and thus producing a colder situation. A slush mixture with a cold towel works well. You must alternate the towels during therapy so the cold temperature will not go above 35-45 degrees F. Also, the towels must be changed because of the heat transfer between the body and the towel. You can also try a plastic bag with ice cubes or ice cubes on a towel.

For ankle injuries, ice immersion can be used. An ice slush can be provided and the ankle or foot immersed into the slush. The foot should be removed every 30 seconds and allowed to return to its normal temperature and then returned to the slush.

The easiest technique is ice massage. One simply takes an ice cube or cup of ice and massages this over the injured area for a recommended period of time—eight to ten minutes.

During ice therapy, the first response will be the shock of cold on the skin followed by an aching sensation. The skin will become numb in about three minutes, followed by a reddening or erythema of the skin. Ice therapy should be terminated at this point.

Contraindications to cold therapy must be considered before application. Patients with cardiovascular insufficiency or poor circulation condition in the extremity would be considered risks for ice therapy.

LIBERTY
BONNE BELL
24

12

Psychology of Competition

The woman's new role in sports: running as a developer of confidence, motivation

Dr. Thomas Tutko

AGGRESSION

There is probably no personality characteristic that has taken on more importance in athletics, competitive or recreational, than aggression. During the second International Congress of Sport Psychology, an entire section was dedicated to the topic. Warren Johnson, the chairman of the Congress, aptly introduced the topic: "It is evident that the concept of aggression is of most pressing importance these days. However, there is much confusion associated with this word and there are various ways of talking about it."

If such a statement can be true of athletics in general it becomes that much more confusing when applied to women in athletics. There are few areas where there is more conflict and greater evidences of a double standard than aggression in women's athletics. At a recent research conference on women and sport, Dr. Michael Smith presented a paper on aggression and the female athlete. Several statements presented in his paper are relevant to aggression in women in general. For example, Smith said, "The evidence overwhelmingly points to culturally shaped sex-role learning as the chief determinant of masculine-feminine differences in aggression."

Sports, however, may be an exception to such learning as expressed in the following statement later in the paper:

> Nevertheless, there is some reason to believe—with possible exceptions in sport and in some extremist women's organizations—that both males and females look askance upon female violence.

In order to deal thoroughly with the topic of aggression and include all of its ramifications, we must first consider aggression as it is usually described in the literature. Later, we can and will discuss the topic in its broader perspective. For example, some male behavioral traits are not described as being aggressive, but the same behavior in a female would most certainly be described as aggressive.

Aggression in Psychological Literature. Perhaps an appropriate beginning would be to provide an acceptable definition of aggression, or at least a common definition used in the psychological literature. An overview of the literature reveals that one problem with searching for a common definition is that there is no clear meaning. For example, in *A Dictionary of Psychology* (J. Drever, Penguin Books, 1952), aggression is defined as "attack on another, usually, but not necessarily, as a response to opposition."

Roger Johnson, in his book *Aggression in Man and Animals*, however, devotes a subsection in the opening chapter "The Concept of Aggression" to the very topic of a definition, and after making 21 statements reflecting behaviors that may be described as aggressive, asks the question, "Can aggression be defined?" Johnson finally resolves his dilemma by stating that aggression is a multidimensional concept.

Female Development and Aggression. The female is trained rather early that her role is primarily passive, even subservient. During her developmental stages there is often a period early in life (six to twelve years) when being a "tomboy" is tolerated. Certain forms of aggressive behavior are acceptable, but usually in a clearly defined circumscribed way. Athletic participation is one such acceptable form, although girls are expected to eventually "grow out of it." To be assertive, outspoken, or independent meets with rebuff—and slowly but surely the female is molded into an unassuming individual who expresses herself only within clearly defined limits, usually the kitchen of her household.

Women have traditionally been protected from many forms of aggression. One conspicuous example of this is the military. Women who volunteer for the armed forces are assigned noncombat duties. Although this is not true in all nations, in the United States it is virtually unheard of for a woman to be assigned to combat. Women's military responsibilities are primarily those of professional women in the community-at-large, such as secretarial or nursing (the latter due to special recruitment).

In athletics the same attitude prevails. Contact sports in particular are the male domain. Women are not sanctioned to compete in sports where there is body contact. P. Weiss, in his book *Sport: A Philosophic Inquiry*, points out that in the Olympic games, females are guided toward individual sport performances rather than team performances. Obviously, the team performances foster more aggressiveness than individual sports. Only recently have women been able to participate in Olympic team sports such as volleyball. And even now, women are generally discouraged socially from participating in contact sports such as boxing, wrestling, and football.

Language of Sports. The language of sports is primarily couched in aggressive "masculine" terms that are rarely used to describe female behavior. For example, headlines describing victories might read: "Lions Crush Browns"; "Tigers Smash Red Sox"; "Bruins Maul Tarheels"; and such. Rarely is such language used to describe female or "feminine" behavior. Hence, if women's contests are described in the same manner, a great deal of role conflict may result since females have been taught since an early age that such language is unacceptable because it reflects primarily male behavior, not the unaggressive female behavior.

Overt aggression is apparent in the verbal language of athletics. In order for males to express frustration, anger, or disgust, swearing is a common form of venting hostility although it may not be particularly acceptable. However, swearing has become relatively common behavior at sports events that generate high tension and a high level of competition. It is far more acceptable for a male to swear than a female. Hence, many spectators express surprise and shock to hear such language used by a female. The rarity of occurrence is a reflection of the depth of the early training in language habits regarding hostility and aggression, i.e., a female is more apt to be chastised for expressing aggressive hostile language than a male.

A further extension of this attitude is spectator reaction to females who express anger toward officials. Any sports enthusiast has had the opportunity to view athletes arguing or challenging an official. At times this may result in the expressions of a few choice descriptive terms. The possibility of a female displaying such behavior is relatively remote, in part because the usual expectation of a female in a frustrating situation is to "grin and bear it," or not let her feelings get out of control. The male, however, is permitted to "let loose." And at times it may appear even more masculine to challenge the official, a representative of authority. Hence, the athlete may be supported by the crowd.

A second reason why women athletes display fewer outward expressions of temper and frustration is that officials are usually male. Many years of training immediately come to the fore when a female athlete faces a male official. She is more inclined to "back off" because she may feel intimidated. Moreover, she is less inclined to be supported by the fans, and so she must stand alone.

Aggression and Hostility. One aspect of aggression that is continually confusing is the tie between aggression and hostility. Although we respond to the two as if they were synonymous there are clear and distinct differences between the two. The main difference seems to be whether there exists an intent to be destructive. Aggression implies assertiveness but not destructiveness. Hostility implies destructive and harmful intent whether or not it results in assertive behavior. It is possible, for example, to be aggressive without harmful intent; for example, a salesman may be aggressive but not destructive. It is equally possible to be hostile without being aggressive; for example, an individual may wish an enemy bad luck or failure.

Several individuals have attempted to clarify the confusion between the two. L. B. Sechrest and J. Wallace, in their book *Psychology and Human Problems*, describe aggression as one tactic of adjustment. They refer to any outward assertive behavior with harmful or destructive intent as *hostile aggression.* I have defined the two terms separately and delineated their relationship by describing each of four categories: hostile-aggressive, hostile-nonaggressive, nonhostile-aggressive, and nonaggressive-nonhostile.

Of particular importance to women regarding the dimensions of aggression and hostility is the fact that aggression is related to athletic success. It is possible that women may be trained to become more assertive, and over a period of time it will become more accepted culturally. The feminist movement is an example of aggression that embodies productive action. However, for women to demonstrate hostility in an aggressive fashion still remains beyond the realm of acceptability. The general halo about women is that they are incapable of hostility, at least in an open, direct fashion. The form that it takes is usually less recognized as a destructive force. J. M. Bardwick, in *Psychology of Women: A Study of Bio-Cultural Conflicts,* points out that female aggression or hostility usually takes indirect and covert forms. For example, it is manifested in interpersonal rejection, passive negativism, and indirect forms of verbal and social aggression. Crying tears of anger is a common form of such hostility, as well as gossiping or making cryptic remarks. In my classification, these would be labeled as hostile-nonaggressive symptoms. The clinical psychological literature commonly describes a covertly hostile female as a "castrating" woman, implying indirect forms of expressing hostile aggressiveness.

Early training of the female to express negative feelings indirectly has a great deal of carryover in athletics. Women are allowed to participate in most individual sports and some team sports. The line seems to be clearly drawn, however, when contact or aggressive sports are involved, as explained in P. Weiss's *Sport: A Philosophic Inquiry.* As far back as 1882 Herbert Spencer noted that such delineation was marked rather clearly. Although the lines have changed somewhat, women in contact sports are still considered an anomaly, freakish, and bizarre. The main reason for this attitude is that contact sports such as football and hockey have an element of hostility. Males can ease tempers, start fights, indulge in physical attacks, and take on the role of being tough and strong—and end up being heroes. In fact, by indulging in such behavior they become more herolike. For females to indulge in the same behavior is a ticket to being ostracized. For example, in professional female wrestling (although pro wrestling is theatrical) and roller derby skating, hostile aggressive behavior, although it is considered a part of the game, is viewed by others as masculine behavior. The female who participates is thought of as being like a man and she is accused of acting like a man. This behavior does not make a heroine of her nor is she given greater social sanction. Instead, she becomes marked as weird—a freak. It detracts rather than adds to her sex-typed role.

Aggression as a Multidimensional Concept. Aggression as a personality trait has been operationally defined in several different personality tests. In the Edwards Personal Preference Schedule (EPPS), aggression is defined like this:

> To attach contrary points of view, to tell others what one thinks about them, to criticize others publicly, to make fun of others, to tell others off when disagreeing with them, to get revenge for insults, to become angry, to blame others when things go wrong, to read newspaper accounts of violence.

Although one might accept this as a clearly defined, operational definition of aggression for women, the concept is somewhat broader and more multidimensional. Any behavior that lends itself to acting out—whether against the environment or as a defense for oneself—is seen as aggressive in women, although it is rarely labeled as such. Women who are independent, tough-minded, outspoken, nonconforming, and in general outgoing in defense of themselves or others, are seen as aggressive. This label is not applied to males but is, rather, considered to be a positive asset. If a male defends himself or others he is usually considered strong and admired. This "independent" behavior has positive connotations. If the female exhibits the very same behavior she is considered to be "out of line" or "aggressive," and the usual connotations are usually negative. There is clearly a double standard in evaluation of outgoing behaviors for males as compared to females.

Women's Athletics and Research Results on Aggression. Not surprisingly, one of the personality characteristics related to success in women's athletics has been aggression, or some form of assertiveness. Researchers in the area of personality and motivation indicate that the female who is able to express herself in an outgoing way is more apt to be successful than one who is less inclined to do so. The more inhibited, timid female sports participant is less apt to reach full potential. Listed below are some research results that substantiate this assertion. These results focus on aggression in its many manifestations such as dominance and tough-mindedness.

Differences have often been found in testing, even using similar questionnaires commonly used in personality testing. In E. Bird's article, "Personality Structure of Canadian Intercollegiate Women Ice Hockey Players," the findings were that the women have a greater degree of tough poise and that they are more independent than the female norm group. C. L. Mushier found that female lacrosse players are significantly more dominant and tough-minded, once again comparing these athletes to the norm group. T. Malumphy found that team and individual female athletes were significantly more tough-minded than nonparticipants. B. C. Ogilvie found female swimmers to be significantly more dominant, achievement-oriented, aggressive, venturesome, and bold. J. M. Williams and his associates, in testing fencers, found them to be significantly more dominant than the norm groups. In a study of Pan-American women athletes, P. Neal found significant differences between the athletes and the norm group on the traits of achievement, aggressiveness, and autonomy.

In general, it would appear that superior female athletes do score higher on traits that can be classified as aggressive or on certain ones labeled as "acting out."

DEVELOPING AGGRESSION

One of the most difficult tasks confronting a coach in the development of motivation in female athletes is the problem of developing aggression. In essence, the coach must undo years of previous training in sex-typing, socialization, and child rearing. Moreover, the coach is confronted with reeducating the female athlete to an alternate lifestyle, one in which she is to act out aggressively, to assert herself, to resist intimidation, and to defend what might be classified as "her" territory. Rather than using indirect or covert means, she must come face-to-face with the problem of assertiveness.

The problem, of course, is that years of training have led her to feel she will be ostracized if she is directly aggressive. She fears rejection for being "different"—for violating the cultural norm. There is a great deal of guilt associated with acting out, for included in this total behavioral picture is not only the possibility of being isolated by men and women alike, but the possibility of being stigmatized as "bad." The female athlete's feelings of having done something *wrong*, together with having been rejected, are two powerful forces that keep her from acting outwardly.

The coach must recognize that the female athlete finds herself in more conflict over aggression than males because of her culturally ascribed role. A male can be aggressive both on and off the athletic field congruent with his male role. But the female who is aggressive both on and off the field finds herself being positively rewarded on the athletic field and negatively rewarded in other spheres of life. She must quickly learn to discriminate between these two areas when she manifests aggressive tendencies. This burden can pose a difficult problem for her.

It is very important that coaches of women's athletic teams discuss their players' attitudes toward being aggressive. Do the players feel guilty? Are they being rejected? Do they experience a personal conflict if they think they are playing a dual role? Do they fear what others may think or do? For example, some girls may have boyfriends who may be threatened by such behavior, or a girl may refrain from being aggressive because of what her boyfriend or potential boyfriends may say. By discussing these problems as a team, the players can mutually share any concerns, anxieties, fears, or problems that arise from being aggressive. In some respects, this may add to a team's cohesion since a greater degree of empathy may be expressed for any one player who is going through some difficulty. More important, others may offer overt support when an athlete is facing such problems.

A frank discussion with the team and/or individual athletes may often reveal reasons for not being aggressive that are extremely personal. For example, aggression and hostility are often so inextricably linked in one's mind that to be assertive produces the same feeling as being hostile or angry, or having feelings of wanting to be destructive. Some deeply religious individuals find such behavior in great conflict with their personal moral code. They are more comfortable accepting aggression *from* others than asserting themselves *toward* others. To do the latter would be akin to committing a sin. The coach can only discover these personal reasons by having individual as well as team discussions.

In some cases, the female athlete will be more comfortable if she is aware of support from her coach, for the coach must not only sanction aggression, but clearly illustrate its value in being a successful athlete. Moreover, the coach must be available to work with anyone who finds herself in great personal conflict as a result of being aggressive, since guilt feelings that often accompany expressions of aggression should be explored if they are to be eliminated or reduced. One way that some women deal with these relatively negative feelings is to withdraw, since embarrassment often results from undertaking atypical behavior. Or, at times the athlete may unconsciously punish herself by failing as a direct payment for being aggressive. This is one of the reasons for "success phobia" or the tendency to fear being a success because of its adverse consequences.

Developmental Steps

Since aggression appears to be related to success in athletics, its development would seem to be of great importance in that area. Moreover, it has been advocated that some "masculine-type qualities" found in athletics can be used to advantage in other aspects of a competitive life situation. Aggression is obviously one of these qualities.

Some individuals have indicated that freedom to release aggression may actually be easier for females than for males. Ogilvie, for instance, made this comment: "When (male) competitors lose, they feel subtle anger and hostility. Women are much more honest about it. When a woman loses, she doesn't want to shake hands with the winner or hug her unless she's a teammate and the team has won. There's a hurt, resentment, anger—a whole variety of feelings."

To encourage this ability to release aggression, the coach might foster its development in a step-by-step progression:

(1) A confidential discussion with each athlete about her attitude toward aggression—including such aspects as guilt and fear—may reassure the female athlete. For example, some females fear aggression because of the possibility of injury. Since women have been trained to be body-conscious, injuries can take on far deeper meaning than for men. Women's fear of injury that might lead to disfigurement or complications in bearing children may loom as an important factor in deciding whether or not to be aggressive. If the coach discusses these problems confidentially with team members, they may become more apparent.

(2) A history of the athlete's family may reveal attitudes toward aggression. A sports-minded family will be more accepting of aggression in their daughter than a family with little or no athletic interest or information. Religiously oriented families are less inclined to condone or accept aggression in any children because of the destructive connotations. Hence, the coach who becomes acquainted with the family lifestyle of an athlete can often find clues to determine if the athlete may have conflict in expressing aggression.

(3) The coach should inform the athlete or the team of her intent to support and/or emphasize aggression at certain times. She might explain that she wants to help the athletes protect themselves from intimidation and other problems. Moreover,

the coach can explain that aggression is related to being successful and reaching one's potential in sports.

It is at this point that the coach can make it clear that he or she is talking about asserting oneself toward a goal rather than using assertiveness as a destructive tool. S. Feshback, in his article "Dynamics of Morality of Violence and Aggression: Some Psychological Considerations," describes this as *instrumental aggression*, which is quite different from destructive aggression.

(4) Periodic assessment of each athlete as aggressive can be undertaken by the coach, particularly for those who find it difficult to aggress. Part of the coach's organizational plan might be to provide strong positive reinforcement for assertive behavior. Work done by Rushall and Siedentop (detailed in the book *The Development and Control of Behavior in Sport and Physical Education*) indicates that prescribed plans for developing certain behaviors can work, with aggression being one of the areas of consideration.

The coach might also refer to those athletes who are aggressive as models of such behavior, clarifying for the athlete just what can be expected of her.

The development of aggression is not an easy task, but there can be little doubt of its influence in athletics. Goodhardt and Chataway, in their book *War without Weapons*, see aggression as one of the prime movers in the Olympics. To develop this characteristic in a healthy, productive way can be of great value in helping each athlete reach her potential.

Stress and Anxiety

The world of athletics invariably involves stress. The stress of practice and competition, the pressure to do well because of internal pride as well as the influence of outside sources, and the stress of maintaining any success that may be gained as a result of competition are all part of athletics.

Accompanying the stress and the pressure is *anxiety*—either chronic uneasiness or the uneasiness related to competition.

The female athlete faces more stress and anxiety than the male, for she must also carry with her the feeling that she is not totally accepted in the athletic world. She cannot be expected to have full support even from those who regularly follow athletics. At times this may be related to her own self-doubt for she may have internalized the cultural edict that women who participate in athletics are weird.

Another facet of female athletic anxiety is that some women find themselves in a relatively select group. The number of female athletes in the country is relatively limited, particularly those who consider sports to be a serious endeavor and in some way hope to make a sports career, directly or indirectly. Stated in another way, the female athlete is alone, and in many instances, she must fend for herself in a not-too-accepting environment. Perhaps the only support she can realistically expect to receive is from her teammates, close friends, and coaches.

An added burden has been the traditional model to which women are exposed throughout their lives regarding feelings. Quite simply, women are expected to be emotional. In fact, one of the most common cultural stereotypes is that women are the "emotional sex." More often than not, this image implies being nervous or tense or anxious.

Anxiety not only accompanies stress, but very often the lack of confidence. If any one expectation depicts the general attitude of the outsider toward women's athletics, it is the lack of confidence. Whereas a number of European and Asian nations have accepted females in athletics without prejudice, the general onlooker in the United States relegates women's sports to an inferior position. The female athlete is inclined to accept that attitude herself. Naturally, there can be nothing more self-defeating than feeling defeated. Wilma Rudolph, three-time sprint gold medalist at the 1960 Olympic Games, has often been used as an example of a woman athlete who has overcome insurmountable obstacles to achieve athletic greatness. In her case, as a child she could not walk and had to be carried everywhere she went. Hence, she had to overcome not only female stereotypes but early childhood experiences as well. Unfortunately, if one expects to lose, very often one *will* lose because one "sets up" the circumstances, often unconsciously. This phenomenon, known in psychology as the "self-fulfilling prophecy," serves as a self-deterrent in athletic success.

An example of how anxiety and lack of self-confidence work together is reflected in the conflict described by Canadian diving champion Beverly Boys. Although her coach, Don Webb, described her as a hard worker, tough competitor, consistent, steady, and very dedicated, Ms. Boys needed to overcome anxiety due to her lack of confidence. During a crucial workout, one which would determine whether or not she would become a member of the team going to Britain to compete, the coach insisted she make an inward 1½ dive off the tower. At the "moment of truth" she froze at the 10-meter (30-foot) board. As Boys describes the incident, "I was certain I wouldn't be able to make it. It wasn't too difficult from a board that has a bit of 'spring' in it, but I was absolutely positive I would hit the solid hunk of concrete on the way down if I tried it from the tower. I was scared stiff and I just couldn't do it. And the coach—boy, was he mad."

Ms. Boys was able to overcome the anxiety about her lack of confidence only because of the challenge offered by her coach. All this was accomplished at age 13!

In this example we can see how anxiety (fear and being scared stiff) was tied to lack of confidence. Only the confidence exuded by the coach finally enabled the athlete to overcome the difficulty. Unfortunately, the average female athlete is constantly told directly or indirectly she is less capable than a man, which serves to reinforce her personal lack of confidence and prohibits her from taking that one step that will propel her toward her peak in athletic excellence.

The fact that female athletes in general have low self-confidence has been borne out by several research studies. J. E. Kane found that women track and swimming athletes have significantly less confidence than a norm group. The same was found when comparisons were made between female physical education majors and both a norm group and male physical education majors.

Anxiety in athletics for women may be attached to other aspects of personality besides lack of self-confidence. It has been found in previous research that women in athletics are also more inclined to be more achievement-oriented, tough-minded, intelligent, creative, self-sufficient, and aggressive. The picture of an ambitious, tough-minded, intelligent, creative, self-sufficient, and aggressive female athlete is inclined to give one the impression that anxiety should be rather easy to handle—and in many respects this may be quite true—but such an individual constantly seeks and faces challenges not only for self-satisfaction but because these challenges arise from the environment. From a personality standpoint, this rather remarkable individual is quite apt to be faced with challenges from her own sex as well as from the opposite sex. The continued challenges are likely to lead to undue amounts of anxiety.

The commonly accepted contention that women in athletics are more anxious seems to be borne out by research evidence. A number of studies have indicated that female athletes are indeed significantly more anxious than other women. In comparing women track and swimming athletes to a norm group, Kane found the athletes to be more anxious. Similar findings resulted from a comparison of women physical education majors to both a norm group and to men. Compared to the norm women, the physical education students scored low on emotional stability, and were more anxious; and compared to males they were significantly more tense and less composed. T. Malumphy found female team athletes to be significantly more anxious than individual players and nonparticipants. And in summarizing the research findings, Kane states that in general, anxiety is reported to be higher for women than for men, although there are many exceptions.

Two additional findings are relevant to the general topic of anxiety and women athletes. First, there seems to be a cross-cultural difference regarding anxiety in women's athletics. Kane reports that British women athletes are significantly less anxious than their female counterparts in the U.S., in part because the British are more generally accepting of females in athletics than Americans.

Second, women manifest more anxiety than men *in general.* Equally important is that women are more inclined to freely express *other* emotions freely as well. Even more important, however, is that women are also more sensitive in general. Women feel freer to express not only anxiety, but also joy, sorrow, and other sensitivity. Supporting this contention is the finding that one scale on the Jackson Personality Research form, *sentience*, shows a higher mean score for females than males. To possess sentience means that one "notices smells, sounds, sights, tastes, and the way things feel; remembers these sensations and believes that they are an important part of life; is sensitive to many forms of experience; may maintain an essentially hedonistic or aesthetic view of life."

The Jackson Manual goes further in defining trait adjectives or other terms that could describe sentience. They include: "Aesthetic, enjoys physical sensations, observant, earthly, aware, notices environment, feeling, sensitive, sensuous, open to experience, perceptive, responsive, noticing, discriminating, alive to impressions."

Perhaps we should consider women as free to express *all* emotions, rather than just one emotion—anxiety—that might in the context of sports appear to be somewhat negative.

We might also consider a more fundamental question regarding society's attitude toward those who express emotions. The typical male model, for the most part, is emotionless. This is of particular significance for athletes since the entire concept of masculinity is brought into focus if a man expresses his feelings. Men are expected to remain "cool," although this may actually be a rather unhealthy reaction. If we extend the concepts presented above relative to joy in female athletics, the male model may actually be self-destructive. Unexpressed anxiety can result in some form of psychosomatic illness, the number one problem in maintaining mental health. It is entirely possible that the female model for expressing emotions in athletics should be encouraged and emulated, not the male model at all.

There is a need for greater acceptance of the emotional side of athletics. Athletics have become progressively more mechanistic, trying to fit the athlete into the mold of a machine, devoid of feeling and functioning efficiently like some mechanical contrivance. One of the highest compliments that can be paid to a team or an athlete is to describe a performance as having functioned like a "well-oiled machine." If athletes act like robots, or teams function like complicated machines, the joys of athletics and the growth that may occur as a result of the sorrow of athletics both vanish. To accept the emotions of athletes renders athetics more human.

Humanistic coaching also involves a concern for the attitudes and feelings of the athletes, and how such attitudes and feelings may be subject to development in the same way that physical talent is developed. Successful play requires more than just the development of skills. There must be emotion behind skills and a positive attitude toward oneself and others. Humanistic coaching involves setting goals with each athlete, working toward productive influence of feelings, teaching how to respond productively to setbacks and to handle overconfidence. All these tasks fall within the realm of humanistic coaching and, by and large, all have been omitted from the training of male coaches.

BONNE BELL
129
246
00 METERS
057

The reader may want a clearer definition of humanistic coaching, which perhaps can be best described by two athletes who were interviewed by L. Percival during his study of athletes' impressions of coaches. One said, "I want a coach who I feel cares about me whether I win or lose." The other commented, "I don't know if my coach is telling me the right thing, if he is the smartest coach in the league, but I do know how he makes me feel when he corrects me or bawls me out when he doesn't notice that I am improving or trying hard."

Many suggestions for this style of coaching have been described in *The Psychology of Coaching* by myself and J. Richards, a book which was written primarily as an individualistic, humanistic approach to the coaching process. Further steps in the development of better understanding and communication have been described in a series of articles in *Scholastic Coach* by Lyon, Ogilvie, and myself. In essence, it is the responsibility of the individual coach to develop his or her unique style, using some basic guidelines.

Some women would tend to take issue with this approach, asserting that women are no different than men and ought, therefore, to be treated the same. Some might go so far as to argue that bringing up these considerations may tend to exaggerate those elements that might not otherwise exist. Others would argue that if all athletes are treated alike they will perform similarly.

For some athletes this may, in fact, be true. To ignore the conflicts that some girls and women might be undergoing, however, and bury one's head in the sand, hoping the problems will simply go away, might cause many athletes to quit who wish to verbalize the internal struggle they face. There are times in which a female athlete, despite the fact that she may have years of competition behind her, questions her identity. She may wonder if she is weird. Moreover, it must be remembered that because these moments of doubt are relatively fleeting, immediate reassurance by the coach as well as discussions at appropriate times may well eliminate the periodic doubts of female athletes.

Humanistic coaching involves more than a discussion of personal conflicts. It involves a genuine interest in the individual rather than a concern for just her talent. An athlete who feels accepted only because she swims very fast or runs with great speed on a track can feel that only part of her is being accepted. Should that part tend to falter, or should the athlete tend to lose that "edge," there is the constant fear of abandonment.

We often hear of an athlete who returns to his or her coach years after his or her competitive days are over to thank the coach for personal concern expressed during periods of crisis. Contests will come and go, records will be made and broken, but the relationships that are formed in athletics, positive and negative, last as long as the individuals who form them. If they are positive, those relationships may have a strong beneficial effect in helping athletes face crucial periods later in life.

GREATER ATHLETIC COOPERATION

It has been suggested by some that one form of working out the controversy of women's participation in athletics is to combine women and men on a single team so that they must work together. In other words, half of the members of a volleyball team would be female, and a certain percentage of women would participate during each game.

Another suggestion has been to combine the scores of a college's women's and men's teams to determine an overall winner. In this manner, the males and females become dependent upon one another. Having one strong team and one weak team would not be an advantage to either team, and thus players would show greater concern for the total unit.

Obviously neither proposal will be realized at the instigation of men; an initiative must come from women. Either proposal could make a marked contribution historically to the direction in which athletics will go. And the second proposal would help athletes work more cooperatively in reaching achievable solutions. It is a model to help young athletes work toward mutually desirable solutions in other aspects of life after their competitive years are over. This is far more productive and more akin to actual life than the present model.

In some respects the second type of model is presently emerging in many athletic areas. For example, in some athletic clinics women have been strongly encouraged to attend along with the men. Some women are even developing their own clinics, with men as the prime teachers in some, but both men and women to instruct in others. This is a productive, realistic model for the athlete to observe and a step toward the kind of cooperation necessary in athletics. It is a stepping stone toward breaking down long-standing barriers between males and females in athletics.

The above proposals, then, represent some of the unique contributions that women's athletics can make to the future, not only to women's athletics itself but throughout the field of sports. There are those who would prefer continuing to follow only the male model. And there are also those who would say that because men have been given a free hand, because they have dominated and dictated for a long period of time, women should be given an equal chance at formulating policy.

The female coach need only review the number of problems and misapprehensions in athletics resulting from male domination to determine that the present model is far from ideal. And although women obviously cannot produce an ideal replacement model, they can improve upon present standards.

Joy and Exuberance

If one single dimension differentiates male from female athletes, it is the freedom to express emotions. There are perhaps few events that depict spontaneous joy and exuberance more than female athletics. A spectator need only look at the faces of the athletes and it is apparent who is winning and who is losing. As the expression goes, these athletes wear their "emotion on their sleeves."

The reasons for this freedom in athletics are many:

1. Women, in general, are permitted greater freedom of expression of positive feelings of all types. The classic stereotype of females is that they are emotional, and this stereotype includes positive emotions. The emotions of tenderness, love, and sensitivity are more acceptable in females than males. Carried to the athletic arena, these same feelings are expressed as a reaction to the consequences of athletic contests. Women can, and do, openly express affection for one another, whereas males expressing the same behaviors would be considered not only odd, but perhaps homosexual.

2. Participation in athletics for females carries with it a greater personal investment in others than for men, particularly for team sports and on lower levels of competition. This greater investment in others provides a greater source of pride in the team and thus more joy in what all contribute rather than

merely personal concerns. Results of research using the Edwards Personal Preference Schedule indicate that women exhibit a great tendency to be nurturant and thus display great empathy when someone on the same team does well. It is as if each team member is being looked after by the others. There is thus greater responsiveness to teammates.

3. Most female athletes have volunteered to participate rather than being invited or persuaded to participate. Any volunteer makes a greater investment in any job or activity than someone who has been pushed or forced. As a result, there is a greater feeling of accomplishment when one does well. Success is appreciated more.

4. There is less emphasis on the "win-at-all-costs" philosophy that dominates male athletics, and thus there is less personal threat if a team member does well. Teammates take more genuine pride in each other. In his book, *The North Dallas Forty*, Peter Gent points out that it is often threatening to a second-string player when the person against whom he is competing does well. And, of course, the second-stringer also has little to be enthusiastic about should the team do well when he or she is not participating at all.

Another problem of high-level competition is the temporary nature of joy. An athlete can only be happy for a short period of time because it is soon time to begin worrying about the next event, the next game, or the next meet. Rarely can an athlete take any comfort in victory, for a challenge always lies ahead. Female competitors can enjoy success for longer periods of time than men simply because for most of them winning has not become a life-or-death matter. Should women compete with the same intensity as men, and should their expectations be the same, much of their spontaneity will be lost, for competing will soon become somewhat of a job, one in which victory is expected. The machinelike functioning of the Miami Dolphins in the Super Bowl of 1973 detracted much from the joy of the game. In fact, some people have begun to classify all professional football—a sport previously known for its excitement and joy—as a dull pastime. The businesslike attitude and methodical approach of many golfers fall in the same category.

5. Athletic victories for females represent more than wins or success. Because females are not supposed to compete or do well, any success constitutes a challenge to that myth. It is as if the female is saying, "I *am* capable. I *can* do it." A victory

represents not only success but a blow toward dispelling prejudice, and thus it can generate great joy.

6. Not only are females *permitted* by society to respond spontaneously to joy, but this response is, in fact, expected. Emotional reactions to tense situations have become the norm, not the exception. Females might even feel they are letting others down by not freely expressing themselves.

There are many sources of joy in athletics. The sense of accomplishment in completing a task that may have taken many hours of hard work to overcome; facing a challenge that tests one's limits; defying and defeating the odds in any uphill battle; and the feeling of pride when a personal goal is reached are all sources of joy. These things bring joy in athletics, although in many instances the athlete is the only one to experience it or even know about it. To turn these accomplishments into work, or to minimize the joy, would be a disservice to athletics. Women in athletics, more than men, reflect the joy of accomplishment.

Sorrow

There is a natural response to disappointment, failure, or defeat. The most therapeutic response to such circumstances is to handle the depression by crying. Women usually respond spontaneously to sorrow in this manner. This is a far healthier model to follow than many of the models followed by men.

In athletics one must expect setbacks. The nature of competition is such that each event or contest produces disappointments. By expressing sorrow, athletes who have encountered defeat give vent to internal emotions, decreasing the likelihood that such emotions will be kept inside, waiting to be expressed in other ways or attached to other incidents.

The female model for expressing sorrow is the more productive. Expressing sorrow decreases the chances that sorrow will erupt in some other form, as it often does with men.

Male Reactions to Defeat

A highly competitive environment does not allow for defeat. To be defeated in the male athletic world produces conflict in the expressing of emotions. Males are not permitted to cry. It is a sign of weakness or emasculation, and is very often referred to as a woman's way of handling emotions. Men have always been told to take defeat or disappointment "on the chin" without flinching. When he is injured, a man must act as if the injury does not exist. Instead of counseling men to deal with sorrow in the most natural way, the male athletic coach perpetuates defenses against defeats and setbacks by training athletes to respond in a way that may be more damaging than helpful. Whereas women are able to let out the tears and be partially rid of the sorrow, males take a more defensive tack. Little boys are told to "act like a man" and "not cry like a girl." They are trained to accept irritation, sorrow, and grief by grinning and bearing it or by repressing emotion altogether.

For example, one rather common method for dealing with defeat in male athletics is to attack, become hostile and accusatory, and in general defend against accepting defeat. Men who adopt this approach may blame the officials, the field, or any other extraneous cause for their setbacks. This male model may be rather detrimental physiologically. For example, a psychosomatic illness may result. According to Dr. Walter C. Alvarez, Professor Emeritus of the Mayo Clinic:

"Deep emotion that has no vent in tears makes other organs weep instead, thus upsetting glandular balances. Repressed grief, rage, or irritation causes profound chemical changes, wreaks havoc with your nerves, makes your body ill. Crippling migraines, high blood pressure, disorders of the digestive tract, and a host of other vague but neurasthenic reactions result from not opening nature's safety valve when you need to."

Because of the tremendous stress of athletics, and the continual pressures exerted to bring success, the potential for such psychosomatic difficulties is very great. Women in athletics are, in general, in a much better position to deal with the sorrows in athletics than are men. Whereas men generally must follow a cultural stereotype that may become personally destructive, females are inclined to respond in a way that is therapeutic. It is rather ironic that males must be trained to respond unnaturally in order to perpetuate a myth, a myth that may be instrumental to their destruction in the long run. For the female to follow the male athletic model in expressing sorrow would be akin to committing a strange type of psychological suicide. However, by accepting the overall male model for competitive programs, it is very likely that the female will end up accepting the same psychological responses as the male.

ATHLETIC ADAPTATION OF THE FEMALE

It has long been commonly accepted that women have a difficult time withstanding emotional pressures of any type. Because women are freer to express emotions, this expression has unfortunately been interpreted as weakness. In addition, all too often women are thought of as less capable physically. Thus the picture becomes one of total ineptitude.

This image has been perpetuated not only by men, in sport philosophies, and by coaches, physical educators, and athletic fans, but by athletically interested women, as well. In an article entitled "Giving Women a Sporting Chance" (*Ms. Magazine*, July 1973), Brenda Fasteau quotes a presentation by Agnes Wayman, president of the American Physical Association in 1933, that expresses this now debunked theory:

"External stimuli such as cheering audiences, bands, and lights, cause a great response in girls and are apt to upset the endocrine balance. Under emotional stress a girl may easily overdo. There is widespread agreement that girls should not be exposed to the extremes of fatigue or strain either emotional or physical. . . . In addition, custom and good taste should always influence in questions of public display, costume, publicity."

Ms. Fasteau then quotes another female physical educator of the same era:

"Girls are not suited for the same athletic program as boys. Under prolonged and intense physical strain, a girl goes to pieces nervously. A boy may be physically so weak that he hasn't the strength to 'smash a cream puff' but he still has the 'will' to play. A girl is the opposite." (Ethel Perrin, chairperson of the women's division of the National Amateur Athletic Federation, 1928.)

This attitude obviously has long pervaded the women's physical education field, and it is highly unlikely that it will be suddenly eliminated. Rather, any change will take place over a period of several years. The main reason for the change in attitude is that evidence is being accumulated, based on research and repeated observation, that not only refutes many accusations but indicates that in some cases the opposite is true.

One of the unfortunate "links" in women's athletics is the supposed tie between physical inferiority and psychological "weaknesses." These two shortcomings are in actuality separate and distinct problems. However, one is usually tied to the other with the usual assumption that the female is poor in both. Ironically, it is entirely possible that the female athlete's greatest asset is her psychological strength, a result of earlier training in handling emotions.

For example, Dr. Joyce Brothers states:

> Anthropologist Dr. Ashley Montague explains this (women's intuition) by saying that the female's inability to cope with the physically stronger male obliges her, from an early age, to develop traits that will enable her to secure her ends by other means. Being forced to sharpen her wits in this way, she develops a sharper intelligence. He feels that women are, on the whole, more quick-witted than men, not because they are born that way but because culturally they have been forced to develop a sharpness of attention to small detail quite unchallenging to the male. A woman's training in picking up subliminal signs is in part responsible for her greater thoughtfulness, tact, and discretion.
>
> Because women have not been taught to repress their emotions or keep them in check, they are not afraid to exhibit their feelings—thereby using their emotions a great deal more efficiently than men. Though quicker on the uptake, they do not jump to conclusions as hastily and unconsiderately as men. They avoid trigger responses.

This explanation of why women use emotions more effectively and productively than men is of great value in athletics. Not only are females as capable as males in meeting the stresses in athletics, they may well be superior. At least the hypothesis stated by Brothers would so indicate.

This conclusion seems to be borne out by observers of women athletes who were under great pressure. In their writings, Ernst Jokl and a team of investigators who observed the women who participated in the 1952 Olympics indicated surprise to see women perform so well under such a challenge. Their final impression was that women were quite capable of active participation in the sports movement.

One reason why people look on women as less capable psychologically is because this concept has been tied to physical comparisons. Since women have been led to believe they are less capable physically, they have automatically assumed the same is true psychologically. Thus, mental barriers to competitive sports have been perpetuated without foundation, and can only be seen to be a myth. The greatest injustice growing out of the accusations that women are physically less capable is that women have developed a deep psychological doubt about their ability to handle stress. The irony is that the reverse is in fact true.

To stress this point in a more humorous vein, let us consider a statement made by Will Rogers, as quoted in Brenda Fasteau's article:

"Another American woman just now swam in France. Her husband was carried from the boat suffering from cold and exposure. She has two children, the smallest, a girl, who is swimming over tomorrow. Yours for revised edition of the dictionary explaining which is the weak sex." (Comment on the English Channel swims by women in 1926.)

If the cultural stereotypes were changed and women were more accepted in the athletic realm, perhaps their self-doubt might be eliminated. Dr. George Dintiman believes that the Russian women athletes are superior to U.S. women because they are given equal status to males and because there exists a national pride in their accomplishments. Whereas Americans are less inclined to consider women's athletics seriously, and continue to take greater pride in our male athletes, and often in team sports rather than individual sports, Russians are more likely to see sports as a total unit whereby men and women alike are entitled to equal opportunity. This attitude probably helps to account for Russian successes against American teams, for Russian women do not face the problem of behaving counter to cultural expectations in order to compete. In fact, sports constitutes an acceptable activity wherein one may be able to participate in whatever aspect of sports one excels.

Some research has indicated rather strongly that the limiting factors in women's athletics are more a sociological than a physical or psychological factor. Roberta Angeloni approaches the subject in her article "Women in Sports: Which is the Limiting Factor—Physiological or Sociological?" She said, "Sociological sanctions should not be confused with physiological limits as far as sport is concerned. And frankly, most of the sociological sanctions are pretty silly, too."

Dr. George Dintiman makes this point somewhat more strongly in pointing out the prejudice against females in athletics. Dintiman said, "Obviously, women do not progress in sports at a rate comparable to men. Tradition, custom, prejudice and outright ignorance retard the influence of sport for women. These factors continue to plague the woman athlete. Biological, sociological, psychological, and philosophic justification is given to keep women in a mild form of sport."

As further proof that there is little to support the contention that women need to be treated differently or are less capable of handling stress, Deryk Snelling, coach of the National Swim Team in Canada, has pointed out that male and female East German swimmers are treated alike. In an article entitled "Where Women Train Like Men" Snelling explains that East German female swimmers were not taken seriously until the 1973 world title events in Belgrade, where they won 10 of 14 world titles. Snelling believes that their remarkable progress is due to their difficult nonsexual conditioning, since the training for males and females is the same.

There are many women who were able to withstand enormous amounts of pressure and achieve success. It has been mentioned elsewhere that Canadian diving coach Don Webb places great pressure on female athletes, who respond as well as males. He feels strongly that "champs get tough when the pressure goes on." Another example is Australian swimmer Shane Gould, who has been described not only as a good competitor, but as emotionally capable of being a champion. Ransom J. Arthur, Gould's coach, said of her, "Having the right temperament means she can see the purpose of the long hours of training and school—she can organize herself to get the essential things done—in her case training and school."

Perhaps few athletes have faced as much pressure or carried with them as much responsibility as Billie Jean King in her nationally televised tennis match with Bobby Riggs on September 20, 1973. Not only was she able to meet this challenge, but she responded to it in such a way that she gained respect and admiration of many athletes and nonathletes. One could hardly ask for better testimony that women are able to handle the pressure and stress of athletics.

ATHLETIC MOTIVATION

Little research has been done to assess the athletic motivation of women per se. One reason has been the lack of adequate instruments to measure athletic motivation. One such instrument, the Athletic Motivation Inventory (AMI) developed by myself, Lyon, and Ogilvie, is used to assess the motivation of athletes. The traits or characteristics assessed on the AMI are found in Table 1. Several studies have been completed with women athletes to determine their motivation at various levels of participation. Acampora compared women field hockey players on the high school, college, and club levels. Overall the AMI was found to discriminate among the three groups on the following variables: self-confidence, determination, conscientiousness, trust, leadership, and emotional control. When comparisons were made between any two of the groups, the results were as follows:

- College athletes scored significantly higher on trust than the high school athletes.
- Club athletes scored significantly higher on self-confidence and emotional control than the college athletes.
- Club athletes scored significantly higher on self-confidence, determination, emotional control, conscientiousness, trust, and leadership than did the high school athletes.

In addition, a hierarchical effect was noticed. For example, the higher the level of competition the higher the score on the majority of the characteristics. The three levels of competition are compared in Figure 1.

TABLE 1. Interpretation of the AMI Traits (Description of High Scorer)

Introduction

The Athletic Motivational Inventory is designed to yield a set of scores for personality traits relevant to the functioning of individuals in the field of athletics. The definition and interpretations of the traits as given below are short and nontechnical. It is recommended that you study them before examining the ISAM reports to enhance your understanding of each athlete.

Trait	Description of a High Scorer
Drive	Desire to win or be successful; aspires to accomplish difficult tasks; sets and maintains high goals for himself in athletics; responds positively to competition; desires to attain athletic excellence.
Aggressiveness	Believes one must be aggressive to win; releases aggression easily; enjoys confrontation and argument; sometimes willing to use force to get his way; will not allow others to push him around; may seek to "get even" with people whom he perceives as having harmed him.
Determination	Willing to practice long and hard; works on skills until exhausted; often works out willingly by himself; persevering, even in the face of great difficulty; patient and unrelenting in his work habits; doesn't give up quickly on a problem.

Guilt-Proneness	Accepts responsibility for his actions; accepts blame and criticism even when not deserved; tends to dwell on his mistakes and to punish himself for them; willing to endure much physical and mental pain; will play even when injured.
Leadership	Enjoys the role of leader and may assume it spontaneously; believes others see him as a leader; attempts to control his environment, and to influence or direct other people; expresses opinions forcefully.
Self-Confidence	Has unfaltering confidence in himself and his capacity to deal with things; confident of his powers and abilities; handles unexpected situations well; makes decisions confidently; speaks up for his beliefs to coaches and players.
Emotional Control	Tends to be emotionally stable and realistic about athletics; is not easily upset; will rarely allow his feelings to show and his performance is not affected by them; not easily depressed or frustrated by bad breaks, calls or mistakes.
Mental Toughness	Accepts strong criticism without feeling hurt; does not become easily upset when losing or playing badly; can bounce back quickly from adversity; can take rough coaching; does not need excessive encouragement from the coach.
Coachability	Respects coaches and the coaching process; receptive to coaches' advice; considers coaching important to become a good athlete; accepts the leadership of the team captain; cooperates with authorities.
Conscientiousness	Likes to do things as correctly as possible; tends to be exacting in character, dominated by sense of duty; does not try to "con" his coach or fellow players; will not attempt to bend rules and regulations to suit his own needs; places the good of the team above his personal well being.
Trust	Accepts people at face value; believes what his coach and teammates say and does not look for ulterior motives behind their words or actions; free of jealous tendencies; tends to get along well with his teammates.

Used with permission of Institute for the Study of Athletic Motivation, A Division of Winslow Research, Inc., Santa Clara, Calif.

Figure 1. Comparision of AMI Traits on Three Levels of Competition

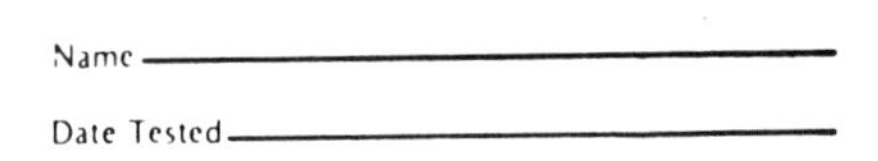

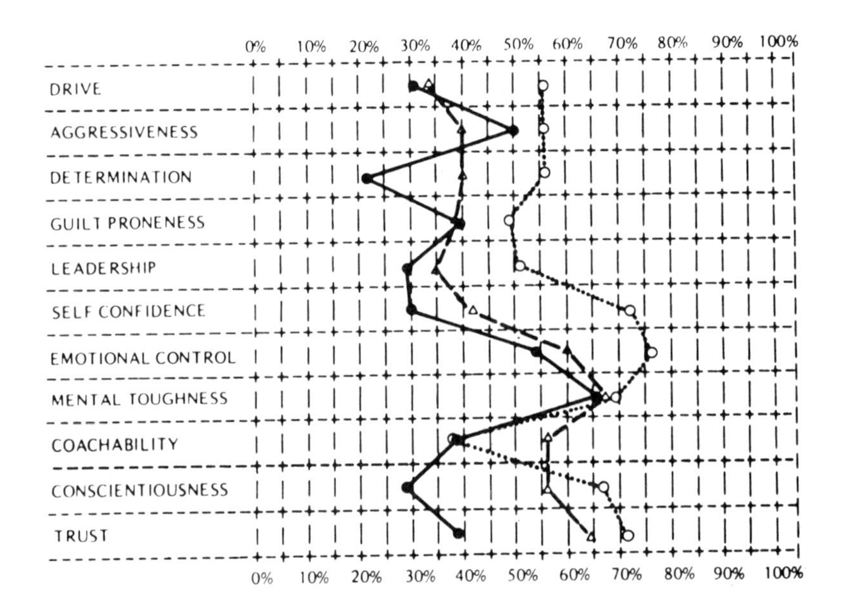

NOTES

Key—Women's Field Hockey

High School N = 47

College N = 37

Club N = 33

*Based on High School Norms N = 387

Used with permission of Institute for the Study of Athletic Motivation, A Division of Winslow Research, Inc., Santa Clara, Calif.

Of particular interest is the hierarchical effect of determination, leadership, emotional control, conscientiousness, and trust. These traits would seem to be particularly likely to indicate women who move to higher levels of competition and who can handle stress and pressure.

In a study assessing high-level competition among female intercollegiate basketball players, Higgs and Higgs, in their master's thesis, asked coaches to assess the motivation of their athletes on the AMI. The top athletes scored significantly higher on drive, leadership, self-confidence, and conscientiousness.

In a study comparing three levels of men and women club tennis competitors, P. Slack found that the more highly skilled tennis players scored significantly higher on determination and mental toughness. Of particular importance was the fact that there was only one difference between the two sex groups. For example, the women scored significantly higher on conscientiousness.

Perhaps one thing that has been overlooked in women's athletics is the degree of dedication manifested by women athletes. It would appear that once a female has decided upon athletics as a way of life she becomes entirely devoted, and this rather quickly separates her from her peers who are nonathletically inclined. This theory tends to support the view of Jack Donohue, technical coordinator and national coach of the Canadian Basketball Association, who has stated, "Those girls are fantastic. To begin with, I have never seen such dedication. They are also much easier to teach than men." In any event, there is little doubt that women are capable psychologically of facing the challenges encountered in the athletic world.

Part 3
The Destination: The Rough Roads Behind Us

LIBERTY
296

13

History of Women's Running

The twentieth century: Olympic triumphs, male prejudice, long-distance victory

Dusty Rhodes

With the overwhelming surge of women's running today, it is difficult to believe that women were not allowed to run in marathons six years ago. It is equally hard to believe that until the latter part of 1972, there was a limit of ten miles placed on all women runners, basically because the common view was that long distance running was harmful to women. A woman risked the death penalty in ancient Greece for even so much as watching the Olympic Games! Now the popularity of women's running is booming—and there is no sign of it stopping.

Since women have historically been considered the weaker sex, their running events were limited to short, sprinting events. Ironically, these short sprints take more explosive muscle power than the more aerobic and endurance demanding distance events. But it has taken nearly a century since the first marathon race in 1896 for women to convince the medical and sporting establishments that long-distance running is not detrimental to a woman's health. The old-fashioned, ill-informed medical and sports community tried to protect women from irrevocable damage, or even death, by limiting their running distances to a half-mile. As recently at 1967, the medical establishment reacted in shock when a 13-year-old Canadian, Maureen Wilton, ran a marathon in 3:15:22.

Marathon running as a truly human and healthy endeavor for women is, therefore, a very recent contemporary conclusion. Raging concurrently with the feminist movement of the sixties, physical fitness and jogging for fun has allowed the spectacular growth of women's participation in marathons all over the world.

Women have probably been running long before man saw fit to record it:

At the 1896 Olympics Melpomene participated in the marathon race as an unofficial entry, the first runner to have her entry refused because of sex. She completed the 40-kilometer course in four and a half hours accompanied by a bicycle escort. (The modern marathon course is 42.195 kilometers.) Sportswriters said the Greek officials should be reprimanded because it was discourteous to refuse the lady entry. They wrote, "We can assure those concerned that none of the participants would have had any objections." All the Greek male runners came in well ahead of her.

Unfortunately, Melpomene's assertiveness did not inspire any other women. There were only sporadic attempts at marathon-type running by women in the next seventy years. The male attitude forty years later remained well behind that of the Olympic spectators.

Sporadic as the attempts were, they were not shy in distance. At the Comrade's Marathon in South Africa, several women finished and were afforded the same regard as the winners. The distance was not unusual, as the Tarahumara Indians of Mexico (long known for their endurance running) had for centuries seen women running fifty or more miles a day. They ran as transportation through narrow mountain paths. In 1936, there was a 13-mile footrace in Pike's Peak, Colorado—only two women entered. Twenty-three years later, however, Arlene Pieper ran 26 miles (up and down Pike's Peak) in 9:16.

But what happened since the 1900s when the British called women distance runners "brazen doxies" because of their habits and attire? The answer to women's acceptance in distance running lies not in the individual efforts of women, but in the collective efforts of organized women's races. Some of the milestones included the following, listed by year.

1921. The Feminine Sportive Foundation Internationale (FSFI) was formed. This was the international governing body for women's athletics.

1922. The FSFI sponsored the first women's world championship. The longest race was 1,000 meters.

1924. Several international meets had already taken place, and the FSFI requested that the 1924 Olympics include events for women. The International Amateur Athletic Federation, which controlled the Olympics, denied their request.

1928. An agreement was worked out between the International Amateur Athletic Federation and the FSFI which provided dual control of four women's events for the 1928 Olympics, including an 800-meter event. It turned out to be a disaster. Instead of pacing, the women runners sprinted the entire distance. Through their enthusiasm, high competitiveness, and lack of proper training for this type of event—most of them collapsed, reconfirming everyone's beliefs that women were incapable of distance running. Even after six women finished within ten seconds of each other, and three bettered an old world record, officials from several countries still demanded cancellation of this "frightful episode" and horrifying event. One can assume the officials thought it was more horrifying to see women collapse than men.

Why were the women so ill-prepared? For the answer, we turned to Harry Eaton Stewart, physician and president of the American team participating in the 1922 FSFI games. He said: "The longer runs—300 meters and 1,000 meters—have been used abroad with no ill effects. It is believed that these events may be used by certain types of girls, but it must be understood that they need longer training periods and repeated medical examination if they are to be free from danger."

Certainly not helping the effort in those years, Daniel Ferris, secretary-treasurer of the Amateur Athletic Union (AAU) from 1927-1957, said, "When we took control of the women's track and field in 1922, it was decided that a 220-yard race would be the longest women's event in the program." This proposal was made and supported by elderly leaders of women's physical training, and the AAU kept this attitude for years. Clearly a weighty factor in the development—or lack thereof—of women's long-distance running in the United States.

1930. In April 1930, the National Amateur Athletic Federation petitioned International Olympic Committee president M. le Compte de Baillet Salour to eliminate women's track and field events from the 1932 Olympic Games, citing that the "Olympics offered opportunity for exploitation and commercialization of women." The petition was greeted with strong world-wide support.

Later the same year, the Women's Division of the NAAF adopted new resolutions and philosophies with regard to the women's program. Specifically, all games and sport for women would include every member of the group; be broad and diversified; and be adapted to the special needs and abilities of the participant, with emphasis on participation.

Interestingly enough, however, this philosophy is still reflected today—with the attitude that women are competitive within themselves, not against each other. This rationale has been spread over the years by physical education instructors.

Helen Manley, supervisor of physical education for the University City, Michigan school system said, "Athletics is now looked upon as educational, whereas formerly it was considered a form of amusement. Let everyone play for enjoyment, not to specialize and to win." She also said, "I am against highly-trained competition for women athletes. Women are not physically fit for the excitement and strain that this competition affords." This was not the only philosophy Manley had that later would be challenged—she also felt that as time went on, fewer and fewer women would participate in athletics.

The attitude was a long-founded one. A 1901 article called "The Athletic Girl" set the stage for decades to come. The article stated, "The aim of athletes among women has been the establishment and maintenance of a high general standard of health and vigor, rather than some single brilliant achievement."

A TIME OF CHANGE

With the Depression of the 1930s and World War II, little development in women's athletics occurred. The issues were of little impact in those years, and the participation, even less.

In 1957 things started to change. An organization called the Road Runners Club of America (RRCA) was formed specifically to promote long-distance running. The club's philosophy was, if women were capable, and wanted to participate in long-distance running, they should have equal consideration at race time. Because of the RRCA persistence, race directors began accepting women in their races—unofficially, at first. Then in 1960, the 800-meter race for women was reinstated as an event in the Olympic Games, and distance running for women increased in popularity. But the United States, so long against distance running for women, was years behind other countries. Nonetheless, attitudes were slowly changing around the country as more and more *avant garde* women were starting a trend by jumping into men's races. They were still considered "radicals" but at least the battle was on.

Julia Chase, a 19-year-old New England runner, participated in a 1961 Manchester, Connecticut five-mile road race. Her official entry had been refused, and she was threatened with the revocation of her amateur status if she went through the finish line. Regardless of the consequences, Julia crossed the finish line. That same year, while women were battling the opinion that running would make them musclebound, Chris McKenzie, a British 800-meter record-holder, challenged this point. She went to a local running club's monthly meeting bundled in a coat, hiding her bikini. As the subject of musclebound women came up, Chris emerged wearing the bikini. She was granted permission to run a longer event—the quarter-mile.

Dr. Ernst van Aaken and Dr. Charlie Robins were the first from the medical profession to speak out in favor of women distance runners. Dr. Robins predicted that competitive times between men and women would get closer together as the distances increased. This, he said, would be because distance running is primarily a test of heart and circulation, not brute muscular strength.

Soon after Lyn Carmen and Merry Lepper were training together, preparing specifically for road races and marathons. Naturally, they were usually unofficial entrants. That year the Western Hemisphere Marathon was being held in Culver City, California, and Lyn and Merry hid on the sidelines. As the gun sounded the girls jumped out onto the roadway, only to be attacked by a race official who tried to push them off the road. "I have the right to use public streets for running," yelled Lyn. Lyn continued the race for 20 miles, and Merry finished in 3:37:07, officially timed by a somewhat amused AAU official.

It must be pointed out that women physical education instructors were a strong force in keeping women's distance running stifled and stagnant. As recently as 1963, women AAU officials were quoted as saying that if women continued to train for long distance events they would not be able to bear children. But nobody told Sara Mae Berman that. As a 26-year-old mother of two, Sara watched her husband run, and run, and run. So Sara decided to take up jogging, and went from a half mile a day to an eight-mile a day routine in a short time. She could not understand why women, some younger than herself, were afraid of running even a half-mile. She soon found out why—the AAU, the governing body for women's running in the U.S., did not allow women to compete in races over a half-mile. Prior to Sara Mae's attending the annual AAU convention, she had her third child. The child, apparently, was not hurt by her running routine. Sara Mae continued lobbying for increased distances for women. Slowly, and with the help of several members of the Men's Long Distance Running Committee, the AAU's Women's Committee began to increase the distance women were allowed to run. By 1968, the AAU Women's Committee increased the length to five miles for races, and the women were exceeding these limitations faster than they could be established.

The 1966 Boston Marathon, the granddaddy of all marathons, would allow *anyone* to run. Anyone but a woman. Roberta Gibb Bingay didn't know this. She saw the Boston Marathon in 1965 and was so inspired she wrote for an application, only to be denied entrance. The reason given—because she would get hurt.

Funny, she managed to survive her five-hour runs. Though Roberta never met Lyn Carmen and Merry Lepper, she knew the tricks—the bushes. Not any old bushes, but the bushes at Hopkington. As 445 runners celebrated the joys of running the Boston Marathon that day, so did Roberta. She finished in 3:21. She took a lot of attention away from the men runners that day; attention, she hoped, that would be turned to show that women were capable of long distance events. Will Cloney, director of the Marathon, tried to discredit her effort by saying she didn't actually run the race, she just followed the course. But nonetheless, Roberta Gibb Bingay was the first woman to run Boston. . . unofficially.

It was still enough to make the AAU Women's Committee paranoid. Fearful of losing their sanctioning power, the Committee declared that they controlled all women's running and all women's running events. The female long-distance runners in 1966 just *were not* going to go along with the declaration.

For the 1967 Boston Marathon, Roberta had company: a K.V. Switzer. Never dreaming that the "K" stood for Katherine, Boston officials sent K. V. a starting number. Wearing a hood helped preserve her anonymity until the press saw her. The melee that followed will go down in history. Race director Cloney tried to catch her, but couldn't; co-director Jock Semple tried to rip her number off and Katherine's boyfriend went after him, sent Semple reeling into the curb. Roberta finished the race in 3:27, and Katherine Switzer finished in 4:30. Perhaps not a winning time, but a victory nonetheless. Katherine Switzer was the first "official" woman runner in the Boston Marathon.

"OFFICIAL" VICTORIES CELEBRATED

That same year in other parts of the world other "victories" were made. In Toronto, a 13-year-old Canadian, Maureen Wilton, ran a world's best with 3:15:22.8, breaking the record held by Mrs. McKenzie of New Zealand, who ran a 3:18 in 1964. In September of 1967, Anni Pede-Erdkamp of West Germany ran a 3:07:26, setting a world record that would hold for years.

But during these years something much bigger was happening. The women's liberation movement was moving fast and furiously. By the end of the 1960s, women were no longer taking "no" for an answer—on anything. Word was getting around about running and its inherent values. Books such as 1967's *Jogging* by Bowerman & Harris, and *Aerobics*, written by Dr. Kenneth Cooper in 1968, were selling. The books were selling running. As the popularity of running increased, more men entered marathons. The more men there were running marathons, increased numbers of women were watching. Soon, watching just wasn't enough.

Watching was certainly not enough for Nina Kuscsik. She was twenty-nine, had three children, and thirteen years of athletics behind her including basketball, speed skating, and bicycle racing. She had excelled in events requiring a lot of stamina, yet she too believed what they had told her—twenty-nine was too old to do the stuff that would ruin you. But she applied her past training experiences to a running program, and worked up to a marathon distance. Once Nina learned that she wasn't being "ruined" she went to Boston.

Not one for bushes, she jumped in from behind the spectators at Hopkington. Just jumping in was no small task. The Boston Marathon was getting big, and it was getting harder to find room to plant even two feet. Sara Mae Berman had the same problem that year, as she entered Boston unofficially for the first time. They discovered how they did in the race by consulting the *Long Distance Log*, put out by *US Track & Field* months later. The women were forced to look for the closest male finisher through the gate, look up his name in the program, and correspond that name to the time in *Long Distance Log*. That would be "official" time for "unofficials" like Nina and Sara Mae.

While most distance running women in the late 1960s were young, possibly had children, and invariably were married to a distance-runner, someone totally new entered the scene in 1970. Her name was Caroline Walker, a 16-year-old who set a new record of 3:02:53 in the Trail's End Marathon in Seaside, Oregon. That day in February saw not only a barrier of age broken, but one of time. Caroline had set an incredible pace of under seven minutes per mile—a new plateau. A new plateau, and a new decade with new attitudes. Not only were people like Nina Kuscsik, Katherine Switzer, Sara Mae Berman, and hundreds of other determined women responsible for the changing attitudes, but the Road Runners Club of America put the whole issue right out front.

In October of 1970 the RRCA sponsored the American National Women's Marathon Championship. Since it was a club race, no AAU sanction was needed. Even though the American National Women's Marathon Championship was held in conjunction with the AAU Men's Marathon, it was still a landmark race. Sara Mae Berman, one of six women starters, won the race. Club officials decided that because the RRCA was founded to promote running, they felt that women who wanted to run should run and should be encouraged to run. The RRCA also gave women equal consideration at race time. And it was with the RRCA's persistence that more and more race directors at least let women run their races unofficially.

By 1971, records were being shattered left and right. Beth Bohner brought the marathon record for women down to 3:01:42, and later Sara Mae Berman came agonizingly close to breaking the three-hour barrier with a time of 3:00:35. Soon, all attention turned away from whether one was "official" or not, and moved to who would hit that magic mark of under three hours. The training that year was fast, hard, and furious.

The 1971 New York City Marathon was in September and all eyes were upon it. The time and place were set, the record would be broken in New York. Nina Kuscsik entered, confident that she would be the one. Beth Bohner also entered. They ran neck and neck at the beginning. Nina took the downhills better, Beth the uphills. After 14 miles, Beth picked up and passed Nina. Nina never saw her again until the twenty mile mark. At that point, Nina recalled later, "The closer I came, the faster she went." Indeed it was a close one; Beth Bohner finished with a world record time of 2:55:22, and Nina in 2:56:04. Beth and Nina became the fastest women marathoners in history.

Later that same year, the AAU raised the legal distance for women runners to 10 miles, a direct result of the enormous pressure from women runners all over the country. But there was a qualification. Only *selected* women would be allowed to run in marathons, subject to the approval of the national chairman. *Selected women* were those who had run in marathons previously. But women weren't allowed to run in marathons previously.

Before the close of 1971, Cheryl Bridges of California ran a 2:49:40 in Culver City, California. It was fifty years and more than twenty-five miles longer than the first women's race sponsored by the Feminine Sportive Foundation Internationale—a race of 1,000 yards.

As 1972 began, so did a new status for women runners. Assisted by the efforts of many male distance runners, women could now enter and be sanctioned for a marathon distance. Race directors could run women's marathons along with the men's.

On March 30, 1972, Pat Tarnansky, a marathoner who attended that pivotal AAU Convention in 1971, contacted Will Cloney. Cloney announced that the forthcoming Boston Marathon would be the first Boston Marathon to include women as "official" entrants. Eight women stood at the starting line that year in Boston.

The eight women who entered, however, discovered that their troubles were just beginning. The Women's Committee, in sanctioning the race, had made the stipulation that women either start at a different time or place than men. Boston Marathon director Will Cloney became a new-found friend. He made a different starting line—by extending the starting line to the sidewalk; the women lined up, and the race was on!

Nina Kuscsik won the race, but not easily. Starting the race well, Nina hit the half-way point in 1:27. About that time she suffered from intestinal cramps and ran the rest of the race with diarrhea. She recalled later, "I never thought I'd be running the streets of Boston with diarrhea." But she ran no matter what, and crossed the finish line in 3:10:21. The most important thing to Nina at the finish was not being the first official woman but finding her warm-up suit to "cover up the source of her embarrassment." The press might have been able now to accept a woman in the Boston Marathon, but she wasn't sure about how tastefully they would treat this. So, after the race Nina's response to the press was merely, "the race proved that I had guts."

The challenge of women's complete acceptance in distance running was becoming a game of wits. At the New York City Marathon in October 1972, the issue of inequality in races exploded head-on. For years men and women worked to organize races for men and women in New York. But Pat Rico, AAU Women's Committee chairman, told marathon director Fred Lebow that the women's section of the race must be separate. The event must begin 10 minutes before, or 10 minutes after, the men's race. The participating women countered with the fact that separate prizes warranted a separate race. The AAU Women's Committee didn't quite see it that way, and sounded the women's gun 10 minutes before the men's race was to start. As the gun went off, and those precious official seconds ticked away, the women sat down and waited. They waited precisely 10 minutes, then the real race was on.

That wasn't the only race going on. Discrimination lawsuits were popping up all over the country. The AAU was challenged on the issue of practicing discrimination in a public place. On the west coast, another lawsuit emerged when women were required to get doctors' notes endorsing their health before a race, and the men were not.

Following the New York City Marathon episode in 1972, the Women's Committee of the AAU met at the annual convention and concurred that they were fighting a losing battle. Two key positions were announced at that convention. They were: (1) AAU distance limit for women would be the marathon distance, and (2) men and women may start from the same line in long-distance running, and from the same gun. As long as women were scored separately and competed for separate prizes, they were considered competing in a separate event.

It followed suit in 1973, and after women runners sponsored legislation, the AAU agreed to establish a national marathon championship for women. Even though West Germany was the first country to hold a national championship that year, and the Road Runners had sponsored a championship marathon in 1970, this was the first national, and American, and sanctioned marathon distance race for women, in the country.

On September 1, 1974, the first International Marathon for Women, and the first United States AAU National Marathon Championship for Women were held in San Mateo, California. In a few short years, there would be over 500 such events. There were 57 starters, and 44 finishers in this race. Judy Ikenberry won the race, registering a time of 2:55:17. Other runners were:

Marilyn Paul	2:58:44
Peggy Lyman	2:58:55
Mary Etta Bortano	3:01:15
Nina Kuscsik	3:04:11
Lucy Bunz	3:05:07
Marjorie Kaput	3:07:46

The following year the times dropped significantly:

Kim Merritt	2:46:14

Miki Gorman	2:53:02
Gayle Barron	2:57:22
Joan Ullyot	2:58:30
Marilyn Bevans	2:59:19
Diane Berrett	3:01:41

At the 1975 race, the world record stood at 2:46:36, set by Miki Gorman in the December 1973 Culver City Marathon. Miki was thirty-eight at the time, and shed new light, and hope, upon runners who felt they were too old to run. (Miki later thrilled spectators when she ran a 2:39:11 in the 1976 New York City Marathon.)

In 1975 the world's record fell three times. First, Liane Winters of West Germany with a 2:42:24; then, Christa Vahlensieck of West Germany with a time of 2:40:15, and finally Jacqueline Hansen of the United States with a time of 2:38:19.

Many things have happened to women's running since 1975, and the goals have become quite different. Some of them include:

- More countries participating in the International Women's Marathons sponsored by Dr. Ernst van Aaken.
- The marathon be an event for women in the Olympics, and the Pan-Am Games.
- Conquering the misconception that women are physically unfit to run marathons.
- Get the delegates to the IAAF to support the international and Olympic marathon concept.
- Get the delegates of the International Women's Committee and International Medical Committee to certify to the International Olympic Committee that marathon running is not detrimental to the health of women.

In an effort to achieve these goals, the New York Academy of Sciences Marathon Conference passed a resolution that should have far reaching consequences. It reads:

To: All member countries of the IAAF
IAAF Continental Associations
IAAF Women's Committee
IAAF Technical Committee
IAAF Cross Country Committee
IAAF Medical Committee
IAAF Council
United States Olympic Committee
Amateur Athletic Union of the United States

RESOLUTION, which was passed unanimously by over 500 participants and attendees at the New York Academy of Sciences' "Conference on the Marathon: Physiological, Medical, Epidemiological, and Psychological Studies," held in New York City, October 25–28, 1976.

Whereas:

(1) Current research including that presented at this conference demonstrates that female athletes adapt to marathon training and benefit from it, in virtually the same ways male athletes do.

(2) There exists no persuasive scientific or medical evidence, nor has any evidence been presented at this conference that long distance running, in particular marathon running, is in any way contraindicated for the trained female athlete.

THEREFORE BE IT RESOLVED: That it is the considered judgment of the participants of this conference that a women's marathon event as well as other long distance races for women be included in the Olympic program, forthwith.

Since 1976, the attitudes and goals have changed. Women are running not so much for their rights, as they needed to before, but for more personal reasons. And those personal reasons for running are not exclusive to women marathon runners.

Thousands and thousands of women started to focus on the shorter distance races. Bonne Bell started a series of mini-marathons that have become very popular.

In 1972, Fred Lebow and the New York Road Runners Club sponsored a 6.2 mile race (10,000 meters) and called it the Mini-Marathon. Held in Central Park and co-sponsored by a now-defunct company called Crazy Legs, the race attracted 78 women. Over the next five years, with the support of businessman Arno Niemand, the Road Runners Club, and the tireless Fred Lebow, the race grew steadily, yet conservatively.

In 1977 Bonne Bell sponsored the New York Mini-Marathon with the NY Road Runners Club. To everyone's astonishment, 2,064 women descended on Central Park on June 4, 1977. That day was a turning point in the history of women's running. Jubilation was in the air.

Katherine Lance, a writer for *Runner's World*, recalls that race: "Jess Bell, president of Bonne Bell, was so enthusiastic about promoting women's running, he contributed medals to all the finishers." In Bell's heart, every runner was a winner. It was the beginning of a love-affair between Bonne Bell and women's running.

Today, there are more than sixteen Bonne Bell races for

women all over the country, attracting more than 30,000 women runners each year. There are more than 500 women-only races in the country, as many other companies are finding the advantages in promoting health, exercise and fitness, and their products as well, all at the same time.

But with Jess Bell, the alignment and the endorsement with women and running goes much further. He is an apostle of women's running. Like many runners, he was at one time an overweight, overindulgent, overworked businessman. He took up running six years ago to combat these problems, and he swears it changed his life. His changes have changed even more lives. He made sweeping changes at the Bonne Bell plant in Cleveland. Soon, his running philosophy was rampant among the employees, and Jess built the facilities for the employees to keep fit, including a gymnasium, track, locker rooms, exercise equipment, and tennis courts. But his message did not stop there. "Participation as well as competition" is the theme of Bonne Bell races, and with it the "everyone is a winner" philosophy. Housewives, students, professionals, children, and grandmothers all can run—and have run—in those 10,000 meter races. The joys of an elite group, so few years ago, are now shared worldwide.

There are more than 8,000 road races in the country today, and ten percent of them are women's races. Truly, the worst battles are over in the U.S., but such is not the case for the women internationally. Parts of Canada still have a 3,000-meter limit, and in Europe, many women are barred from road races, particularly in France and Belgium. The fight for the admission of a women's marathon to the Olympics rages, but hope is dim for a change from the 1,500-meter limit by 1980.

At the recent Avon Women's Marathon Championship in Atlanta, Dr. Ernst van Aaken, the long-time spokesman in favor of women's running, said: "I cannot understand how much proof is needed before there are distance races for women in the Olympics. I think it's a tremendous shame that throughout there are people who decide who should run or not, when they haven't even run a marathon themselves."

The ultimate decision rests with the AAU and International Olympic Committee. IOC is comprised of mostly men, and according to Penny DeMoss, AAU representative and marathon runner: "The all-male IOC lives in the past. They have proof that we can run marathons, and even ultramarathons up to

100 miles and the IOC chooses to ignore it. We'll probably have to wait until they all die off before we see women's distance (races) in the Olympics."

Since there are many countries around the world that forbid women to run in marathons, no matter what the US does, it will wait until the rest of the world catches up, before there is significant change.

Meanwhile, the avid participation in women's long-distance running is evidenced in the incredibly fast progression of records. While the men's marathon record remained untouched for nine years (set by Derek Clayton of Australia in 1969 with 2:08:33.6), the women's record has been broken every year. For example:

1967	3:15:22	Maureen Wilton (Canada)
1967	3:07:26	Anni Pede-Erdkamp (W. Ger.)
1970	3:02:53	Caroline Walker (US)
1971	3:01:42	Beth Bonner (US)
1971	3:00:35	Sara Berman (US)
1971	2:55:22	Beth Bonner (US)
1971	2:49:40	Cheryl Bridges (US)
1973	2:46:36	Miki Gorman (US)
1974	2:46:24	Chantal Langlace (Fr.)
1974	2:43:54	Jacqueline Hansen (US)
1975	2:42:24	Liane Winters (W. Ger.)
1975	2:40:15	Christa Vahlensieck (W. Ger.)
1975	2:38:19	Jacqueline Hansen (US)
1977	2:37:57	Kim Merritt (US)
1977	2:35:15	Chantel Langlace (Fr.)
1978	2:34:48	Christa Vahlensieck (W. Ger.)

This remarkable progression is a direct reflection that until 1971 only a minute number of women were running at all. With thousands of women now testing their capabilities, speed and capacities are blossoming. Until 1971 a three hour marathon for women was impossible. In 1975 twenty-seven women ran sub-three hour races. The new "impossible" barrier is now sub-2:30. If as many women as men had been running since that first marathon in 1896, it is very possible that there would be no gap between the world's best time for men and women.

Training methods, mental attitudes, and hormones are only partial answers for the gap in men's and women's running speeds. More and more, running enthusiasts and experts agree that equal records will come with equal opportunities and recognition.

RALEIGH
TRACK
218-A
ull striders
725

14

Politics Behind the Movement

Behind the scenes: AAU committees, the Boston Marathon, race sponsors

Ruth Anderson

I wasn't properly aware of the true significance of the First Women's National AAU Marathon Championships as I stood near the starting line of the West Valley Marathon that February 1974 in San Mateo, California. Joining me were 57 women and 250 men. Preceding the event were years of women struggling for recognition and equal opportunity as long-distance runners. My limited experience had brought me to this milestone in women's racing with only two marathons and little more than a year of running behind me.

Judy Ikenberry led the 44 women finishers across the line in a fine time of 2:55:17, becoming the first senior woman champion. "Masters women" (age 40 and over) was a nonchampionship category not recognized by the AAU until that organization's 1975 convention.

My 3:20:59 time was good enough to win the master women's division, and also to lower the national record by six minutes for women over 40. I realized how lucky I was to be "old enough soon enough" to get in on the ground floor of the master women's movement. This, understandably, became a cause to which I could devote much effort and interest.

The 1975 Boston Marathon taught me a lot more.

There were more than thrills and anxiety of competing in our country's most prestigious marathon. By attending a women's meeting before the race, I met many of the crusaders and pioneers of women's long-distance running. Here were Sara Mae Berman and Kathy Switzer, about whom I had read so much; along with Nina Kuscsik and Jennie Taylor-Tuthill, whom I had first met in San Mateo. (Nina and I had experienced the thrill of competing in Waldniel, West Germany, at the September 1974 International Women's Marathon sponsored by Dr. Ernst van Aaken. It was an inspiration to meet this outstanding sports physician and coach.)

With so much evidence of progress behind us, I was surprised and a bit shocked to learn how much inequality and prejudice still remained against women's marathoning and other long-distance running. The women at this meeting concluded that a need existed for a women's long-distance AAU committee, separate from the Women's Track-and-Field Committee, which still held views similar to the International Amateur Athletic Federation, i.e., that 1500 meters was perhaps even a bit too far for the *fragile* female athlete. Aldo Scandurra presented much wise council from his years of experience with the long-distance men's movement and their separation from the National Track-and-Field Committee's domination. That the Women's long-distance committee evolved from the AAU convention that fall was largely due to efforts by Nina Kuscsik, supported by many at the meeting.

The "official" Boston Marathon results of 1975 listed 28 women finishers under the 3:30 cutoff time (at least two more also made this mark, Marcie Trent of Alaska and myself, who were "lost" in the backup at the finish line after three hours). This was very different from the early days beginning in 1966 when Roberta Gibb Bingay jumped into the race from the bushes at Hopkinton and finished in the respectable time of 3:21. Not until 1972 were women officially accepted as entrants in the Boston Marathon. The intervening years had many milestones.

The publicity surrounding the Boston Marathon provided a showcase for furthering the women's long-distance cause.

Still, it was a difficult concession that raised the distance from 800 meters to five miles set by the Women's AAU Committee in 1968.

Several events of 1967 contributed to this decision. Kathy Switzer's entrance in the Boston Marathon wearing a number (supposedly issued to a male entrant) caused official reaction highly publicized by the news media. The unsuccessful attempt by Jock Semple to remove her number drew much attention to the unofficial status of women in marathoning. But, for the next several years the only way these plucky women could determine their times for the Boston Marathon was to accept the time of the nearest male finisher.

The year 1967 was also the year that the report of a 13-year-old Canadian girl, Maureen Wilton, running a 3:15:22 marathon, was released. Anni Pede-Erdkamp, a protegee of Dr. van Aaken, ran a new world best of 3:07:26 later that fall, which was not beaten until 1970. Sixteen-year-old Caroline Walker completed the Seaside, Oregon, Trails End Marathon in 3:02:53. Women continued to challenge this record, driving it under three hours for the first time in September 1971 at the New York City Marathon with both Beth Bonner and Nina Kuscsik breaking the barrier with 2:55:22 and 2:56:04 respectively.

These achievements did not have official AAU approval until the pressure from marathoning women bore fruit in the fall of 1971 at the AAU national convention. The AAU Women's Committee ruled that women would be allowed to run marathons on approval of the national chairman (this was essentially women who had already proven themselves at the distance). The Women's Track-and-Field Committee also raised to 10 miles the distance women could compete nationally.

Thus, the 1972 Boston Marathon officially welcomed eight marathon women ready to compete. The AAU stipulated, however, that women should start from a different time or place than the male entrants. Fortunately for these women, Race Director Will Cloney simply extended the starting line to the sidewalk, affording the women a "separate" spot to start. All eight women finished this historic event: Nina Kuscsik first in 3:10:21; Elaine Pederson second in 3:20:35; and Katherine Switzer third in 3:29:51.

The issue of starting with the men was again raised at the October 1972 New York City Marathon. The AAU Women's Track-and-Field Committee Chairman Pat Rico issued an edict that the women's event must be separate and must begin ten minutes before or after the men's start. Women participants protested by sitting down at the starting line for ten minutes following the first gun, starting only after the second one was fired. Such obvious discrimination could easily have produced a lawsuit against the AAU under existing human rights laws in New York state, but the Women's Committee of the AAU capitulated without a fight. They not only ruled that women could start with men in long-distance races, but legalized the marathon for all women. Separate scoring and prizes were recognized as the definition of a "separate event." Thus the AAU responded to pressure from the long-distance running women with these 1972 Convention rulings.

Still, by 1975 it was the underlying attitude of the AAU Track-and-Field Women's Committee of "over-protection," from dealing with the younger track-and-field women, combined with a poor understanding of the long-distance running women's needs, that promoted the push for a separate long distance women's committee. We were amused by the ruling, still in effect for traveling U.S. women's teams that required a chaperone, when the nine of us competed in the September 1974 International Women's Marathon in Germany. The youngest of our group was in her mid-20s; two of us were over 40. Yet to satisfy the AAU Women's Committee, we assigned Dr. Joan Ullyot as our "chaperone" as well as our physician and interpreter. She was also a competing member of the team. She preferred the title "Head of the U.S. Expedition."

Humor aside, long-distance running women needed to run their own programs to establish an Olympic marathon and longer track events. They could then set up national championships at all the standard distances; administer their own travel funds; select teams for international competition; and in general be more responsive to the long-distance running women athletes' interests at all levels.

The 1975 AAU convention accomplished this division between long-distance running and the track-and-field committees. All road racing (plus track events longer than a mile not connected to a specific meet, plus cross-country) came under the jurisdiction of the newly-formed Women's Long-Distance Committee.

Women "masters," aged 40 and over, became a recognized group for both track-and-field and long-distance running. A separate committee was also created for masters at this same convention. The initial jurisdiction of this committee required a judicial interpretation by the AAU Law Committee. It ruled that *all* masters, including long-distance running and race-walking for both men and women, would be governed by Track-and-Field Masters Committee. The title left some confusion, perhaps even doubts, as to how all interests would be served. Indeed, by the following year's convention much clarification and restructuring were necessary.

The new regime of 1976 saw establishment of a Masters Long Distance Running Committee for men and women, separate from the Track-and-Field Masters. Master women were thus able to participate in their first national championship on November 14, 1976. The event was a 10-kilometer cross-country race in Belmont, California, run as a separate competition. Miki Gorman was an outstanding winner, setting a course record for all women in 38:54. Twenty-six other master women finished this difficult course.

This represented a tremendous success, considering the lack of previous recognition master women had received. It made the lonely "unofficial" and nonchampionship events of 1974 and 1975 appear to be things of the past.

Be that as it may, I had trouble forgetting the 1974 Masters National Marathon Championships on Sauvie Island, Oregon. There had been no objection to my entry, and I did receive the certificate of completion all finishers were awarded. But I didn't exist as either a division winner or a national champion for my first-place female placing. At least I didn't have to contend with the hassle that confronted Catherine Smith when she tried to enter the track-and-field portion of this championship meet. She was allowed to compete only after threat of court action on discrimination grounds. The Track-and-Field Championships welcomed all master women to participate the following year in any events they wished to enter. On the other hand, the marathon championship was held separately in Medford, Oregon, and I found myself in the same unofficial and nonchampionship situation as before.

Master women were treated more on a par with the master men at the 1975 First World Masters Track and Field Championships in Toronto, Canada. The marathon had age divisions for women 30-39 ("sub-masters"), 40-49, and over 50. Appropriate medals were awarded all placers, first through third. The 10-kilometer cross-country event was the only one that "permitted" participation by women, but certificates were awarded the finishers. Track-and-field events again had medals for the scoring women in the same categories as for the marathon.

On the other hand, the 1975 Senior Women's National Marathon Championships did not offer the master women championship status. Miki Gorman was the over-40 division winner, well deserving the title of national champion.

Obviously there was a problem for the master women in deciding where to turn for their national championships. Polling as many competitors as possible before the 1976 convention indicated a trend toward giving the new Masters Committee the authority to include the women masters in their national programs. Many of the husbands of these women and their male running friends were also master competitors; so both the pleasure and finances of traveling to national championships together were desirable considerations. For the vast majority of master women, the ultimate goal was not of an open Olympics as it might well be for the younger women governed by the new Women's Long Distance Running Committee. Rather, the World Masters (Veterans) Championships with peer competition in five-year age groups was rightfully a valid goal. Such five-year age group divisions would put quite a stress on the open women's competition structure.

The complex nature of the AAU Committee's jurisdictions caused problems this first year for both new committees, requiring the AAU's Judicial Committee to rule on the Marathon Championships sites for both 1976 and 1977. The Southern Pacific Association was awarded the Senior Women's 1976 Marathon Championship to be run with the Western Hemisphere Marathon in Culver City, California. The Hawaiian Association and Mid-Pacific Road Runners hosted the Masters, Women's, and Men's Marathon Championship along with the Honolulu Marathon.

Both were outstanding marathons scheduled only a week apart; both drew top runners from the championship divisions away from each other. Kim Merritt, Gayle Barron, and Cindy

Dalrymple, to name a few, ran in Honolulu rather than Culver City. Toshiko d'Elia and Martha Klopfer competed in Culver City, missing the masters championships in Honolulu. Thus when Minneapolis/St. Paul was to be the 1977 site for all women, including juniors, it was hoped all top contenders would be there. Certainly an outstanding group of women was present, October 23, for this women's-only marathon, the first such event in the United States. For this historic event, Nina Kuscsik presented a very inspirational address on the history of women's marathoning, much of which I've tried to include in this chapter. All 79 finishers in this race were a credit to women's marathoning. Fifteen of these women broke three hours, topped by Leal-Ann Reinhart of California in 2:46:34.

October 23 was also the date of the 1977 New York City Marathon. Among the 5,000 entries there were some 200 women competitors, including several outstanding ones, Miki Gorman and Kim Merritt in particular. Perhaps this merely indicates that women have reached the level of the men, where they can pick and choose which races to run. The potential rewards are the same when dealing with record times, outstanding competition and in some cases trips and prizes.

Fortunately for the cause of the Olympic marathon for women, priorities helped bring an exceptional field of women to the 1978 Avon International Marathon in Atlanta. Nine countries were represented among the nearly 200 women entered, including 15 of the top women marathoners in the world with marathon times of 2:50 or better. Californian Martha Cooksey's fine winning performance of 2:46:16, followed by Sarolta Monspart of Hungary, Manuella Angenvoorth of West Germany, and Cindy Dalrymple of Hawaii in the top 10, all breaking three hours, ably demonstrated the capability of women to make an exciting competition of the marathon distance. Will the International Amateur Athletic Federation take notice? The U.S. representative to this body was there to take notice. Dr. Ernst van Aaken was there to lend his support, plus the much needed attention of the news media that has followed his work closely.

The very next month the Boston Marathon added more fuel to the mounting statistics. Twenty-nine women broke three hours, with over 100 finishing under 3:30. Women marathoners are succeeding, bringing along all the long-distance events from 1,500 meters in their wake. Surely the Olympics are the next step. "In due time" is an unacceptable concept for women who have come this far. Further support from the news media, writers, sponsors, even whole communities should continue this growth of women's participation.

Indeed, just this past June 10, 1978, the Downtown Council of St. Paul, Minnesota and the "Natural Light" division of Anheuser-Busch, sponsored a 10-kilometer race. A portion of all entry fees from this race was donated to the Women's Long-Distance Running Committee to campaign for the longer distance women's events in the Olympics. A press conference with the local news media had been held the day before; from the types of questions asked and by the response to the answers given by me and Alexandra Boies (a panel of two), I felt there definitely was good support for the women's cause. This was particularly true once it was made clear that no events over 1,500 meters were scheduled for 1980. "Natural Light" plans to sponsor a series of such races across the nation with continuing support for the Long-Distance Women's Committee. Hopefully these funds can "talk" in the right places.

Another recent development, brought about by participation of commercial sponsors and race organizers who recognize women's potential as athletes, is the establishment of equal prizes for men and women. Both woman and man overall finishers of the "Natural Light River Run" in St. Paul were awarded airfare to the New York Marathon. More attempts are being made to offer travel invitations to top men and women. An outstanding example was the field of women and men invited by Nike Sportshoes to the 1978 Cascade Run-Off in Portland, Oregon. The list included Gary Bjorklund, the overall winner; and Marty Cooksey, the women's first place finisher, both in very fast times for a hilly 15-kilometer race (44:06 and 51:36, respectively). I felt very privileged to represent the masters women with such notables as Kim Merritt, Carol Cook, and Leal-Ann Reinhart. Again the first-place prizes for men and women were comparable: travel to Fukuoka, Japan, for Gary; to an international race of her choice for Marty. To have a woman runner of Marty's excellence competing with women from other countries on their home grounds should be a positive way to demonstrate the desirability of this competition at the Olympic level. I would like to see more race awards for women like these to make it possible to get more of our outstanding women athletes into foreign competitions.

As Dr. Ernst van Aaken has been the international mentor for women long-distance runners, so has Walter Stack of the San Francisco Dolphin Southend Runners been our local and national mentor. Even in the founding years of the DSE ten years ago, he encouraged and promoted women's participation in his club's runs. He says that the percentage of women members is the greatest nationally for a club of its size (the club has 3,000 members, 38% women). He was also the prime mover in promoting the Pike's Peak Marathon as a women's participation challenge. Trophies, T-shirts, even establishing a "Peak Busters Club," were the rewards he originated for all women finishers.

Another man with an interest in supporting and encouraging women in running is Jesse Bell of Bonne Bell Cosmetics. He has furnished great opportunities for women's competition nationally with the sponsorship of the 10-kilometer Bonne Bell "Mini-Marathons." Numbers of women ranging from 800 to over 2,000 have turned out in the cities where these races have been held. There have also been some outstanding times by the women winning these races. Sixteen-year-old Roxanne Bier started the once-a-month series in San Francisco with a 36:20 to her credit. The fastest time so far was recorded by Marty Cooksey in Phoenix on March 5th; however, Cindy Dalrymple came within three seconds of the same time in Washington, D.C. May 28, 35:41 to 35:44! Such facts should also help impress the doubting international officials about women's abilities to run 10,000 meters well.

On June 3, the L'eggs 10-kilometer "Mini-Marathon" in New York's Central Park added the most impressive statistic yet for this distance. Martha White, eighteen years old, won in 33:29 out of a field of over 4,500 women. This would have been a world record for a women's 10,000 meters a year ago. But track times are improving dramatically, too. Loa Olafsson of Denmark lowered her record of a year ago from 33:34.2 to 31:45.4, April 6, 1978 in Copenhagen.

If only more countries around the world would observe favorably all this progress and allow their women the same opportunities. . . . Perhaps the examples of masters women already competing in world veteran championships will add further credit to the need for international competition for all women in the Olympics.

15

Breakers of Barriers

Some running pioneers: Roberta Gibb,
Kathy Switzer, Nina Kuscsik, Sara Berman

Kathy Switzer

ROBERTA GIBB

"The first thing I thought of when someone told me that there was this race, the Boston Marathon, and that people ran 26 miles in it, was 'Twenty-six miles! People can run 26 miles?' I could hardly believe it. Then, the next thing I thought was, I wonder if I can run 26 miles."

Somewhere, Roberta Gibb and I must have breathed the same molecules at just about the same time. Ever since we were young girls, there was a fascination of running through woods, across fields. Of her beginnings, Roberta says, "I run for the same reason a bird flies. Even as a child, the sight of a wide open beach was an expression of joy, and summer camp was a time to run across fields and jump the horse fences.

"I never could wait to get out and run and run. I loved seeing how long I could go, and always loved exceeding what I *thought* were my physical limits."

Later on, as a teenager, Roberta met a boy who told her that he ran five miles a day. That was the longest she had ever heard of and she began running with him to see if she could do it as well. Later, on her own, she liked the idea of running from her house to another village and back again without any consideration to time or distance. It just felt good to her, so she did it.

Roberta Gibb is a New Englander. In many ways, her soft accent, slow speech, and blonde hair, and wide-eyed look reveal her as an early California flower-child...but the impression is fleeting. Her measured speech is perfectly structured; each sentence is a philosophical reasoning of her thinking—her explanations are often syllogisms.

The philosophy is a very New England outlook on life: the way she lives, the way she regards her son, and the way she runs. She takes pleasure in the roughness of the New England terrain, the challenge of the hills, the easily-found solitude of the New England woods, and her own sense of history.

Despite living near Boston all her life, Roberta had never heard about the Boston Marathon until she was in her early twenties. At the time, her family lived in Winchester, and her father was a chemistry professor at Tufts, in nearby Medford. Roberta drove over to watch the marathon in 1965, and instantly fell in love with it. "I was really moved by a group of people doing together exactly what I was doing alone," she said. "It just set in my gut; I really identified with all those people. Quite frankly, it didn't occur to me that none of them were women, and I came away from the race knowing I just *had* to run the marathon.

"My family has lived in this part of the country—Rockport, Marblehead, Winchester—for hundreds of years. In fact, they came over on the Mayflower. When I watched the race, I knew that it was partly my love for Boston, and the fact that I had been running to some of the small villages around here—like Concord and Winchester—and that endeared me even more to the Boston tradition of this race."

It was after viewing her first Boston Marathon when Roberta knew that maybe the physical limits she had arbitrarily established were false. Five miles seemed easy to her, and she knew now that she could work to 26. How far could people really go, she wondered? Could they go as far as horses, for instance?

An annual event in the early fall in Woodstock prompted her to try to find out. The event was a three-day, 100-mile horse and rider event where the first day 50 miles was covered, and the second 25, and the third also 25. Roberta decided to see if she could run the same rocky trails under the same schedule. The prospect did not seem formidable, as the kind of running Roberta liked best was running through forests and fields, with no real idea of distance or speed. Roberta ran by "feel" and it's the way she still prefers to run today. That day in Woodstock, Roberta covered 40 miles the first day, but her knees bothered her; she wrapped them for the second day and ran 20 miles but "it was no fun anymore." She was satisfied in knowing 40 miles was probably her limit for having fun; and she knew for sure 26 miles was not going to be a monumental undertaking for her.

In January of 1966, Roberta went to live in La Jolla, California and discovered a completely new communion with nature in running. She was fascinated by the brilliant sky and the soaring mountains...but mostly, she was drawn to the beauty and power of the desert.

"I was getting ready for the Boston Marathon, and of course, I had no idea whatsoever of how to train. I didn't know what shoes to wear or what to eat, how to run, or how far to run, so I just went out and ran almost a marathon a day. Of course, after a few days of running like this, I'd be really tired and have to take a day off and then go out and start in the next day. Most of these long runs were done in the desert. There was nothing better than running there.

"I just loved the desert. I would take a bus out there and run back. One day, on an especially long run, I had gotten lost and apparently run across the Mexican border. I could see the border patrol stop following me when I must have crossed back into California.

"The desert was fantastic, because it was totally still, totally quiet. The air was clear and smelled like sage, and I'd run for hours. I'm convinced my best runs were made in the desert that winter. You know how well you feel, how easily you're running. I know that even that first Boston was not a good run compared to some I had had."

It was also a time that Roberta's running was the most important thing in her day, and she could devote as much time as she wanted to it. She was looking forward to Boston in April, not for any competitive reasons, but because she loved the celebration, the carnival-like atmosphere of everyone running together. She submitted a request for an entry in January, and it was refused by the race directors for two reasons: (1) they couldn't take the responsibility in case she got hurt, and (2) she was not allowed to run anyway.

"I was really disappointed because I had done all the training and I knew I was ready," she said. "So I decided to come anyway."

It was a four-day bus trip from San Diego and Roberta didn't exactly eat a training diet on her way to Boston. By the time she arrived, she was tired, cramped and had an upset stomach. She ran Boston two days later.

Since her entry had been rejected, Roberta felt a little uneasy about her reception in Hopkington, so she decided to wait in some bushes for the start of the race. But she also felt a little smug. "Here was a 23-year-old woman getting ready to share a secret or a joke with all these men—that a woman was going to be able to trot along with them all the way to Boston. It was important not because of the 26 miles, but of limits and options—that women *were* capable. If the limit imposed were a false limit, perhaps other limits were also false. The whole idea was to open possibilities to ourselves, to realize and go beyond our limitations."

When the gun went off, Roberta jumped into the passing throng and was on her way to Boston. "The men were very supportive," she said. "Most of them would say things like, 'Don't worry, they can't do anything to stop you,' 'Gee, I wish my wife would run,' or 'Good luck!'"

But some of the race experiences were totally unexpected to this young woman who liked running alone in the desert; the cheers and excitement from the spectators, the comments and questions from the press and the sudden feeling that she wasn't just running alone—she was being noticed.

"I was actually quite touched by the people along the way," she said. "The idea of spectators in the race never occurred to me, and as I never felt like a woman as separate from the rest of humanity, the attention that was focused on me gave a sort of stage fright. I felt I had to be very polite, and whenever I could, I said 'thank you' to the people along the way. I'm basically a very shy person, and after the race was over, I felt in a way that the whole thing intruded on my life."

Roberta ran the distance well within herself. She said she really had no idea what she was running or could run, that in her daily workouts she never timed herself over any distance, she just ran as long as she felt she could. The Boston effort was a 3:20—considered incredible at the time, and prompting many to say she really didn't run the full distance. Of course, as more and more women began running marathons and 3:20's are commonplace, many of the early disbelievers have changed their minds. After the race, Roberta went back to California and began her studies at UCLA where she was majoring in philosophy and pre-med. She began spending more and more time studying, and less time running. In 1967, she ran Boston again, although she felt she wasn't in as good condition as 1966.

Unbeknownst to Roberta, I was also in the 1967 race and running considerably slower than she. When my infamous shoving incident took place at about the four-mile point, Roberta must have been ahead of me and knew nothing about me or the incident. But when she came into the finish line area, a group of race officials stepped out on the finish line with locked arms and wouldn't let her cross. Roberta just stopped and walked around them, got in her car and went home.

Roberta competed in no other events except the Boston Marathon. The 1968 race was her third and last competition. By 1968 she was, as she says, "out of shape and losing interest. I really did not have that time to run because of school, and I really had a bad taste from being blocked in the 1967 race. I hated the hard roads, I hated the exhaust. Primarily, I run for meditative and not competitive reasons. I use running for the time alone and not for social reasons. Running is my rejuvenating force."

And Boston had lost its rejuvenating spirit for her. "For a while, I did feel compelled by the other women and the women's movement to continue running—I certainly believed in what they were trying to accomplish by being allowed into the marathon. But just the fact that I did it seemed enough for me, and that others could find what was needed for themselves. Basically, I am not overt, and my fight is not a public one. I felt my contribution was just to keep myself in harmony, and other women, who were better adept at it, could fight for acceptance in public.

"I feel that women must begin their changes within themselves. They must become unlimited. There can be no outside changes until the inside ones take place. Running is a part of that for me. And, I think the growth that's taking place in running among women is one sign that those changes are taking place in them, too.

"Perhaps I lost a chance to give women runners a stronger boost, but I wanted to retreat afterward, to be alone, and I do feel that the entering wedge was important."

Suddenly, we're back in the present, a decade later. Our discussion turns toward the search for realization in general—how it has expanded from running to include jobs, lifestyles, and people. We are interrupted by a bubbling voice and an equally effervescent presence—Leif, Roberta's three-year-old son, who crawls into her lap and puts his arms around her neck, obviously signaling that his mother has done enough talking for one day. Roberta neither ignores him nor continues on with her regular conversation but directs her remarks to him for awhile. Since she doesn't talk baby talk to him, for a second you think she is still addressing you. "What have you been up to lately? I guess it is getting late—are you hungry?"

Roberta considers children "rays of sunshine" and Leif is certainly hers. "The best thing I ever did was to have Leif. He is definitely the most important thing in my life," she said.

She has devoted the last three years to her child, feeling that in his formative years he needs her constantly. Whatever else she wants to do in her life will have to wait. "I'm very worried about the quality of life Leif will have when he grows up. That's why I'm trying to get closer to the earth, to keep life simpler and be more natural for him and me. It's the same reason why I run—it brings the various moments into a whole big picture—and harmony. When I go back to work, my job interest will be in this area too—environmental law and human welfare."

What about your future with running?

"Oh, I will always run, but I like running just the way I do it now. Some days two miles, some days 10. Whatever I feel like." She laughed. "My running ideal would be to have family-oriented megamarathons up in the Vermont hills. I think a family run where we all go out and do 100 miles, away from the roads and confusion, and stop and have picnic lunches would be great. A lot of the running now just seems too professional." She pauses. "I do entertain a fantasy, though. I think about someday getting a coach and really doing it right, of training hard, and running marathons, or longer races. I do feel I could run as well as ever."

She pauses and nuzzles Leif. "You're going to be a runner, too, aren't you? You've got good, strong legs." Then to me, "I'm not going to push him though. I just want it to be part of him, for him to enjoy it."

K. V. SWITZER: A PERSONAL PROFILE

I am often asked about the people who have influenced me to become a runner, particularly women influences. Although there are women I respect, sometimes even emulate, I always answer that question in a truthful, but joking manner. The fact is, it was men who influenced me; the only woman who played a major role was Mother Nature.

Making the decision to run came long after I did it naturally as a child playing running games, and as an early form of survival: I had to show the boys in the neighborhood that I was as good in sports as they were. Because there were several things I just *couldn't* do as well—like throw a ball as far or run as fast—I had to make up for it with persistence. I had an uncanny ability for any endurance activity—I could out sit-up anyone, ride my bike uphill when others had to walk and I could also run further, if not faster. In all things where I could push myself, I could excel.

I suppose, however, that I had my first outright passion to run when I was thirteen and my family was on a lengthy camping trip to the Pacific Northwest. For the first time, I had the greatest sensation of being a part of nature. One day, we were driving through the Grand Tetons, seeing one soaring vista after another. We stopped for awhile and I couldn't hold back—I had to race as far and as fast as I could through the meadows of blue and yellow mountain flowers as if somehow I could bring it all into my arms. It was an incredibly profound moment for me.

The next was equally profound. I was out of breath in about 300 yards, and the beauty of the moment was slipping away from me. I felt very sad that people have to get tired, that running forever is only a fantasy.

The next summer, I entered high school and wanted desperately to make the field hockey team. I asked my father for some advice and he said I should just run a mile a day and I'd make the team.

I tried to hide my shock. A *mile* a day! Why not the Matterhorn?! We measured off our yard and I plodded my seven laps as if I were being sent to execution. Suffice it to say, despite the relative anonymity of my own backyard, anyone who saw me—neighbors, milkmen, mailmen—expressed grave concern for my sanity. The boys in the neighborhood were hysterical.

I look back on that summer, hot and oppressive as only days in a Washington, D.C. suburb can be, and marvel that I prevailed.

I made the field hockey team in the fall with flying colors. As much as I was in good condition, I thought God was paying me back for my suffering and I promised that I would always run my mile in the off-season.

I kept my running promise and I became a very good athlete in all offered sports—lacrosse, field hockey, and basketball. Determined to do well in college, I expanded the mile-a-day theory: "If one is good, two is better, and no one can run more than three." I ran three a day, and was, in my mind's eye at least, "queen of the hill."

The running continued for two years in college, where I lettered in three sports. But something was happening to me. I was taking sports too seriously. Once, I shouted at an incompetent fullback that I had covered for once too often. She shouted back, "It's only a *game*!" And something clicked inside of me.

I went out for a run to think about pursuing an individual sport. That way no one would tell me it was only a game; *I* could decide whether it was a game or not. I also realized that when school was over, so were team sports. I'd better discover something I could do alone. Tennis? Too confining, need a partner. Golf? Too slow, too much equipment. Then, the light bulb. Running—what I'm doing right now and what makes me feel better than anything.

I was grinning like a fool when I told my coaches I was forsaking all for the sport of running, and was bewildered by the stony glances. Again, the milkmen, mailmen, the neighbors. You've got to be out of your mind. It was 1966.

I didn't care. It was like being blind and in love. One coach said to an ex-teammate that "Kathy will never make it as a runner," and that really frosted me because as far as I knew, *no* women had made it as runners and her dismissal was so unnecessary. I lamented over her remark, too, because it seemed then that women were not out to help each other but instead were their own worst enemies. . . I wondered why they didn't put that energy into being supportive of each other. Also, why were women lacking the camaraderie that the men had?

It was to be only a year later that I would find out, but in the meantime, I couldn't seem to communicate to other women the fun and friendship that women could find in sports.

Although I never was, and never wanted to be, "one of the guys," most of my support came from male athletes—particularly those involved in running sports. Sedentary men were my most vocal critics. They still are, for that matter.

Just about the time I was running all of this through my mind, the men's track coach asked me to run the mile for the track team—it appeared that eligibility requirements had changed, he was short a few runners. He had only one miler, and if I could finish a mile, I'd get points for our team. It was understood I wouldn't beat anybody, but I didn't mind helping out.

I didn't think a thing about it until I walked on the track the next week and saw three times as many spectators than the school had students. I was a little naive in not realizing I would

AVON
21
Marathon
31

be a side-show attraction. I wanted to tell everyone to go home, that I was going to finish last. Which is what I did, in my first-ever timed mile, a blistering 5:58.

But a Rubicon had been crossed. Such scandal the sports world never saw. Debate after debate—can women run, should they run, what would happen to them eventually? Ultimately, I ran in one conference, but couldn't run in another. My fellow students were as divided over this invasion into a male domain as the athletic conferences. I attributed a lot of this haranguing to the provincial quality of a small southern school.

I decided to transfer to Syracuse University because I wanted to major in journalism, and I welcomed the liberalness and anonymity of a large eastern school. Once there, I boldly asked the cross-country coach if I could practice with his team. Although he said I couldn't officially be *on* the team, I could run with them.

During my first week of loping around the golf course, I met a nice little old man named Arnie Briggs. He had been the "unofficial" track coach for about 20 years, which meant that he trained with the university boys and offered some coaching help on the side. In "real" life, he was a mailman. He was also—years before—a nationally ranked marathoner, had run in 18 Bostons (16 medals), but was now so injured he could hardly jog. We bobbed around the course doing eleven-minute miles, and occasionally sprinting through ten-minute miles. It was strange, though, that no matter how injured Arnie was supposed to be, he could always keep running and talking and I was always the first to call it a day. He always ran with me, though, and regaled me with tales of old marathons, and occasionally told me to lean more and drop my arms.

We abandoned the cross-country course and began running the roads. Months slipped by. Inexplicably, we were doing ten miles a night, often slogging through the bitter snow and cold. Arnie kept telling me how good I could be, what natural talent I had, etc. My confidence was rising. After one particularly tough run under conditions like this, I knew Arnie was no longer holding my hand throughout our workouts. I announced that I was going to run the Boston Marathon. The "once before I die" kind of thing.

Actually, I was really fascinated by the idea of the race—the history, the freedom, and the whole mythology of Phidippides and the marathon in general. It truly appealed to my romantic nature; I felt like just being involved with it would give a sense of eternity. It was like scaling Everest, to overcome yourself, to cover ground by your strength alone, to feel, for a second, immortal.

I was also overwhelmed by the "big time" aspect of sports—both those in college and professionally. I loved the idea that there existed one last event that was open, free, and appealed to the sense of personal accomplishment. For awhile, I was totally absorbed by the thought of it.

By the time I decided to tell Arnie about running Boston, I was so sure of my decision that I was almost casual. He, contrary to everything he'd ever indicated before, instantly dismissed it.

"Ridiculous. No woman can run the Boston Marathon." I suddenly realized that Arnie still felt he was holding my hand, and that all the "great natural talent, etc." was just poppycock to get me through workouts. I was incredulous. I reminded him we were doing 10 miles a day. "Law of diminishing returns," he answered.

I pulled a trump card: A woman named Roberta Gibb did it last spring. I read it in *Sports Illustrated.*

Arnie replied that she probably jumped in at Wellesley; people always did that kind of thing in Boston.

I was indignant; Arnie was sullen and unmoved. We mutually reached a compromise: If I could show him in practice that I could cover 26 miles, we'd go to Boston.

The plan was 10 miles a day and a long run on Sunday, increasing the long run "by feel" over the weeks to a full 26 miles. Long runs started at 12, then 15, 18, 20, and 26. Some weeks took repeats at the same distances. Some pretty respected people told me I could be injuring myself, but I dismissed them. Still there was a shadow—we really didn't know anything for sure. It was like sailing uncharted seas. Exciting, but sometimes scary.

The day of the 26 miles was special. I felt great—a little glass-kneed toward the end, but after all, we'd been running nearly all day. (Arnie told me later it would hurt less when I went faster, which is something I couldn't possibly understand for a few years.)

At any rate, when we were about to finish our 26 miles, I suddenly thought that if the course were somehow mismeasured short, that maybe I'd not be able to do Boston. I convinced Arnie I just couldn't feel totally secure about it, so we ran another loop.

When we finished our practice (which was about 31 miles) I

was ecstatic and really sort of stoned on the distance. I threw my arms around Arnie and pounded him on the back, yelling: "We did it! We did it!" Arnie passed out in my arms. When he came to, the first thing he said was "you can run the Boston Marathon."

The next day, Arnie was authoritarian. "Go to the infirmary—get a health certificate." "Fill out the entry form." "You're qualified as any man, got to go by the rules." Obviously, in our scruples to follow the rules, we didn't know women weren't allowed to run. Nowhere did it say that women weren't allowed—it wasn't printed anywhere and both of us simply felt other women weren't interested. I signed the form K. V. Switzer, because that is how I most commonly signed my name. Ultimately, it was this signature that probably led to all further problems.

We went to Boston with my boyfriend (a 225-pound hammer-thrower), who was letting me know that if *I* could run the Boston Marathon so could he. The trip to Boston was fun; we felt like a merry band of Indians.

The morning of the race it was sleeting and raining. Awful, but after Syracuse, I could run in anything. Arnie went inside and picked up the numbers. I stayed outside and did my stretches. I had on a hooded sweatshirt and a bulky grey sweatsuit, which I wore because we were going to throw our clothes away as we warmed up during the race and I didn't want to wear my good sweats. . . . As I look back, if I'd worn my good sweats, someone might have pulled me out of the starting lineup. As it was, the officials couldn't tell I was a woman in all those bulky clothes, although all the runners could. I've never shaken hands so much before the start of a race before or since that 1967 Boston. The male runners were so pleased it was really wonderful. I felt totally relaxed—high, even—when the gun went off. Mecca!

After a couple of miles, we started peeling our sweats. I was down to hoodless shirt with numbers and just getting ready to take off the long pants when the press truck went by. We waved and laughed, and they were having a great time taking pictures and asking where I was from. The officials' truck was right behind us.

Then the bomb went off. Someone was running down the street after me, grabbed me and spun me around, trying to rip off my numbers. Someone was screaming at me to get out of his race. (*His* race?) I was terrified, everyone was bumping and yelling, and I was trying to run but this man kept grabbing at my sweatshirt. Arnie was yelling, "Leave her alone! I've trained her and she's alright!" He kept batting at my assailant. It was Jock Semple, the co-director of the race, and I'd never seen a more fearsome face. I'd never been so scared in my whole life, in fact. Suddenly protective of my numbers, I jumped away. Safe. No! Here he comes again! Then, a streak of a Syracuse sweatshirt, a weird crunching sound of impact, and Jock literally flying through the air. There was an insane moment of silence when it registered that my friend had blocked Jock so hard that he was on the side of the road. We all looked at each other, terrified. Arnie yelled, "Run like hell!" and we took off, everyone yelling again, and acting like in 100 yards we'd be at the Prudential Center. I began to cry, the press truck accelerated, knocking over cameramen. Everyone was cursing. The officials' bus went careening by and Jock was standing on the running board and shaking his fist at us. "Yourrrrr in big troooouble," he yelled in his Scottish burr. Everyone told him what he could do and where he could go, except me; I looked straight ahead, I was so scared.

Eventually the press truck drifted away, and we were alone. I was so emotionally drained I felt like my knees were rubber. We had 22 miles to go and I couldn't get the lump out of my throat. But more than anything else I had ever felt in my life, I knew that I was going to have to finish that race, blisters, dehydration, whatever, even on my hands and knees. Telepathically, Arnie said, "You know, you're going to have to finish the race." I snapped back, "Just don't worry about *that*. There is no way I am *not* going to finish this race."

I must confess, it was tough. I thought at every intersection that one of those big Irish cops was going to arrest me and I'd be too tired to fight. It even crossed my mind that what I was doing might somehow be illegal, that's how Godawful confused I was.

The more I ran, the more the fear turned to anger. At first, I kept thinking, "How could he have done that?" Why didn't he listen when Arnie said that I was alright? Why didn't he give me a chance? His first—only—reaction was that I was a female. Doesn't he realize that I have a brain, that I have trained hard just to be here? I began to think that no wonder women didn't run, they're too afraid to. And they'll never try without encouragement or opportunity.

It wasn't the *women* at all, it was their lack of experience, the way society regarded them, and their own awareness (or lack of awareness) of themselves as physical beings. I knew that women could not make changes within themselves if their whole upbringing and self-perception were restricted. I concluded that it probably wasn't just running, either; it was probably all of women's sports.

As I ran further, my anger was becoming defused and was instead becoming a philosophical resolve. By the time the race was over, my radicalization was nearly complete. We dealt with a couple of crabby reporters, and went to find a hot bath and a beer. I was frozen, but still ecstatic. We had, after all, really done it, and I felt I'd triumphed over a lot more than myself.

A few days later, the second bomb was dropped. I received a letter from the AAU suspending me from any further competition for the following reasons: (1) fraudulent entry (the initials on the entry blank), (2) running in a race with men, (3) running in a race of more than 1½ miles (longest allowable distance for women), and (4) running in the Boston Marathon without a chaperon.

For a long time, I couldn't even answer those charges because they were all so ridiculous. Fraudulent entry! A couple of dozen men had signed up for Boston using their initials that year (I counted them in the entry list) and nothing happened to them. Besides, they were *my* initials; they were certainly not fraudulent.

Like a draft-dodger, I went to Canada and ran that summer. Then, I began to run unofficially in every men's road-race I could get to. It became quite ridiculous, as race directors began inviting me to events, giving me "unofficial" numbers, "unofficial" awards, "unofficial" results, and times. My appearance was helping to hype their events. And I felt the more visibility I got, the more other women would run, and the more the officials would notice and change the rules.

The male runners were encouraging at all times. The press jumped on the issue as good copy, and that helped the cause a lot. But the officials seemed to ignore the whole thing.

Finally, the women's issue became clear again when, in 1971, Nina Kuscsik and Sara Berman were battling it out for a world record at Boston. Most of the top men skipped Boston that year, and the media focused on the two women. How ironic it was that they didn't even count. The press made quite an issue of it. So did the runners. The Road Runner's Club of America spearheaded the legislative attack, and their work was prodigious. By

1972—at Boston—the women were official and it was really an historic day to be running Boston.

Although the toughest technical barrier was crossed, the tough internal barriers were often as difficult to overcome—that was to be able to run as an *athlete,* to go all out, and not be afraid of looking tired, or getting hurt, of not finishing simply because we felt we had to carry the banner for the whole female sex.

After about two years, most of us felt that the stigma was washed away by the presence of other women and of a social acceptance. We could see that the sport was really going to grow, and it was a time for giving it everything we had.

From my point of view, I trained my brains out for two years, and had more success as an athlete than I ever dreamed. My 2:51 in the 1975 Boston was really good for that time and gave me great satisfaction, and I knew then I was ready to move on to other things that were really needed in sports for women—to help create opportunities to develop talent, to reward effort. I guided my career in this direction, and ultimately it will be more satisfying to me than competitive running.

I suppose as I look back, I have only one *if only* and that, of course, is just speculation at this point. I often wonder what it would be like for me *now* if I were that 19-year-old just starting to concentrate on running, but to start with no social restriction and no doubts about physical limitations. . . . Could I have been better? Or, would I have not even reached this modest level, since every step of my training seemed to have profound significance?

I'll never know, of course. But I do know one thing, and that is my future and my career are dedicated to the principle that no other women will have to ask that question.

THE WOMAN RUNNER TOMORROW

Among all runners there exists a nagging dread that on the day of marathon competition, something unexpected will happen that will thwart all the hours of pain and months of training. And, it is always the surprise element after all the preparation that is so ironic, unfair, or just so bewildering: Blisters from otherwise faithful shoes, an unattended water station, a missed time, a loose dog.

The stories of the early women in the marathon read the same way: Sara Berman's 3:01 world record in 1971 not "counting"; Australian Adrienne Beams's 2:46 in 1972—ignored to this day; Nina Kuscsik told to start her marathon ten minutes after the men when she could beat two-thirds of them; Roberta Gibb refused an entry to Boston because women might hurt themselves running; an attempt at physically removing me from the Boston Marathon, and suspension from the AAU for running the race. And many, many more incidents that are left unrecorded.

In their own right, the first women runners are early pioneers of female distance running; some are still competing today, others have rechanneled their efforts for the sport, and some are relegated to history. For the most part, the women became pioneers as a surprise to themselves—they were only doing what came naturally to them.

But the show is far from over. As the sport of women's distance running has years to go before reaching maturity, some of the most exciting changes are undoubtedly before us yet, and we can only hope that our progress will be more swift and less painful than in the past.

Still, what has transpired in the sport since the late sixties has been phenomenal. When Roberta Gibb ran Boston in 1966 without numbers, there were rumblings, jokes, outright dismissal. There were also inklings of future possibilities. In 1967, when the Boston race director tried to eject me physically from the competition for wearing numbers, the catalyst for much change in running for women occurred. The impact of this event was due in great part to the fact that the whole series of blocks and tackles took place, incredibly, right in front of major sports media of the world, and offered everyone an instant display of injustice at work.

Fortunately, the media ran the stories of early women finishers of marathons, and most even took them seriously, which helped to work wonders on the dubious public. The press, it seemed, knew that if *any* person ran 26 miles, that person would *have* to be serious.

The issue also rose at a time when women across the country were feeling the first wave of the feminist movement. Women were questioning all areas of social limitation and bias, and athletics were included.

So, much in the same way that Roger Bannister's breaking of the four-minute-mile barrier brought a flood of sub-four-minute milers, these incidents helped women to realize they could do more athletically. Those running tried harder, gained more confidence, and began turning in respectable performances.

The woman runner of the era knew that her right to her own

physicality was so basic that it was beyond question. And yet, time and time again she was questioned about her "true" motives, and throughout her performances, the woman distance runner had to justify her own existence and simultaneously fight for official status. As late as 1971 she was shrugged off as an athletic oddity, a person who insisted on running in a "men's" event with no official recognition possible.

The ancient rules of sport stated authoritatively that women could run races only up to a certain distance, and that they were restricted from longer competitions to protect their health. Moreover, running with men was considered unacceptable. It was a time when recognition from our running companions was always there, but a feeling of sensationalism at best and disgust at worst seemed to ooze from the public. The implication, however shrouded, implied that women running in the same competition as men was somehow sexual.

Oddly, the women were not as strident as one might think they would be—instead, they were more like Johnny Appleseeds—trying to spread the message of how much fun and how healthy running was, and how women especially would fulfill so much of themselves if they could participate in a physical activity.

A lucky break occurred in 1971. Most of the top international male runners skipped Boston to train for another race. And, in the wake of rumors that a women's world marathon record was in the making, the million or so Patriots Day spectators focused their attention on the Tebaldi-Callas-like duel between Boston's Sara Berman and New York's Nina Kuscsik. Both women narrowly missed the record, but they had finished in the top third of the men's field.

Despite this achievement, women were still accorded an unofficial status. In effect, we were considered to be nonrunners. But people were forced to admit that we did exist, and public pressure on marathon officials gradually mounted.

At the same time, the Road Runners Club of America turned legislative wheels in the direction of Boston, where the ear grew ever more attentive. And at last, in 1972 women were made official entrants. Imagine our exuberance: real official honest-to-goodness numbers, separate trophies, even our own podiatrist.

But among women marathoners there was still a sense of uneasiness. Every time we ran we faced considerable pressure; obviously, a handful of women among more than a thousand men would be noticed. Thus, our first obligations seemed to be to perform well on behalf of our sex, while our sense of athletics ran a not-too-close second.

The official recognition had worked wonders. In February, 1973, the first AAU women's championship was held, giving the women the bona-fide status they sought. That year, West Germany, with the coordination of Ernst van Aaken, hosted the first international championships, paving the way for international change.

In 1977, business began sponsoring women's only competitions, initiating the total emergence of this sport as an entity for women as well as allowing them to continue in mixed competition.

In 1978, the Avon International Women's Marathon Championship was moved from Germany (along with Dr. van Aaken) and held in the United States. The Avon Marathon brought together, for the first time, 14 of the world's top 20 marathoners, showing that corporate strength can join hands with some of the early visionaries of the sport and create the changes needed in a very rapid and very broad way; in fact, Avon's backing in this endeavor is now laying the groundwork for the first comprehensive international program for women.

In the wake of these long awaited revisions, women marathoners are springing up everywhere. Every year their numbers increase geometrically. From this growth (actually, from the freedom of this growth) has obviously come a great deal of talent. After the Boston Marathon in 1971, some runners asked me what I felt the "ultimate" marathon for women was going to be, and although I could not predict ultimate performance, I said that a woman would run 2:35 within the next ten years. The men—friends and respected runners themselves—thought my words were absurd. Of course, six years later Christa Vahlensieck ran a 2:34 in Berlin. The same runners are now admitting that a 2:20 is not just possible, it is probable.

However, the true emergence has been among the masses of women. Most incredible is not just the fact that they are running, but that by so doing thousands and thousands of women are undergoing positive personality changes.

From the simple act of one woman runner gaining inspiration from another woman's jogging, and having, often for the first time, a great sensation of her own physicality, is going to be quite profound indeed—because active running not only gives a woman a fast return on her investment in terms of physical fitness, but also a great sense of freedom, a joyful sense of play, and sense of self-realization. In short, running makes women feel very strong, very beautiful, and that, more than anything else, is going to pave the way for all kinds of ultimates in the future.

16

All the Miles of My Life

A lyrical tribute by a running poet

Grace Butcher

I ran in my first track meet in May 1949. In May 1969 I was still running. I anticipate that I will be running in May 1989 and May 2009. How can I ever die with the old heart perfect, the lungs perfect, the entire body machine perfect? I feel like Ponce de Leon with my own personal fountain of youth. In 1968, at age 34, I had one of my best seasons, winning both Ohio AAU district cross-country titles and finishing high in the nationals (15th of 150 women). In 1972 I won the state two-mile, and in 1977 won my first masters titles (age 40-44) in the mile, 600 and 1000.

Running has been one of two tremendous shaping forces in my life. I was a self-conscious, scrawny adolescent who dreamed of being *somebody*, knowing that if only I could run distance, I'd be the best runner in the country. Many years later, I was.

There was no distance-running for women in the United States beyond the half-mile until 1957. It was considered physiologically dangerous—and worse, unfeminine. The Hungarian revolution of 1956 saw many of that country's top athletes and coaches fleeing to the United States, and in the spring of 1957 I met Alex Ferenczy, coach-refugee. He was amazed that I could not run the events I dreamed of (880, one-mile, cross-country) because they did not exist in our national program. We began a campaign to have these events included, a campaign that met with much opposition from the powers-that-were in women's track. Our campaign picked up momentum, however, and during the indoor season of 1958 the first half-mile for women in this country in thirty years was run in the Goodyear Gym in

Akron, Ohio. I won that race, beating Stella Walsh, the woman who had been my coach in sprints and hurdles many years before, and former world record-holder in many events. The headline about *my* race read: "Walsh Finishes Third."

From 1958 through 1961, I won several more U.S. titles and established or broke the U.S. indoor and outdoor record a half-dozen times. Though I'd had to wait about ten years, my dreams had come true.

There have been periods in these nearly thirty years when I have not competed, thinking I had retired and continuing to run only for fitness. But I kept "unretiring" to compete again. A compulsion. An obsession. A fantastic love of the beauty of the run and the ever-possible chance of recognition. I cannot imagine ever stopping. Barring some total physical disability, I will always run.

I feel great joy these days as I see the thousands who are running to improve their physical fitness. They have at last discovered the best thing for putting and keeping their only body in top shape. People no longer stare at runners, male *or* female, and ask, "What are you doing?" At a shopping center (where I'd gone to run on the sidewalks during some very bad weather) I noticed one little old lady nudge her companion and say knowingly, "She's a jogger." Well, I felt somewhat put down to be called just a "jogger," but smiled at the knowledge that running has finally come into its own: a do-it-yourself aid to achieving the best possible condition.

As an athlete, I've kept endless training diaries over the years. As a poet, I've also felt the compulsion to write poems about what I feel while running. Yet the *feeling* of the run is as difficult to describe as any other deep feeling. But because I am a poet obsessed with the need to share, I have felt this essay building up in recent years. I am frequently overwhelmed with the feeling of beauty and power and confidence that running brings. And because I live in the country, I have access to many beautiful places to run. But the beauty of the run is *within*, for I have had the same remarkable feelings about myself running through factory yards and city streets.

There are strange times and places to run. There are high school tracks after dark, for instance, with lights on nearby buildings to keep me oriented. Running in the dark and unable to see where I plant my feet, yet knowing I am on a smooth track and unlikely to stumble, gives a strange impression of fluid, effortless movement, like swimming at night in black water.

Once there was downtown Rochester, New York, where I ran laps around the block, smiling graciously at officers in the patrol cars that appeared every so often. They were not accustomed to seeing young ladies in long underwear, running around the block, especially in ten-degree, snowy weather. I know of many runners picked up by the police as suspicious characters simply because they were "caught" running out of an alleyway in some tough neighborhood at night.

And the miles of deep snow running—plunging over the white hills and through valleys of the golf course marked with tall pines black against snow and sky—like running straight through a Grandma Moses Christmas card.

Once, for a television appearance promoting the Cleveland Knights of Columbus track meet, I had to run at the downtown YMCA with a couple of men stars. The only problem was that the only access to the track was through the men's locker room, a very busy place that day. I was told to dress in a restroom off the lobby, then to present myself at the door to the locker room. A large towel draped over my head, I was led blindfolded through the locker room to the track. All I saw en route were many bare feet—not very sexy unless you happen to have a thing about feet.

The dark, cold, echoing Cleveland Arena was the site for indoor training when I was an instructor at Cleveland State University and trained with the boys' team there. We ran the cement corridors in the semidarkness, dodging unexpected workers and the nauseating smell of tons of popcorn being prepared for the game that night, and climaxing the training with a dozen calf-cramping assaults on the steps leading from the drafty playing floor over the hockey ice to row *Z* up under the rafters in stifling heat.

There was always the Chardon High School gym when there were no classes, only students passing through. Or the empty halls after school. ("That's Mrs. Butcher. Claar and Dan's mother." "No kidding! How old *is* she anyhow?")

I ran in meets with the boys at Hiram College, going half the distance so the times would come out right for me. But back then, all my motherly instincts rebelled against what I was doing. "Hey, that *girl* is going to pass you!" boys on the visiting teams would yell to their teammates. (The Hiram boys were used to me. "We think of you as just one of the guys," they told me.) So I would slow down my tempo a bit, thinking that my time didn't really matter so much if this kid had to face his teammates' scorn on the bus ride after the meet. I'd pat him on the fanny and murmur breathlessly into his ear, "Come on, we'll run this hill together." My coaches never seemed to understand my explanations about why my time wasn't any better. But that was years ago. Now, less motherly and more mature, I run with men in road races and in masters' meets, and I run hard!

There were the fairgrounds where the trotters and pacers spent the winter months, and where I'd share the track with the drivers stretched out on their sulkies, wrapped against the cold. The horses would spook a little if I'd approach from the opposite direction, and I'd always apologize to the drivers who would just smile and nod. The horses were in their shaggy winter coats, snorting and blowing, their nostrils white with frost, shoulders and flanks lathered with sweat even in the freezing air. I watched the fantastic, controlled bodies, the high pounding driving steps—all that energy in harness always seemed more impressive to me than a "flats" horse. And I did my own seemingly small, insignificant run, feeling the half-frozen earth vibrate under me as they pounded past.

At out-of-town meets in bad weather we'd use the hotel corridors with their plush carpets for training areas. It was a delight to run there on such fine footing, and fun to see the doors open after we'd run by a dozen times or so as the guests checked on what was happening. What they did not expect to see was men and women in very brief attire sprinting madly up and down the halls. They were wise to look both ways before venturing into the traffic pattern.

I sometimes run trainings inside my home, putting wild classical music on the record player and running laps through the living room, dining room, and kitchen, which happen to be arranged in a circle.

There have been strange and funny trainings. And there have been thousands of just ordinary trainings, on tracks all over the country, in parks, on golf courses, in gyms—wherever there was running room. I've sweated, struggled, cursed, laughed, cried, flown, and staggered through more trainings, heartbreak, and glory than I can remember now. Yet several things remain as a common denominator to all the runs: the intense awareness of beauty, pain, joy, and sorrow, and the great need to try to share these feelings. So many people today are in psychiatrists' offices "to discover the *real me*"; there are few more direct confrontations with the self than the physical and mental confrontations with body and soul that the runner experiences. It's my theory that the innate hunger for self-awareness is part of what makes the runner run. When the body says "No!" and the mind says "Go!" which one is going to win?

Years ago I got permission to run on a beautiful golf course near my home. I wait until nearly dark when most of the golfers will be gone, park my car under gigantic maples on the top of a hill just behind the 17th hole, and look out over "my" golf course. The hills roll away into the shadows of twilight. Mist starts up from the creek at the bottom of the hill. I breathe in all the cool colors of the air: dark green and blue and purple. They are very clean. I feel majestic and alone on the hill, surveying the miles I will run. Tall pines turning black against the flow of evening mark my course of these past ten years.

The run is a love, an anguish, a beauty, a fulfillment, a creation, a birth, a death. I begin. The hill catches my feet, pulls me down into the deeper twilight.

I move, shining, over dim hills.
The grass unwinds a blur of rivers on the bottom
of the night;
I cross with no bridges.
My hair is heavy with fog,
and my breathing is the force that spins
the universe.
There is more to the spectrum than was supposed;
beyond violet are endless miles of impossible colors.

Surely I am God. In the deepening dark there are no differences between my body and the air through which I move. Oh, it's for this, for this, for times like this that all the sweat and pain were made. I am the ground I run on, the tall pines. No one sees. No one. My shirt is black, and my shorts. I look down at my legs as they move, and they are beautiful. God, I am so alone. (I am not God.) No one sees how beautiful I am. To stop when the miles have stopped moving under my feet is to see my body shine in the last light. My heart fills my whole body and is more powerful than I am. I can never die. I see myself bright against the dark. There is more love here than I can ever account for.

In my car over the dusty dirt roads to a narrow lane through deep woods where I will run today. The dust hangs gently, moves away over the fields. Years and years ago there was, I am told, a railroad line here, going on for miles, connecting the little towns to the big city. Now there is nothing but this dark slash through the woods. Flat and smooth it is, and black cinders like the most beautiful track. It stretches away through the woods, straight for a mile. The trees are close on either side, and in the summer they touch over the top.

Running here is like running in a tunnel. Sometimes on a white-cloud day the sun may be covered where I begin but shining down there at the far, far end. Symbolic gold at the end of the runner's run. I see the seasons change here. My impressions are always blurred by my movement, like time exposure photographs of star tracks or jeweled traffic on science-fiction highways.

There are animals sometimes—rabbits, skunks, deer—suddenly and astonishingly real out of the underbrush onto the road. I would share the right of way with them but they don't understand my unbroken rhythm or the loudness of my breathing. Sorrow, small sorrows because they are afraid of me. But dogs sometimes, loping from the woods, go my miles with me. Beautiful Irish setter once, shining red-bronze and dappled in streams of sun and shadow. Up and back, up and back along my miles he went.

The woods move over my eyes like a painting through all the seasons. Blurred, blurred, while details jump out. The black bars of endless shadows of endless trees across the snow ripple like op art, purple-black and bright, moving, almost hurting my eyes. The blaze of gold and red in the dusky smell of autumn; the sweet heavy breath of clover almost too rich for my lungs; the jungle smell of spring; the warm rain like love and the snow on my hair and the blizzard that whips my eyes to tears. And the one red leaf or the one white stone, sudden in the blur. Or the one flower, caught by a turn of the head, held without motion for the space of several strides.

I am held, I am the same through all these years, I am held by these walls: green, red-orange, brown, gray, black, white. The seasons turn; it is I who am motionless.

In these woods trees are always running
and clover drifting smells like pain
or sometimes very sweet and fast

with the speed of the long green tunnel
rushing by especially to the end
which is always there and very golden.

Even the wind makes no difference
for the leaves fall when they will
and I have no feet only swirling leaves
golden below the knees a blur upward
to where woodchucks climb trees
did you know that
and skunks stop all traffic on this road
even when all traffic is only
back and forth facing
the miles on both sides
are just as long.

These woods are blurred
with very green breathing or sometimes
gray and brown and black breathing
in a cathedral running gothic trees
leaning over center aisle running
towards golden shining at the end of
sometimes very white breathing
and my feet are diamonds up to my ankles
to my knees to my thighs
and I disappear into blizzard
into blossoms where pain drifts up
on thin white wings or butterflies
and ripe fruit is golden when it falls
from running trees into my quiet hands.

But the pain sometimes. What kind of words are there for that? My big dream for medical science is that some day there will be some kind of electrodes that transfer pain from patient to doctor, from runner to coach, so each can know what the other feels. "I have this terrible pain in my knee, coach." "OK, let's see how it feels." The coach takes the electronic devices, hooks one to the athlete, the other to himself. The athlete runs; the coach collapses in agony. "Take a couple days off," he says, staggering to his feet, yanking off the device. The runner goes gratefully free, knowing that the coach knows the impossibility of running this day's training.

But until then the runner is alone. Can I finish the ten miles? Can I go that one more 440? Or am I doing some irreparable damage to my foot/calf/knee/thigh? I run crying sometimes. The pain is my only opponent on the empty track, in the deserted park, along the dark street. The fear is of the endless weeks and months it has taken to achieve this condition and of the blink of an eyelid it takes to undo it all.

Where is the point where the muscle tears loose? Is it here? Is it this hill? This lap? This mile? Between this bush and that tree? Where does the bone in the foot crack, the Achilles tendon rip free of the heel? Is it this downhill, that sharp turn?

The landscape moves by me
so slowly now.
The wings of my heels
do not scrape the glittering snow
into showers of diamonds,
showers of crystal spray.

My feet with their wounded wings
do not leave their strange marks
in the snow anywhere.
Nor on any roads.
Nor on any tracks.
Nor on any grass.
Not anywhere.

I am afraid to look at my feet
to see why they are so still.
Maybe in the spring,
with all its other blossoming,
new feathers will replace the old.

But for now, the world seems
to lie still outside my window.
I cry at the silence
that wings, not moving, make.

The sun, the clouds, the blinding snow, the blood-colored sunset—they stay the same. But in all the loneliness inside the shape of my skin, over the roaring sound of my heart, I have to decide again and again in the passing years about my relationship to this pain. I cower, curl up in agony in a very small space at the very top of my skull, and ride there while my body does the rest of the training. Or there is the breathing. Escape into the breathing. Go into the center of the body; stay there. But stay out of the legs. That's where the pain is. There are things I can do to get away, but it isn't real, of course, the escaping. I pretend for a while that I am not me.

Pain is whispering
talking
shouting
screaming.
Who is making all this noise?
Not I.
I concentrate carefully
on twenty-seven butterflies
white and yellow
exquisitely hovering
over a dead black snake.

There have always been those eyes. The runner likes eyes when they are understanding. But when they stare without comprehension, there is usually no time to stop and give the lecture about *Why*. I want to tell all the people about the beauty, to shake their fatness until it quivers, to tell them to run themselves out of their fat bodies. "Feel how sweet the air is when it's close to your bones!" I would tell them. "You have room for too many people inside that skin. Get out! Get out! Free yourself. Feel it, know it, that you are free."

I would tell them that if they ran they would have no more blurred edges. All of their extra images would slide together into one. You get to the center of yourself during the run; you confront what is there and find it beautiful.

And I want to give this to everyone. "The more you do, the more you can do," I want to tell them. "The farther you run, the farther you can run." And I see the people who don't care about their bodies. "It's the only body you have," I say, and am appalled when they just shrug. If at age sixteen all of us were given a car that had to last us for the rest of our lives, we'd dedicate as much time as necessary to keep it in perfect running order. But bodies? Expendable. Just a shrug and a slouch into the depths of the favorite TV viewing chair.

I am sick in the atmosphere of not caring. I can't lift them with some kind of sky hook and manipulate their legs for them, left right, left right, faster now faster. I give them words and love; they have to give their bodies back to themselves.

Imprisoned in the pale thick flesh,
the thin one stands on tiptoe
and smilingly screams
to be let out.

I am ashamed that I have not
loved myself more:
I would give her the tall worlds
I see from my eyes,
and a sharp, sure body
that she need not look at mine
and think it is beautiful.

I would give to her five children
horses of the wind to ride
to the far corners of the earth,
leaving her with quiet meadows,
and cool empty rooms,
and time to read
and wonder.

I think of her as I jog
with a lean certainty
through my own long-enough days.
She would be surprised to learn
I think of her and weep
for gifts ungiven.

I am running on the street in front of the house today for some reason. Too much snow everywhere, perhaps, or the mood has struck me on a day off to run just a little warmup. Not enough to get in the car and drive to the golf course or to my beloved dirt road adjacent to it. So I'll run here, back and forth on the half-mile level stretch out in front. I don't like the pavement; it's hard, jarring under my feet. But just today won't hurt. There are always horns, shouts, whistles, offers of rides. But I wrap myself in the hypnotic rhythm of my stride, of my breathing, and just run.

I remember once years ago when someone said about me during a training session that I had a "saint-like" look about me. I was astonished and amused. She meant, I suppose, that I looked dedicated and alone and suffering and different and content. And so along this road where I've chosen to run for some reason today, I suddenly think of her words again, years older now, and wonder how I fill the bill. St. Butcher? Hardly!

But there is this feeling about the run: it's like prayer, like some kind of communion.

If there is something in us that is divine, it's at the deepest center of our souls.

And that's where I go sometimes during the run.

The run is a meditation, a contemplation of what I am, a discovery of what I can give and of what I've received. There's a feeling of total isolation from a world that plays golf in carts and drives two blocks to the store for cigarettes. I propel myself through the miles with the miraculous power of this body. I sometimes seem to run in a slightly different dimension from that in which I usually exist. The world of the run—its isolation, its beauty—and the other world seem like two identical transparencies laid one over the other without quite being lined up. There is something just a little different here. *I* am a little different here. I run:

. . . and the cars see my face
down, eyes, down: a saint
dedicates the road to herself
and ignores the close fenders,
the swooping vacuum, the monoxide
purified by pure lungs only.

Scan the side of the road
for stones; smooth the foot rides
the tired earth. Patterned the
breath of all saints; into it
is escape. Ease the body into the
head to the top of the skull.

The arms repeat the angle
of calf to thigh. All easily
over the roadside. Cars of
faces press the air to look: see!
the funny saint with down eyes
and lonely face. What useful holy legs!

There's no one around today. The campus seems deserted and cicadas sing on the practice fields. Heat shimmers from the all-weather surface of the beautiful track and pain shimmers from the screaming muscles in my legs. But the sky, the clouds, the sun, the pines are around each curve! Surely I can somehow go into all this beauty and get this training done. I can try drinking the air as if it were some kind of food: tastes like pine and clover mixed with water vapor guaranteed to relieve pain quickly or double my money back.

Let's see—what other games can I play? I can imagine fifty thousand spectators here just to watch this training. Surely I would not limp in front of so many people. The white lines are cooler than the black track; let's see if I can run on the lines. Ah, a car through the parking lot. It must be a reporter who has learned of my dedication and determination and has come to do a story about me (with photos, of course. I must take the clip off my hair, let it blow loose out behind me). No, the car leaves. More likely someone who made a wrong turn and ended in the parking lot. A custodian comes to set the sprinkler up on the infield. Ah, surely I can run better with him watching. He waves. That helps; I feel a great lift.

But the pain! Like black and white streaks through this technicolor day. How many more 440s in this hot light where no one really watches, and no one except me cares? My feet burn a path through all of this blazing summer and I leave a trail of pain behind which anyone could follow. Here is where the inevitable "Why?" makes a difference. I am tempted to stop, to think, but am afraid. Maybe there is no answer.

Rainwings
pain-folded into night colors
running streaked into light and dark
cloud shadows chasing
bright fields of pain
shining wet and moving
hair touching softly
whipping into caress
of steady rhythm flowing
into black river of miles
and white lines of minutes
ticking of pain
in left right rhythm
climbing up above where
must stay here
stay here
stay here
no thoughts
sliding down into pain
only high higher climbing
into wind

where I become the wind
blowing
through bright fields of pain.

Meanwhile, back in the woods, another day, another year, another season, there is an invasion of my privacy. *My* woods, as I choose to think of them, though they are some miles from my house. But today there is the intrusion of hunters. They are—these ridiculous huge men bulking against the snow in their stupid safe brilliant red-orange—they are hunting a fox. Or *the* fox. The skin on my back crawls with imaginary bullets. They know me, of course. I have run here for years. We exchange a few frosty words as I trot by.

I run this
black and white woods:
an easy universe.
I am at home here.

But sudden thick hunters
trudge
and stand.

"I am not the fox,"
I tell them,
and they laugh.

(But my hair flows
loose behind me,
warm and brown,
and my feet are certain
in the snow.)

They neither understand
nor shoot,
and I laugh last.
Today, at least,
I do not die.

Far far down the road, where I have run out of their sight, I have seen the majestic fox in his brilliant winter fur. He glides huge hot circles through *his* woods, *my* woods, *our* woods; but not their woods. We are warm, he and I; the snow melts where we run.

Oh, there is love, of course. It is as gray as November, as black and white and brilliant as January. And it hinders the training or it covers the pain or it tightens the throat or wings the heels or freezes the eyes with tears. I take it—you—with me in every run, and you, invisible, watch every mile, every poem I run for you.

"Look at me!" I tell you out loud. "See how beautiful I am when I move like this. See the words of my feet in the snow."

To run this white weather
is to scour with cold
my lungs and blood and eyes,
but my heart is infinite
and warmer than it is old.

The thought of you,
like a beautiful knife
hot through ice,
cuts me loose
from all my frozen miles.

I create you here too much. Between runs I speak aloud into the soft white space of the winter air. You are too real, too vivid. I try to think you into existence here on this road in the woods. The question now is not "Why do I run?" but rather "For whom?" All this is not for myself, surely. There is too much beauty, too much pain for just one person. I will keep the pain; give you the beauty. Oh please, for once when I am unselfish, be here. I have all this giving, and you are only a dark image behind my eyes, projected onto the snow. Not real, not real.

I guess what is most real and least accepted is that I am here alone. There is no you to see how I am. There is instead this perfect January with its dazzle of ice, and there are memories of pain and memories of all the pain to come. There is all the uneasy darkness of love past, and in this running I carry the load of all my love for you. Sometimes I stop, walk, stare out over the woods and fields, and everything is empty and beautiful. My body is here: the runner in too many clothes, temperature below freezing. And instead of the how-many-times how-many-yards, I think of you not here and wonder why the training goes on.

In this bright glass world
my body sharply rings;
delicate bells of the mind move
into a rhythm of light and ice.
But under the pulse

that perfectly drives me
to crash the white air,
under the blank ice
a black rhythm coils
and uncoils:
it is not spring,
this dim thunder,
nor blood.

Whose faces are those
in the dead water,
covered only by the
thin sound of bells?

My own face hardens
into glitter of ice.
I stand: a stillness of light,
a frozen flow of sun.
The last bell swings, emptying
into the endless glare;
is heard, and forgotten,
by children playing
in the tightening air.

Ah, but there are also days like this new one now. I have had a great insight. The sounds are purely sexual: the rhythm, the increase in tempo, the breathing. It never occurred to me that the great running poem of all time would be a love poem, but of course! It is the endless rhythm of the run that creates my own time, independent of the rest of the world. The waiting is infinitesimal. That you are not here is insignificant. The run says everything. Don't you see what I am doing? I finally see what all this running is about. It's not medals and trophies. Forget those. Forget.

The great running poem of all time
will be written, rewritten, revised
by my indefatigable legs
around the timeless track
of your body. I (suddenly) knew...

I have run a thousand miles of poems
in perpetual training, and feel
the final tilt of the earth
turning me (eager) towards you.

Lost feathers from any birds

for my impatient feet;
the wind in my hair is only
until (gentle) in your hands.

. . . Snow. . . yes. Or white sand.
Or sun on a white bedspread.
There is so little need, really,
and so little to understand.

How simple. I am content for days in a swirl of my own intense understanding. But slowly I lose it. Why don't *you* see how simple everything is? Lord, lord, how can I run like this? The complexities of our relationship tangle my feet and muddy my mind. I cannot run involved in the run. I carry you with me like my skin, my clothing.

I lose count of the times I've run across the snow, across the spring, across the whole of Time. How many quarters make a whole? How many minutes make a mile? How many hills make a cross-country runner happy? And so—and so—where do I go from here? There is only my body left; my head is sometimes not fit for habitation any more. Of all people, of all ironies, I cannot run away from myself. This has been a good head until now. I must get as far away from it as I can for a while. Where can I go? Obviously I must run somewhere, and obviously it must be down. *Vertical therapy.*

If I run long enough
I shall finally (like sand)
fall completely out of my head
into my body—

out of the glare and din of words
spoken aloud alone,
into an endless twilight
of coolness, of silent motion.

Through the sharp snow
my body darkens
like an explosion
of many birds.

There now. . . one more day has gone. One more training. My head has not exploded nor has my heart burst. Oh this fine body! Neither veins nor muscles have ripped apart. Oh this lovely body, this haven. I thank whatever force it is, whatever name it has that keeps this universe "running."

I am alive and here and not insane. The running keeps my head firmly on my body, and all dark thoughts are scoured, brightened in the clean smash of sun on snow.

There is something—even a race—to look forward to. Too easy for the running to become an end in itself. I am supposed to be a competitor, but who is it I run against? I run against the snow, the rain, the heat, the gentle spring, the comfortable autumn. I am dark against sky, sun, snow, and light against twilight and against high school tracks after dark with street-lights nearby. I am light against the dark cinders and dark against white sand. I am heavy against the air and light against the earth. But who is it I run against? In all these years there has never been anyone else on the track or over the hills running against me.

It's not someone I run against, it's something I run *toward.* It's in me whatever it is. I run toward it all the time. It's some center, some knowledge. It's some kind of youth, too.

Across the melting ice and snow
great gray dogs run at me
because I also run. They think
this is their wilderness. I must
prove them wrong. I am ready,
warm and happy, to kill them
as they leap at me.

Also the earth for some reason
pounds at my feet. Yes, I suppose
to have a love like this, I must be
punished somehow, or made to
appreciate the earth more by its
hurting me this way. Whose logic is this?
What is all this pain about?

All this sacrifice of animals and all
this pain I offer up each year to make
the summer come and oil my skin with sweat—
maybe it would come without all this.
But I am afraid to think what would happen
to this earth without me. My running is necessary.
It keeps things the way they are.

People insist on dividing air into time: into minutes and hours. I see thin black lines in the air like measures in music.

But there are no lines in the run. Time opens. Oh, I must run for time, yes. But the two minutes, the four minutes, ten minutes, two hours of the race are of no importance somehow. They are too small in the whole universe. It's the years and years of running that count. And the whole idea of time and the calendar blurs into the beautiful colors of the seasons. I might be spring summer autumn winter. But never ended finished old. Whatever it is in me that runs also runs the universe, and is always new or it is always unchanging. I haven't yet figured which, but it doesn't seem to matter.

There are times when even the woods don't work, however. The flattened days of November that press down with a heavy sky; the road in the woods, straight for a mile, is like a treadmill, and nothing really moves. I weigh a thousand pounds; most of it is clothing. My long underwear twists inside my warmup pants. My underpants twist inside my long underwear. My head-scarf either comes untied or chokes me. My hands sweat in my mittens and are too cold without them. I freeze and sweat in the headwind, tailwind. The track at the school has been ruined by football cleats; it stands wind-swept, desolate, cut up, freezing into clods and clumps and holes. The road in the woods has been ruined by tractors, cars, bicycles. It freezes into ruts I cannot run in without stumbling. I long for the humid hottest summer days when my skin shines as if oiled and my muscles have an infinite reach. I swear violently, choke up with tears, laugh. But then there is an abortive attempt on the part of the universe to make this training easier. Sudden color. Too brief, too beautiful.

A bluejay
threads himself
through dead needles
of swamp grass:
too much reality
for this gray
stiff dream of woods.

I cannot follow him
across decaying water,
and running the long way around
(running forever)
I find no blue thread left—
no path.

Maybe the only real thing, the only certain thing, is to know myself. Then I will know what it is people call God, or the force that created and moves the universe. How can I know myself—my *Self*—without going into the deepest places of my own mind and body?

All the religious dogma doesn't quite work. But they're all involved somehow. Confession, redemption, resurrection, prayer, miracles—some kind of certain feeling of absolute knowledge, an enlightenment, a purification. Every good run is like a final inventory: a rummaging of the unused rooms of the mind, a testing of the untried components of the body.

At the bottom of my lungs
looking for last air;
the deep and bloody rush
through the hot passages
of the roaring heart;
behind the eyes
where seasons blur
like melting wax;
through the mindless pain
of muscles torn, gone wrong;
into feet wounded
by other kinds of nails—
strange ecstasy, this.
I have neither fasted nor prayed,
but I have been clean and holy
all the miles of my life.

I had this thought once: "Running is a poem that spins from my body like a spider's web, hangs beauty on the air behind it."

People ask, "Why do you run?" I have wondered since I was very young, but it is only now that I seem to know. We go through our lives trying to discover what we are, painfully aware of our shortcomings, our imperfections. Yet when I am running there are moments when everything is right. For an instant, I am perfect. There is a place on the high school cross-country course where I come out of the woods onto a long, gentle, downhill meadow. My body is carried by the hill, with no effort. And I am perfect there. A voice in my head says, "Yes. This is what you were born to do." And my body does it. Everything is together, and perfect.

And there is another place: the dirt road in the woods, in the winter when everything is either black or white. There are no questions at all. And the only trouble is—I am alone. There is, as in all perfect moments, no one with whom I can share what I am, feel what I am, be what I am. Even if others run with me and stop for a moment, I am still alone in the fragile clouds of breath that hang in the crystal air. Is this always our condition—the longing for the impossible sharing?

I cry. Running is the most beautiful gift, and it cannot be given. All of us must give it to ourselves, must know for ourselves what it is. It is like love that even words, gestures, looks can never truly express. How can I give the movement my heart makes, the ecstasy and sorrow that flow through my body making it ache with the need to give what I feel? The running, loving, living are all in the final word, *alone.* You can never truly know me, my dear love, my beloved children, my wonderful friends. Take my words, my body. But they are not ever enough. Run. Have these moments that I have had. Know the beauty I know. . . .

When I run, my body
draws in upon itself,
hones down.
My bones are within reach;
old rhythms restore themselves.

Harmonies reappear.
I sing my own comeback.
Each inhalation/exhalation
has so many notes
like a chord of music.

Something in me tunes in
on my own clearest frequencies;
something resonates with a clarity,
the high perfect sound
a crystal bell might make.

I am inside this fine body,
tending to the miles as they pass.
I fit perfectly inside my skin;
nothing is left over. Nothing!
The miles become perfect as I finish them.

I can run only where I am,

each step a new place of its own.
Nothing is more right than this:
the grass, the sky, and my body
in between, moving and beautiful.

Poetry Acknowledgments

"I move, shining, over dim hills." (Appeared as "Runner at Twilight") *Sports in Literature,* Henry Chapin, ed. New York: David McKay Co., 1976.

"In these woods trees are always running." (Appeared as "Training") *The Free Lance,* Vol. 10, No. 1, 1966.

"The landscape moves by me so slowly now." (Appeared as "Runner, Hurt") *Forum: Ten Poets of the Western Reserve,* Peter Hargitai, Lolette Kuby, eds.

"Imprisoned in the pale thick flesh." (Appeared as "Poem Because of a Short Fat Friend") *Kansas Quarterly,* Vol. 1, No. 3, 1969.

". . . and the cars see my face." (Appeared as "I Run") *The Back Door,* No. 9/10, Fall, 1976.

"Rainwings" (Appeared as "Training on the Track") *Rumors of Ecstacy . . . Rumors of Death,* Ashland, Ohio: Ashland Poetry Press, 1971.

"I run this." (Appeared as "Identity") *Small Pond* No. 11, Fall, 1967.

"If I run long enough." (Appeared as "Therapy") *Rumors of Ecstasy . . Rumors of Death,* Ashland, Ohio: Ashland Poetry Press, 1971.

"Across the melting ice and snow." (Appeared as "Responsibilities") *Seventy-three Ohio Poets,* David Citino, ed. Marion, Ohio: Ohio State University, 1978.

"When I run, my body." (Appeared as "Runner Resumes Training After an Injury") *Forum: Ten Poets of the Western Reserve,* Peter Hargitai, Lolette Kuby, eds. Mentor, Ohio: 1968.

Part 4
Profiles: Fifty American Women Runners

Profile of a Typical Woman Runner

After examining the 350 questionnaires submitted by women who took part in Bonne Bell Mini-Marathons, the only conclusion that can be drawn is that there is no "typical American woman runner." American women runners cover the spectrum of occupational, economic, intellectual, emotional, and political viewpoints.

There were trends in some areas. Most women began running for health and appearance benefits. The reasons for continuing to run usually shifted subtly but definitely to psychological reasons. "Laying off would bother me very much," says Jessika Lucas of San Francisco, 23 years old, who runs 6½ miles per day. "It's part of my daily routine and I feel very badly if I miss too much. I feel very good after I run because I know I've done something good for my body. It also clears my mind when I run, and it eases a lot of my problems—or rather allows me time to think them out."

Maryann Mimi Taylor of Boston states rather emphatically: "I already feel guilty if I miss a day. For instance, last week after a party I had a hangover so I didn't run. My dissatisfaction with myself for not running was worse than my hangover."

Although all the women surveyed have run a race of at least 6.2 miles, the amount of training the women do varies from 1½ miles per day to better than 100 miles per week for women who train for marathons.

The majority have run only a year or two and are unconcerned about high fashion, preferring something comfortable (usually a T-shirt or tank-top and a pair of shorts).

Most of the women have been lured into running by other female friends, boyfriends, or husbands; also, most resisted at first, feeling it was either beyond their capabilities or that it was boring. Almost all found, however, that once begun, running becomes a difficult habit to kick.

The response that female runners get from friends and relatives to their avocation is varied. "My husband supports my running as does the rest of my family," says Jessika Lucas. "They all think it's admirable."

Cathie Wheeler of East Burke, Vermont, says that her family and friends think it's terrific and that they all support her efforts.

Nancy Morrissette of Foster City, Calif., who completed her first marathon in 1978 at the West Valley Marathon in San Mateo under conditions of gale-force winds and driving rain, finds a mixed response from her family. "They voice their support but never make it convenient for me to go for a run. My weekend run requests are always met with, 'Don't you do enough of that at work?' or 'Why don't you do something with the entire family instead?' I am content with five days of running but would love to add Saturday and Sunday to my schedule for longer runs." Nancy does most of her training runs at Skyline College, where she is a secretary.

Liz Strangio of Fremont, Calif. reports that her family likes her running and that most of her friends are runners. Her brother, Steve, runs 75-100 miles a week, so she's among people who are on the same wavelengths. Her training reflects her dedication to running as a sport and not just as a lifestyle. She does interval workouts three times a week and runs a 10-mile course over hills on Mondays. Her forte is cross-country.

Robin Holderness of Alexandria, Virginia, reports that her family is supportive, but that they question her sanity, especially when she runs in the rain or in temperatures that top 90 degrees.

Most of the women surveyed indicated that although men and women derive much the same physical and psychological benefits from running, women often find running more important to their lives because it opens doors to appreciating themselves and their abilities that they never knew existed.

"I think all runners derive some of the same physical and emotional benefits from running," said Judith Roeder of

Concord, Maine. "Running gives a person better physical conditioning, increased aerobic capacity and makes them feel healthier, more energetic and alert."

Maryann Mimi Taylor feels that "both sexes share all the benefits and all the agonies."

What Cathie Wheeler derives from running is "almost therapeutic." She thinks with men "it seems to be more of an ego trip. Although I think that the division of what people get from running should be drawn down columns of individuals instead of down between the sexes."

When asked to name the person who has had the most positive effect on their running, women either name their husbands—or themselves. Running brings a belief in one's abilities that women seem to recognize and revel in.

Woman after woman expressed the great freedom running brings into her life and the feeling of accomplishment after running distances. Never believing it was possible to run even a mile, many women are setting goals of running marathons in a year or two. They are finding themselves more capable than the world—and they, themselves—thought they were.

And for some of them, it is making life an entirely new experience for them, something wider and more exciting than it has ever been before.

"I feel good about myself after I run." "Running helps stabilize my life." "It's given me new direction." "Before, I was lazy, too tired to do anything; now I've lost 25 pounds and I'm always active. I can't believe the change it has made in me." "Running makes me appreciate me." "It turned my life around." "It made me appreciate my body, what it can do, what I can make it do, what I can expect from it. It made me confident that if I can make my body do that, run all those miles, that I can make it do almost anything. Anything I want is within reach because I run." "It's a whole new world for me...it's opened a whole new world."

This section, then, represents the feelings, the findings, and the aspirations of 50 American women who are essentially no different than any 50 American women. The only difference is that they run (at varying distances, at varying speeds). And that through running they have found something within themselves that they are anxious to share with other women.

BONNIE STORM
Woodside, California

"The glow of the marathon is constantly around me."

"I run now for different reasons than when I started," said Bonnie Storm, a 33-year-old resident of Woodside, California. "I began running to keep quick for tennis, and as a weight control. Now I run, often in *preference* of tennis, because it makes me feel great. I enjoy challenging myself with longer distances. I enjoy the mental aspect of running—the 'head games' you can play.

"One day a certain distance seems impossible while the next the same run is a snap. I feel I am just beginning to scratch the surface of what I can do and this is really exciting. I love physical exertion and running makes me feel like I really earned anything I do the rest of the day. I feel crummy and even guilty on those days I don't run. I think I'm really getting hooked!

"Running has really made me aware of the foods I put into my body. I want my body to function efficiently so I can run better. I even quit drinking after my first race. Why ask my body to perform and then clog it with all sorts of junk? I am by no means a nutritional purist, but I am aware, and I never was before!"

Bonnie has been running for three years. She trains six days a week, 35-45 miles per week, racing sporadically. Her training is done mostly in the mornings, but she's not locked into any particular time of the day. Warm-up exercises center around the Achilles stretch and she generally runs alone, although once a week she usually runs with friends. Her husband runs, but less frequently because he has less time.

Bonnie's longest run has been 12 miles, but she indicates that it was done with relative ease and she definitely wants to go farther. When asked about marathon aspirations, her response was cautious but not untypical: "The 'glow' of the marathon is constantly around me. I have no definite time reference, but I would bet I run one within a year. Almost guaranteed in two."

When asked what she would tell other women about running if she were given a soapbox, this was Bonnie's presentation:

"From atop my soapbox I would remind my audience that *everyone* can run. This is getting to be a cliche, but it's so true. Success is guaranteed. Lately I have run with friends who were never remotely athletic, and are now running. And loving it."

Bonnie's training pace of 7:40-8:00 per mile is quite respectable; her best mile time is 7:00; one of her goals is to do a 6:30 per mile average time in a race. Her loyalties are still spread between tennis and running, though.

"I am not sure if I am totally committed to training strictly for running, or if I am still basically a tennis player. If I was concentrating on running only, I would want a coach and a definite training schedule to follow."

When asked about her most memorable run, it took no time for her to wax poetic:

"My most memorable run is constantly changing, almost weekly. But I guess the Bay-to-Breakers race would be my most current memorable run, simply because it was such an upper... so positive. Prior to the race, I had pretty negative feelings about participating, but several essentially 'nonrunner' friends invited my husband and I to run with them, so we agreed, more as a social engagement than as an athletic event.

"Our friends 'trained' and talked a lot about 'carbo-loading' for the race, and we (my husband and I) laughed to ourselves at their naivete and wondered how we would survive without being trampled, or even how to bow out gracefully.

"The evening before the race we all went out to dinner together and, of course, our friends ate pasta in preparation for the race. Again, my husband and I shook our heads; we knew we would probably walk the whole distance because of the crowds.

"The morning of the race was overcast and medium cool—a perfect day. All of us drove to the starting locale, and parked next to a car full of unbelievably athletic black runners doing amazing stretches and warm-ups. Eventually, we smooshed to the front of the assembled runners...some 10,000 to 13,000 strong. I hadn't a clue how to begin this thing, but while waiting all of us saw lots and lots of people we knew, both current friends and lots of acquaintances from the distant past. Real carnival atmosphere.

"As the gun went off the start was orderly. We managed to blend in pretty well, found a few feet of room to run and we were off. Well, all I can say is that the race was an absolute gas! Always dodging people, cars, parking meters sounds gruesome, but I loved every second of it! We ran much faster than most, but the race was literally solid people from the start to finish. The dreaded Hayes Hill came and went and we didn't even notice. Lots of cheering from the runners, lots of good feelings and happiness. We kept seeing more friends among the runners and spectators. At the end of the race I felt strong and had tons of kick left. The spirit of participation was elating. Both my husband and I felt super. The best moment of the race was at about five miles out. Remember those athletic black runners we started next to? Well, we passed them easily. . . .

"Looking at the race clips on TV later I couldn't believe we did it. It looked like torture on TV with all those hordes of people. But I would have been extremely disappointed to have seen those shots on TV and not have been a part of it."

MARTIE COMARELL
Benicia, California

"At 30 years old I am in better shape than I was at 20."

"I started running to please my boyfriend," says Martie Comarell of Benicia, California. "He had bought me a pair of Adidas Country running shoes so we started running at Lafayette reservoir. I then gave it up for a while because of being too lazy to do it because I really didn't feel that there was any improvement in my running. I had recently quit smoking and appeared to be having *more* problems with my lungs and weight than when I was smoking.

"I resumed running in May of 1977 by entering a race at Lake Merritt in Oakland. I paid no attention to my time and had to stop a few times but I did finish. I was determined to keep running on a 'fun' level because I knew competition would disappoint me because I was not in shape for it.

"Well, my fun running became serious competition; and although I am still far from a real competitor, I still register at and run races.

"I feel better, both physically and mentally. I have to separate physical from mental. Boy, *am I glad I stuck with running*. My resting pulse has dropped from 61 to 39!! I feel like a finely tuned machine. I look in the mirror and at 30 years old am in better shape than when I was 20!!

"Mentally, my attitude is 150 percent better. Running has given me a purpose, a sense of self. It has opened numerous doors of learning about diet, anatomy, and psychology. Running has helped me to like people again through learning to like myself. It has given me a pride in self and other runners I had forgotten I possessed.

"Running itself is a continual learning experience. The benefits are unbelievable. People now ask me if I am a runner, when before I had to tell them!"

Martie has a weekly schedule that mixes running with exercising and other sports. On Sunday she does a three-mile relaxed run, then an exercise workout at her club; on Monday she does an exercise workout and a fast three miles; Tuesday she does six miles of hills and a workout at the club; on Wednesdays she runs six miles at an 8-minute pace then does an exercise workout; she does an exercise workout and nine slow miles on Thursday; takes Friday off; and races on Saturdays with a sauna and swim afterward.

She has done 10-mile runs, but she reports that her back begins to bother her if she tries to go over that.

Martie's problems are mainly cars. "I've only had one occasion in Oakland where a carload of guys thought they'd try to run me off the road—which, by the way, they did. Only one woman (in Benicia) *really* scared me. She looked right at me and pulled out of a driveway into me. I didn't even have time to stop! I jumped right on the hood of her car."

Her family and friends "now realize I'm a serious competitive runner. Knowing my back problem, they definitely questioned my sanity. Now even the people I work with appear at a race to do splits for me."

How about if she had to lay off running for a while? "I wouldn't go crazy if I had to stop running for very long," she says, "but I would be close to it. Running has become a fair percentage of my life. I am a self-confessed addict, and am *very hard to live with* if I don't get to run. Running is a definite mental and physical 'upper.'"

Martie's observations are similar to those made by most women as far as what men and women derive from running: "All the men I've talked to seem to get the same feelings as I do. Some are intimidated when I pass them, but a guy passing me doesn't bother me at all. I believe the physical and emotional benefits are the same. I feel competitive males and I have a lot in common."

Her goal at the moment is to be a firstplace finisher in six-mile races. After that she isn't sure.

She credits her boyfriend, Tom, with being the most positive factor in her running. "Tom got me to run when I didn't want to run. He bought me my first pair of shoes and has helped see I make it to the races. He has also made sure I didn't overdo it. And he's my greatest fan. After Tom, I guess I'm my own best positive factor in my running, because I always want to keep going, to do more, to do better."

Martie's most memorable run came in a San Jose race when she was injured going into the event. "I had decided to try a tactical race. I wanted to run faster than my LSD (long slow distance) pace, but not at a race pace.

"Arriving at the race location, I looked around at the people to get my first sensory impression. Hot! Boy, I was glad it was an early race. I finished my half-can of beer. We were parking the car and Tom said, 'Yuck, what a place.' I found the toilet as quickly as I could and got myself ready.

"Tom and I talked as I stretched. I was unusually calm, knowing I wasn't there to race all-out. I saw familiar faces. I had decided the first three miles should be at 7:30 pace, but I knew it would be hard to keep that pace. I kept reminding myself to go slow, run tactical, pick it up at four miles, don't die, fly over that finish line.

"The gun sounded. 'Go slow,' I told myself. Tom was ahead, urging me to pick up the pace. I stayed slow. The one-mile split came in 7:30. Good. The two-mile split at 15:10. Better. Hang on. Relax. One more mile. 22:00 for three miles.

"I was hot. There was one woman runner ahead of me. I moved beside her and we talked briefly. She had outpaced herself and had to stop.

"At four miles I was feeling great. Aside from the injury, I was monitoring everything. All signs were go. At 4.5 miles I picked up the pace and gave the two women ahead of me something to think about. At five miles I passed them, then picked off three more. 'Pick it up,' I told myself. So I did. It felt good. I passed a guy who was really tired. 'Give 'em hell!' he said to me. So I did. At six miles I felt light as air. I saw Tom. Correction. Heard Tom. He yelled for me to pass the guy in front of me. I tried, but the guy stayed out in front. The finish came. The guy in front of me turned, his hand outstretched. 'You would have caught me. Great race,' he said.

"I smiled. 'I know,' I told him."

BARBARA CARLSON
Orinda, California

"There will be more talent surfacing as more women run."

Barbara Carlson is a statuesque California blonde, mother of two teenagers, one a student at UCLA; she's been running eight years, trains 7-8 miles a day, and races in Saturday and Sunday events from quarter-mile to marathon. "I was playing lots of tennis and felt a need for additional training," Barbara said. "Once I got started with running regularly, I couldn't stop."

Unlike some runners who prefer solitude when they run, Barbara is amenable to running alone or in groups. She sometimes runs alone in the morning, then joins friends in the evening for an additional run. Warm-ups consist mainly of stretches for the backs of legs which have been causing her problems for the past year. The stretching is augmented by a slow jog to start the workouts.

She runs in the Nike waffle trainer (male version) but, being a frequent racer changes to Nike Stings for competition. To date, she has run 11 marathons.

Her training is done mostly on suburban bicycle paths and roads, and along dirt trails in local parks. The terrain is very hilly near her Orinda home so she travels to flatter sections of the valley to do her daily training runs.

Family and friends are supportive of her running; the only problem her running seems to cause is that her heavy weekend racing schedule keeps her away from home a lot.

The only problems she has encountered while running came during a training run at Oakland's Lake Merritt when two men chased her, and on another occasion when a man ran after her; the second time, she was much more alert to the problem and chased him off by yelling. She makes a habit of running with friends now when she trains at Lake Merritt.

In the matter of the much-touted differences between what men derive from running that is different from what women derive, Barbara thinks that both sexes enjoy much the same things from running; that the differences have been somewhat overplayed.

Barbara reports a feeling of well-being occasionally when she runs, but not necessarily a "runner's high." "It happens when I feel pretty well generally," she reports, "I seem to run better when I'm loose and feel great." Her training runs are done at an 8:30-9:00 per mile pace.

Her running goals are pretty well plotted. "I would like to run a 3:30 marathon," she says. "So far I have a best time of 3:32:18. I've run this same time two years in a row at the West Valley Marathon. Besides, I'd like to improve my speed in races; and I'd certainly like to set a goal of running injury-free."

In the matter of the women's running movement affecting our international competitive edge, Barbara says that women have recently begun to show what they can do. "There will be more talent surfacing as more women run, and we will almost automatically have great women runners on the international level."

There have been two runs especially memorable to Barbara. "One of my most memorable was a 12-mile race at Woodside, California. It came two weeks after I had run a 6:08 indoor mile at the Examiner Games in San Francisco, which came about as the result of doing quite a bit of interval training specifically for that race. I ran as hard as I could, and I passed people I had never passed before. It was just one of those super days. I plan to do more interval and speed work, because it really does pay off.

"One other time," she continued, "I won an open race for women in San Francisco's Golden Gate Park. It was a three-mile race. When I crossed the finish line I was handed a big bouquet of roses. I guess that will stand out in my mind forever. I'm not an especially fast runner, so that was a big moment in my running career."

RUTH WHITE
Newmarket, New Hampshire

"Not for your husband or your kids, but for you!"

"I began running just to see if I could do it; it was a personal challenge," Ruth Ann White, a schoolteacher from Newmarket, New Hampshire, said when asked why she runs. "It was discouraging at first, because I could only run about a quarter mile. This was particularly depressing because I've always been active, from high school where I ran the quarter-mile, through college. As I discovered, unfortunately, most of my exercising wasn't aerobic. I did some skating, skiing, and biking but didn't have to work hard at these.

"I was up to two miles after I had been running a month and was really proud of myself," Ruth Ann continued. "I felt great. I'd come home tired from teaching high school. I'd change my clothing (before I had time to change my mind), do my warm-ups and be off. I could relax and unwind, think, breathe fresh air, and just feel like I'd found a second wind. I definitely had more energy, slept better, ate less, and was less tense.

"I was on a trip recently where running was impossible for about a week; I really felt very sluggish as a result."

Ruth Ann's interest originally came from reading magazine articles that heralded running as a beneficial sport; she also read *Aerobics* by Dr. Kenneth Cooper and approached running as a purely health oriented activity. Being at the point in her life where she was approaching 30, everything seemed to come together for her with running. "If I had to lay off running for any length of time it would bother me quite a bit," she said. "But I know I'd get back to it! I'm hooked."

Ruth runs a conservative 15-16 miles every week, taking Friday and Saturday off and doing three or four miles the other five days, all of it directly from her front door, where she can run on rural roads with farm houses on each side. She is also fortunate enough to take some of her runs near the Great Bay, which she calls the backwashes of the Atlantic Ocean. Ruth's longest run was seven miles; and she's only competed twice—in 10,000-meter events.

She does a 20-minute stretching and warming-up regimen before starting her run, including wall pushups, situps, sitting on the floor with legs spread and bending forward, and sitting on one leg with the other out straight accompanied by a bend forward to the knee. The runs come Sunday mornings and during the evenings after work; when school's out during the summer, she runs mornings.

She reports no major medical problems; her only complaint is an occasional blister, but she says even those are minor.

When asked what she would tell women in general about running if she were given a soapbox from which to speak, her speech went like this: "How are you feeling these days? Could you use a little more energy, a little more zip, a better figure? Well, I have just the thing for you. Go out and run around the block. Of course you can't just get up and go out there and run. Or can you?

"You'd be amazed how in a few short weeks, with the proper training program, you could really develop some self-motivation and some real pride in doing *something good for you*. Not for your husband or your kids, but for *you*. Consider that, after all, you're pretty darned important.

"Let's face it, we Americans are in pretty poor shape as a group. Some of us are downright 'heavy.' Wouldn't you love to still have some sex appeal when you're 50 years old? You sure can, if you want to. Just follow a daily program of exercises and running. Or even walking, as a start, would be good enough. You'll feel like a different person.

"The best part is that the price is right. Why spend a lot of money on diet aids when, in reality, we all know the only way to lose weight is to move your body. Get out there and move it!"

Ruth is not sure whether or not women derive something different from what men do. "I sometimes think women are less competitive. But I really don't know. Maybe I'm brainwashed."

She has experienced the "running high," describing it as a point where breathing becomes very easy and where running is done with little or no effort and the mind is free to wander. Her average speed in her daily training runs is 7:30-8:00 per mile.

"I'm pretty contented right now with my running," she reports, when asked about goals toward which she's aiming.

As the ultimate reaches of a woman's ability in long-distance running, Ruth sees the day when a woman holds a 6:00 per mile pace for 40 miles.

Who is the person with the most positive effect on her running? She feels that, although her "...husband has been helpful and has not bugged..." her about her running, she is her own most positive force. "It's my thing!" she firmly asserts.

This is how she describes her most memorable run:

"I am very definitely a cold-weather lover. Running is the most enjoyable thing to me when I'm cool or cold when starting out. I think it was one Saturday morning in March when the snow was beginning to melt. The temperature was at least 32 degrees, because I passed several puddles and ponds that were frozen. My breathing became easy and I was excited about the beginning of spring. I knew everything would soon be green and fresh and really pretty. I was only going to run three miles but there was such a feeling in me of the run that I went an extra mile just to make it last longer."

ELISE BORTIN
San Francisco, California

"I spent the first half of the race praying I wouldn't have to go to the toilet."

Elise Bortin is a 24-year-old resident of San Francisco who has been running for little more than a year. She became interested in running, she says, "through the enthusiasm of others who were running and because I found regular exercising to be so awful, while running was definitely not such a bad way to accomplish the same thing."

Wisely increasing her weekly mileage by no more than 10 percent at a time, Elise takes a day off every two weeks; her weekly schedule includes 8 miles on Sunday, 10 on Monday, 5 on Tuesday, 10 on Wednesday, 8 on Thursday, 15 on Friday and 5 miles on Saturday, a variation of the classic (and proven) hard-easy-hard-easy training. Elise has run in a dozen races ranging from a 4-mile biathlon (which included a quarter-mile swim) to a 13.1-mile half-marathon. "At this point," she says, "I'm not out to win races."

Her training runs are usually in the afternoon after work, or at 5:00 on weekday mornings if she is scheduled to be somewhere other than at her usual running courses in the afternoon; weekend training runs are either in the afternoons or at 6:00 or 7:00 a.m., depending on what she has scheduled for weekends. Before training runs, Elise does an Achilles stretch, push-ups against a wall, situps, leg-lifts, and toe touches while placing her heel on the hood of a car, keeping the leg parallel to the ground. Most (90%) of her runs are done alone because she prefers it that way. "I like to lose myself in myself during my training runs," she says. Her brother runs 15 miles every day consistently; while her sister runs occasionally, and her aunt and two cousins put in about three miles a day.

Elise hit her real stride when asked why she runs: "In the beginning it was to get myself in half-way decent condition and to look better. Before I started running I weighed 185 pounds, and that's plenty on 5'5". I started dieting, lost 35 pounds, then started running and lost 32 more pounds.

"The reasons I run now are quite different than they were when I started, although the 'vanity' aspect is still present. I would say that now it is a vital part of my compulsive personality. It's something that I almost have to do, and I beat myself over the head when I miss a day.

"Running definitely relieves anxiety, worry, and frustration. I always know how good I will feel afterward, and occasionally during the run! On 95 percent of the days it's like pulling teeth to get myself out the door but I do it anyway. I have a definite marathoning goal now that fits into my compulsive nature."

When asked if she has ever encountered any problems while running, Elise mentioned that during the big races so many runners act like "maniacs at the starting line."

Pretty much her own coach, Elise uses the *Runner's World* article about training for a marathon as a guide for her efforts. "I don't like to listen to men, especially nonrunners, that give advice," she says. "It's really not tailored to my needs."

As with anyone who goes into any endeavor with a compulsive nature pushing her, Elise has suffered some injuries. "A hip problem developed after six months of running," she said. "When I overtrained my hip gave me such pain that I had to cut down my mileage. This cleared itself eventually. Then my right knee started hurting three months ago and got so bad I could barely walk, much less run. (But I still tried.) I went to the Podiatry College in San Francisco, to their runners' clinic. They diagnosed a ligament problem that I had to ice and exercise while laying off running. I had to stop my training schedule for six weeks, during which time I was absolutely wacko!

"The problem was caused by pronating feet. I've begun using foot supports and am having permanent orthotics made.

"I've been training toward the San Francisco Marathon in July; but I'm apprehensive about all the time I had to take off. The knee is okay, but my body feels prone to injury. I hold my breath and hope I hold up until the marathon.

"I fell down the other day and scraped my entire right side, though. It was caused by my own clumsiness."

When asked about her most memorable run, Elise told this dramatic tale:

"That's easy. It was at the 1978 Bidwell Classic Marathon and Road Race in Chico, California. I elected to do a half-marathon. Before this race my longest run was eight miles, and my longest race 10,000 meters (6.2 miles). I drove to Chico the night before and spent the night full of fear and anticipation.

"I woke up with cramps the morning of the race. I had not

had a menstrual period for two years and lo and behold, I got my first period in two years the morning of the race. [Amenorrhea, or absence of menstruation, is fairly common among a high percentage of women who train on high-mileage regimens.—Ed.]

"The course was flat, with pavement, gravel, and lots of *mud*. To further complicate things, as if that weren't enough, I had always sworn I would not run in the rain, and sure enough it was pouring. I debated whether to cop out; God knows I had legitimate excuses. But I instinctively knew that I'd hate myself if I didn't run, and if I did run the worst that could happen is that I'd get dirty, wet, sore, and *happy*.

"I spent the first half of the race praying I wouldn't have to go to the toilet. I was also afraid I wouldn't have enough strength to finish so I paced myself rather slowly (9:10 miles). I found a woman to run with and we stayed together the entire race. After it was over I felt as though I could have run much farther.

"I was just so incredibly high. I was also freezing, hungry, amazed, grateful, hopeful, and in a state of acute disbelief. During the race, and for a long time afterward, I felt like *I was doing it for me*. I really sensed an inner peace and serenity. The experience left me with the feeling that anything is possible if I'm willing to shut up and go ahead and do it."

KATY NASS
Nassau, New York

"I have found something I am good at—that's the best part of running."

Although running for only a year, Katy Nass of Nassau, New York, is doing ambitious mileage. Twenty-seven years old, 5'7" and 120 pounds, Katy's 50-mile week of training puts her into marathon-training class. She does a long run of 10-12 miles on Sunday, 6-8 miles on Monday, 5-6 miles and intervals on Tuesday, 8-10 miles on Wednesday, 6-8 miles on Thursday, takes a rest day on Friday and runs 10 miles or a race on Saturdays. "I have just drastically increased my mileage," Katy reports. "Before I was doing 35-40 miles a week."

Her involvement in running seems to have been preordained.

Her two older brothers, her husband, and her sister-in-law all run. It was apparently only a matter of time before she gave in to the less-than-subtle urging to join the group.

Katy is not the last convert to the group though. "My dad also started running after we all did—he does 25 miles a week and he's 55," she reports. "My oldest (35) brother is the 'pro' of the family—he does upward of 60 miles a week. My next oldest (33) brother does 40-50 miles. My sister-in-law, who is 29, does 40-50 miles a week and is consistently beating me, but I'm gonna catch her."

With all that running going on in the family, Katy frequently finds partners for her runs; or she sometimes takes her dog, Panky, or else goes alone.

Katy has a better warm-up regimen than most runners. She does wall push-ups, toe touches, bent-knee situps and a variety of leg stretches before starting her runs. It is fortunate that she does go heavily on the warmups, because her high mileage would suffer without it. She wears New Balance 320s for training and Lady Nike Waffle trainers for races. Her longest run has been 18.6 miles.

She prefers to run at home, which is rural and fairly hilly. "Here I have a variety of different distance loops. In the winter I run at work (urban), because the roads are usually cleaner," she says. She runs during breaks at work during the winter because the weather is warmer in the middle of the day.

"I started running because I wanted to lose some weight, and because my family was really into it," she says. "I was hooked once I started. I have lost 15 pounds and have never felt better, not only physically but also in terms of my self-image. I'm proud of the way I look in my running shorts; my new found confidence extends to other parts of my life. I *have also found something I'm actually good at—that's the best part of running.* No matter what stage I'm at, there are always new goals to reach, improvements to be made. Running makes me feel alive and very much the woman I want to be."

As far as running problems go, Katy suffers from blackened toenails, a malady common to runners, which can likely be explained by her training in New Balance 320s which are not famous for a generous toe box. "I have no nail on my big toe and parts of nails on the others." Black toenails are caused by the toenail rubbing against the top of the shoe while running; the solutions include using shoes with larger toe boxes, wearing tape over the toes, or cutting holes in the tops of the shoes to relieve pressure.

Other medical problems Katy has encountered were knee problems (which she solved by cutting back a little on her mileage until they cleared up), and occasional aches in the hip joints.

Katy's coaches include her brothers, her husband, and *Runner's World* magazine.

The difference in what women derive from running as opposed to what men derive from it? "I think women have to become even more dedicated and devoted because they are more hassled about running than men are. Women are often more concerned with their looks; and initially it's tough to face the 'hot and sweaty and dirty image.' But women get over this because of the physical benefits, and enjoy their new slim looks. Many of the other benefits apply both to men and women."

How about the fabled runner's high? "Yes. There definitely is a spiritual feeling sometimes associated with running. It usually happens after 4-5 miles and often lasts until the end of the run. It's very hard to describe the feeling—it's as if you'd like to stop and kiss every person and tell them how much you love them. Sounds weird!"

Katy trains at an 8:00-9:00 pace, races at about 7:30. Her goals include a six-mile race at a sub-7:00 pace, running a marathon in the fall—and beating her sister-in-law.

Given the soapbox from which to address women, Katy's speech is short but to the point:

"Women are becoming more and more involved in sports; and in no other sport is this more true than in running. High school track for women is booming; most major races now accept women as full participants. It is up to us females to continue to show that we deserve a place alongside men in international events. I want all of you to do something today to promote sports—not only for your own interest, but for the good of women all over the world."

MARY DAGEFORDE
Los Altos, California

"I enjoy competition—with other people and the clock."

Approximately 200,000 runners know Mary Dageforde. She's the young woman sprinting toward the finish line on the Avon paperback edition of *The Complete Runner.* The picture was taken at a Sunday morning Fun-Run in Los Altos Hills, California, where Mary runs when she isn't racing on Sundays. Addicted to running and to the racing side of running, Mary races two or three times a month, everything from four-milers to 10-milers.

Inclined toward running as a child, Mary began serious running in college six years ago, but it's only during the last year that she's raced frequently. Her training schedule for the week includes a race or fun-run on Sunday, 4-5 easy miles Monday, intervals at the track on Tuesday, 5-7 easy miles on Wednesday, 4-6 medium fast miles on Thursday, 4-6 fast miles on Friday, and a rest day on Saturday. "The actual schedule at any given time depends on my current goals," she explains. "If I'm trying to improve my mile time, I'll run more intervals and less distance; if I'm trying to build up for longer races, I'll increase my distances appropriately. Before I do my first marathon, I hope to be up to at least 40 miles per week."

Mary's workouts come in the early evening—before dinner and before it gets dark. Sometimes in the winter months she will run at lunch because it's warmer then. Training runs come after about 5-10 minutes of warm-up exercises, and usually are done alone. Although she has nine brothers and sisters, no one else in her family runs as much as she does; one of her sisters has shown some promise as a sprinter in high school track. Her boyfriend also runs and has naturally supported her running.

She had been training in Adidas Runners, but a bad resoling job unbalanced them and began causing some problems in the right foot, so she's now changed to Nike LDVs and finds them a good shoe. She does sprints in Adidas Saturns.

Her longest run to date has been 15 miles in the January, 1978 Paul Masson Champagne Marathon. She'd run 10 miles twice before that, and wanted to use the marathon to get the feel of a marathon start and to use it to get to 15 miles.

When asked why she runs and what she gets from it, her reasons were firmly outlined in her mind:

"Basically, I simply *love* to run; I have always loved it and hopefully always will. But *why*? Why does it mean so much to me? Why is it currently my 'main' sport even though I enjoy quite a few sports? A number of contributing factors come to mind, and it's probably a combination of them that can at least partially explain my intense interest and joy in running:

"I enjoy challenges. Running seems to have an infinite number of challenges at hand all the time—challenges both in terms of distance and in terms of speed. I love improving my body's capabilities, testing it, seeing how much it can improve, how well it can do. I'm fascinated and encouraged by the dramatic improvements that are possible. Setting a personal record gives me an intense feeling of satisfaction, joy, and accomplishment.

"I enjoy competition, with other people and with the clock. At this stage of my running, I can't hope to win any races, but I still enjoy competing and seeing just how well I can do, trying to improve a personal record for the distance run. I get great satisfaction out of having a good kick at the end of a race, and want to develop this ability and have it become my 'trademark.'

"I enjoy the camaraderie among runners—I have met quite a few very nice people through running.

"I love the feeling of being physically fit, of knowing that I am capable of running quite far.

"Team sports are fine, but they take a lot of organization and a lot of commitments at specific times, specific places, specific days. Running, on the other hand, is something I can do more or less on the spur of the moment wherever I am as long as I've got some free time, my running shoes, some shorts. It's something I can do on my own, going wherever I feel like going. Sometimes I enjoy group running (e.g., in Fun-Runs and races), and other times I like to be off on my own.

"Being nervous can have a *positive* effect on my running (running faster), whereas in most other sports (and other aspects of life in general), nervousness has detrimental effects on one's performance. So running a race is a situation in which I don't mind getting nervous beforehand!"

Has Mary ever run into any problems on her runs? "Unchained dogs have at times been a problem. They come running and barking at you, baring their fangs. Even though I have not been bitten, encountering a vicious-looking dog while in such a vulnerable position is frightening and I will avoid routes if I know they have such dogs on them.

"I also hate breathing exhaust fumes."

From a combination of increasing her mileage too fast, Mary did suffer some foot problems that laid her up in February. She had hoped to travel to Atlanta for the Avon International Women's Marathon Championships. When asked what kind of a speech she'd have given to the men and women gathered in Atlanta if she had been asked to address them, this is her speech:

"I'm sure you all share with me the thrill and anticipation in running with or watching so many women runners. This is an historic occasion whose importance can not and must not be overlooked. I was inspired from the moment I heard about this event, and immediately planned on trying to make it my own personal first marathon, and then to attend as many subsequent International Women's Marathons as possible. I hope it becomes an annual event. I came here to meet and run with other women runners from throughout the world. And I came for another reason: I feel so strongly that this is an ideal opportunity for us to meet en masse and make a strong statement to the world about our interest in and ability to run distance races.

"It's only recently that women were 'allowed' to run marathons. And look what's happened since then—the world record has plummeted and women have proven that they are just as capable as men in running distance races, and in fact may be better suited for distance running. We've come a long way—and yet, outdated opinions and discrimination still haunt us. For example, I'm sure you're all familiar with and discouraged by the International Olympic Committee's refusal to 'allow' women to run any farther than 1500 meters in the Olympics."

Mary feels that her observations point up the fact that there is no real difference between what men and women get out of running. "Why should benefits of athletics be considered any different for women than for men? Perhaps because of their backgrounds, more women feel less pressure to *achieve* and be competitive, but that's not always the case."

Her goals are pretty firmly set in her mind. "I always have some short-term goals, some 'hoped-for' longer-term goals, and the overall goal to improve as much as possible and see just how well I can do. For each of my routes and distances, I have detailed records of my times for the last few years, and a sheet of all my current records. I love breaking records, and sometimes break 2-3 a week! One goal is to run a marathon within the next year, and another goal is to get under six minutes in a mile (I'm currently at 6:21) and keep pushing that record down as far as I can."

GAIL GUSTAFSON
San Francisco, California

"At Wellesley, I really got excited by the women cheering us on."

Seven years ago Gail Gustatson was getting all her exercise at a gym. She was doing workouts on weight machines and swimming. One day her instructor began brow-beating her into running around the gym 10 times. "I didn't mind the monotony," Gail said, and she went on from there.

Now, at 36 years old, Gail runs an ambitious training schedule each week. On Sundays she competes in races of five to 15 miles, runs 7-10 miles on weekdays (with either Wednesday or Thursday reserved as an interval workout day), and does a long run of 10-20 miles on Saturdays.

She normally runs in the afternoons, but on weekends prefers to go out in the mornings. "I do the George Sheehan exercises for the hamstrings, Achilles tendons and calves, both before and after I run," she says. "I get *very* tight if I don't."

Unlike most runners who do their workouts alone, and run occasionally with others, Gail almost always runs with friends, and runs alone only once a week. On her runs, she likes to wear as little as possible, thereby avoiding the rubbing and chafing that can occur after the first five or six miles are finished. She prefers tanktops and running shorts in the summer and T-shirt or turtleneck shirt and track shorts in the winter. Living in the northern California area, she never wears a sweat suit. As far as shoes go, she wears the Tiger Montreal IIs at the moment; for quite a few years she wore the Adidas SL-72s; she bought a pair of Brooks Villanovas but they wore out in a week.

Gail's longest runs have been marathons, although she hopes to try some 50-kilometer runs, at least in practice.

Most of her training runs are done in and around San

Francisco, with some trips to Marin County for sessions in the beautiful hills in that area. Her runs are with friends, so that they end up pushing each other during workouts, making them less-than-easy workouts.

"I have always enjoyed physical activities," Gail reports. "Though never an athlete, I was an avid walker and hiker who often used my feet instead of a car to get around. I also love to eat and it's a constant battle to keep my weight under control.

"In the beginning, I ran for the most part to keep the weight down. I soon got beyond that and though it still helps in that regard, that is not the reason I run. I run because I enjoy it. It feels good during and afterwards. I feel that I am in control of my body instead of the other way around. I love my muscles. I love to race. There is nothing like the feeling I have after a good race. I have given my all—at times I wondered if I could keep it up, but I did. I am pleased with myself, exhilarated, and if I've beaten my competition, that's the frosting on the cake."

Gail's family and friends support her running, although at first they were prone to question her sanity. "But now they see that I was in the vanguard of this running movement, which threatens to take over everything, and they're great about it. I try not to bore people talking about running too much, but my family seems to get a kick out of how much it's done for me."

Gail's training on extended runs is at 8:00, while most of her shorter training runs are done at 7:00-7:30. Her fastest mile is a 5:54 and in a five-mile race she averaged 6:20.

Her goals are ambitious. She wants to run a sub-3:00 marathon. First, though, she would like to go under 40 minutes for a 10-kilometer race and run a 3:08 marathon. "I had the latter all planned last fall," she says, "but I had a very bad day and fell apart. This winter and spring I have been plagued with injuries, so I'm planning on making another effort in October. After my success then, I will plan my assault on 3:00. I haven't peaked yet and it will come."

Given the soapbox that all the respondants were offered, this is Gail's speech:

"I would just like to say to all you women out there that if I can do it, you can do it. I am no athlete. I have no innate speed or natural ability. I don't look like a gazelle when I run. I plod a bit. I'm not built like a runner. But, after these years of doing my homework, I'm pretty good. I'm starting to get pictures of myself where the muscles really show. I have done well for myself in many races. The rewards are many and they are there for any of you if you are interested enough to do it for yourself."

Gail's most memorable run was Boston 1976. "That was the year of the record heat," she recalls. "I had trained for four months. I ran 20-plus miles every Saturday and averaged 75 miles per week. I even did intervals on the track for the first time in my life. Then that heat!

"I was ready to give up because I couldn't imagine I could do a 3:30 and earn a certificate from Boston. I couldn't even imagine finishing.

"Flory Rodd and Chuck Stagliano came up to me as I was lying in the grass at Hopkington and suggested running easily together. I figured what-the-hell and joined them. We started and felt amazingly good. They were great about getting water and ice for me. After the first five miles they had to practically hold me back. I knew a lot of the women running that year and they started falling back as I went on. There were gals who should have been in front of me.

"At Wellesley I really got excited by the women cheering us on. I got lots of cheers as there weren't too many other women ahead of me. I was feeling so good I was worried. Flory had to drop back but I just zoomed on. I passed some more women and then, at the hills, I passed Kathy Switzer. That blew my mind. Next was Laine Winter—a former world record-holder. I was going crazy with exitement. Seeing me brought out her competitive juices and she later passed me.

"The same thing happened with Judy Gumbs-Leydig. I saw her ahead and told Chuck I couldn't pass her. She was my good friend and we had done the track intervals together. I passed her when she stopped for water and felt guilty about it. She later came past me. That was okay.

"I was delighted. I was on my way to a PR (personal record). I can rememer little else. I knew that last mile was the greatest I've ever run. I was giggling and so excited. As we rounded the last turn I was vain enough to think ahead to the fact someone might take my picture! I had worn a white painter's cap which I kept filling with ice cubes which melted and cooled me off. Of course my hair was soaked, but I whipped off the cap and tried to fluff up my hair so it would look good. I have two pictures which were subsequently given to me. In the first, there I am, cap in place. A few yards later, in the second, I'm grinning from ear to ear, cap in hand, and wet hair plastered to my head. So much for vanity.

"Boston 1976—I will never forget it. It is still my PR. But, I'm ready for another memorable race any time now."

SHEILA PERPALL
Holliston, Massachusetts

"Running really gets your life moving."

Sheila Perpall is a 16-year-old high school runner from Holliston, Massachusetts, who became interested in running three years ago by becoming involved in her school's track and field program. She keeps her training schedule pretty streamlined, resting on Sundays and doing about six miles with some speed workouts the rest of the week. Her training runs come after school in the afternoons, and they are usually done with three or four friends.

She trains in Nike Waffle Trainers and races in Nike Elites and her longest run has been a 10-miler. Most of her running is done on dirt paths.

Sheila's interest in running is buoyed by the fact that she has become rather good at it. "I run because I went out for the cross-country team in my freshman year. At first I wasn't that good," she admits. "I placed about seventh or better for our team in races. But in my sophomore year I won every race I entered except one. I received the award of Most Valuable Player on my team. It has really made running very rewarding. I also run indoor track in the winter and track during the spring."

Her runs are done on trails and paths within a half-mile of her front door. She is cautious when she runs, having almost been hit by a car once. Dogs scare her, too; her friend was bitten by a dog while out on a run once, as was her coach.

Her only medical complaint is that she has occasionally suffered from shin splints.

She gets great support from her family and friends in her running, and her immediate goal is to again be named MVP for her two remaining years in high school.

Her training is done at an eight-minute pace, and her fastest mile time is a 5:43. The biggest shortcoming in her running program is that she doesn't get enough time to train as much as she'd like.

Her message to other females is a simple one: "I think that if some of you have never tried running before, you should give it a try. Running really gets your life moving. And I really think that most women will enjoy it."

Sheila's most memorable run was when she won the conference meet in cross-country. "I love it," she says. "I never thought I could do it! But the weather was just beautiful and everything went perfectly."

She hopes to run a marathon after she graduates from high school.

SOFIA SHAFQAT
Port Chester, New York

"My family cannot understand why I put my fragile body through these 'miles of masochistic tortures.' "

"Please understand," said Sofia Shafqat of Port Chester, New York, "that I run only for my own sanity and very private enjoyment. I have no strict regimen to which I must adhere; I keep no charts or calendars marked with running schedules. I run any route which appeals to me on that particular day. I allow myself one rest day a week, a policy which permits my body to collect itself even though it makes me feel annoyed for being lazy. During cross-country season at Brown, we ran typical cross-country workouts: lots of distance, intervals, fartlek and hills. I now generally do distance runs—anything from 5-10 miles a day."

Sofia represents most runners—both men and women—running today. A large segment of them never race and never have any need to. . .running itself is enough.

Sofia, 19 years old, joined the cross-country team at Brown University as an experiment to have fun. "I am not a terribly competitive person and was therefore not beating the pants off other schools," she admits. "While I ran for Brown, I did compete in three-mile cross-country races, as much as I hated them. Now that I have resolved to run only on my own and only for myself, I have not raced as yet. To train for racing is not the object of my current running program."

She runs alone and with a companion, and the competitive urge that begins when running with someone else causes her to choke. "It's this developing stress that I dislike so much and that causes me to fear racing so greatly," she explains. "I don't mind in the least a companion who sets a good pace and prods me to keep that pace; I hate it, however, when someone wears himself out trying to run me to the ground. I find that I do much better in very large races where, due to the sheer number of people, nervousness does not exist."

No one else in Sofia's family runs. "My family cannot understand why I put my fragile body through these 'miles of masochistic tortures.'"

For running attire, she wears "generally the most comfortable and decently warm rags that I own."

She has run in Nike Waffle Trainers, Adidas SL76s, and now trains in the Adidas TRX; she used the Tiger Jayhawk for racing.

On the question of why she runs: "Very honestly, I don't know exactly why I run," she said. "Probably the reasons are fundamentally very selfish: running affords me some very private and very alert moments with myself, and for that hour, absolutely nobody else counts as much as I do. I don't need to worry about this problem or that problem; my thoughts are generally very fragmented and thus it is pointless to try to achieve any marvelous solutions to hopeless dilemmas.

"I am able to conquer those menacing elements of my environment that confront me pumping up a nasty hill, shaking out my arms that become a burden on endless flats. I can then pat myself on the back for my vast accomplishments, seeing with some satisfaction that a small part of my day has been successful. After all, I just ran a long route and didn't I run it nicely. . . ?

"In a way, then, running gives me a perspective on other processes with which I must deal, by the mere virture of being an often grueling procedure tidily and effectively fitted into a very short period of time. Sailing through a run without pain or difficulty, or better yet surviving any difficulty, is a reinforcing spur for one's general motivation and sense of self-achievement. . .I guess it's sort of like proving to yourself that you're marvelous *every day*.

"Also, I'm very vain about physical toning, and I like to eat whatever I please. Running easily takes care of all that."

Would being laid up bother Sofia? "*Yes.* It would definitely bother me. I have been forced to 'rest' (hateful word) for the past six weeks on account of an injury, and have taken up biking instead, so I am getting exercise, although I cannot help but be envious when I see a lucky runner sailing by. As long as I can substitute the running with some other type of decent exercise, I am reasonably pacified. I have concluded that one cannot become obsessive about running, since the activity can then become unhealthy, and one's chances of being sensible about staying off injuries will be slim. If I had to discontinue running for months at a time, I am sure I would miss it, but I would have to be realistic and find other releases. Thats what it is, I suppose—a release."

Sofia's most memorable run was, paradoxically, not a very positive one. This is her journal entry from May 19:

"The pain is leaving, finally. Perhaps it was a reminder that not everyone can run all the time. Respect your body, I tell myself; no more of this mind over matter garbage.

"It's been more than a week. It happened last Wednesday, when everything went wrong for me. I was so ticked off at Professor R., who had the inconsideration to overlook the grading of my paper. After going to Horace Mann House for the fourth time that day and hanging out on the sidewalk for a half-hour, I was informed that I could have my paper on Friday. I was disappointed and tramped back to Wayland, having decided that *something* good was going to come out of that *bad* day. I would go for a lovely 10-mile run. I put on my shoes and shorts, stretched out grimly, and set off in intense irritation. Ten miles, ten miles... a little chant marched through my head.

"On Gano Street I passed a dead mouse. Up the steps with a little trot, onto the wide concrete bridge. Extended stride, ignoring choking exhaust fumes... Tripping down the grass embankment, sharp turn, First Street to Veterans Memoral Parkway.

Ten miles, ten miles.... beautiful soft grass, smooth slopes and graceful descents. Bright, crystal sunshine... gusty breeze. The run was so easy. I was surprised at having reached the juncture with Pawtucket Avenue so quickly; the way home was even easier. I never felt so strong and light in my life. Traveling fleetly and effortlessly, I showered myself with ecstatic congratulations.

"With two miles left to go, my strained left calf tightened up. Come on... this is nonsense. There's the Science Library in the distance; what's wrong with you—can't you do two more miles? Sharp pain near the knee. You can run it out, just run it out. That's the hard part—you land only so often and so very quickly that you only have a split second to decide what hurts. And if it takes you 25 steps to make the decision, why can't you run another 25 if you have borne pain this far? And so it goes on. You run on a bad injury until you can't run anymore—just a series of desperate limps, but nothing will make you run short of 10 miles. I will *not* run 9½ miles and walk the other half-mile.

"Well, here I am, dangling a last straw which has broken my camel's back."

JUDITH DENNIS
Falls Church, Virginia

"I have stamina on the tennis courts that most women on the intermediate level do not have."

"I run to stay in shape for my tennis game and for my general appearance," says 34-year-old Judith Dennis of Falls Church, Virginia. "I have three children and I don't want to become forty and fat.

"The benefits of running are that I can maintain a good weight for me and not watch my calories. I receive a great deal of satisfaction from completing a three- or four-mile run every day. My self-confidence has increased in other athletic ventures since I started running, and I also have stamina on the tennis courts that most women at my intermediate level do not have.

"I also enjoy the admiration I receive from my peers, since most of my acquaintances do not run and seem impressed by my running.

"Physiologically, my pulse (resting) has dropped 15-20 beats since I started, and my heart-lung capacity has increased tremendously."

Judith has been running for six months, the initial urging coming from her runner-husband. Although she has entered only one race so far, she has steadily increased her training mileage; she does 3-4 miles on Saturday and Sunday, takes Monday and Friday off, and has courses set up where she does 1.7 miles Tuesday, 2.5 miles on Wednesday, and 3.5 miles on Thursday. She does her running in the evening, often with two or three friends. She does wall push-ups and hamstring stretches as part of her warmup routine.

Judith runs in her suburban neighborhood, and her courses are relatively hilly. Training runs for Judith and her friends are usually quite pleasant, since there are few automobiles in the neighborhood and since there are only occasional problems from dogs, none of which has ever been much more than curious.

She reports that her family supports her running efforts, and that her friends are incredulous and envious. Her husband serves as her coach. She feels that if for some reason she had to lay off running, her body would become stagnant and it would bother her greatly.

The greatest shortcoming in her running at the moment is the fact that she must suffer through the hot, humid weather that surrounds the Washington, D.C. area in the summer. Her goals are to increase her stamina and her mileage and to enter some six and 10-mile races.

The many women runners tell her that many talented women are going to be cropping up who will be making a name for themselves on the international competition level; she feels that the women of America have only begun to show their abilities. She also feels that with the proper training, women will be able to equal men in accomplishments in long-distance running.

Judith has no plans to run a marathon; shorter races seem more her style.

The person who has had the most positive effect on her running is one of her neighborhood friends who runs with her daily. "She's very disciplined; she's ten years my senior and is an inspiration to me. We talk the entire run and our running together makes it easier and more fun for both of us."

Understandably, Judith's most memorable run was her single race to date. "The reason it was memorable was that I had never competed before and there were so many people there who were so supportive and excited by the race. The comradeship of the women runners was terrific. I really enjoyed it. I not only wanted to finish, which I knew I could, I wanted to have a better time than I had done on the same course about a month earlier in practice. I finished 20 minutes faster than I had on my practice run. It was just terrific."

SUSAN PRITCHARD
Bangor, Pennsylvania

"Women strive to compete as much as men do."

Susan Pritchard of Bangor, Pennsylvania was initiated into running by her fiance, who had run in high school. She has been running for a year, doing three miles on Monday, Wednesday, and Friday, and a five-miler on Saturday. At 24 years old, Susan has run one race—the Bonne Bell 10,000-meters in Washington, D.C.

Susan trains in the evening, prefaced with 50 sit-ups, some side bends and leg stretches. She enjoys running with friends more than running alone. Her family thinks that she's crazy for running, but so far that hasn't slowed Susan.

She has made a promise to herself that she will not begin wearing any of the elaborate running outfits until she is worthy to be called a runner. She wears Nike Ladies Roadrunners.

"I first began to run seriously in Washington, D.C., while working for the Audubon Society," she says. "My course was the reliable tow path out by National Airport. I am waiting at home in Pennsylvania for a field biology job through Cornell University right now and am running in a very beautiful rural area. I am having trouble keeping to a schedule because my activities are more diverse."

She tries to plan her training runs to avoid automobile traffic and dogs and consequently reports no problems on that front. Medically, she reports having no problems other than occasional cramps.

"I am in dire need of a coach to push me on those days that I find time to do everything but run," she says. "When I moved home from Washington, my running schedule was thrown off. I felt very tired, frustrated, and physically unhealthy. Running seems to cleanse your system of problems and stress."

Her training is done at an 8:00 pace; she has not run competitively enough to have a best mile time, however. Her biggest shortcoming, in her estimation, is her lack of self-discipline. Her goals, however, are mighty. She wants to do a marathon and she also hopes to someday be the best woman runner. She's not setting her goals blindly, however; her Bonne Bell race assured her that to achieve her goals it would take serious training.

"Women strive to compete as much as men do," she feels. "The quality of women racers astounded me. Running begins as recreation until your first race."

She credits her fiance as being the most positive influence on her running. "He pushed me when the only good thing about running was stopping at the end."

Her most memorable run stands out clear in her mind:

"I was on my way to work at the Audubon Bookshop on the dreariest Saturday morning imaginable. Life seemed unfair in that my fiance was on his way west on a well-deserved vacation after graduating from dental school, and there I was, going to work when there were hundreds of things I'd rather be doing. I was very early for work and I stopped in the drug store. There, on one counter, was the Bonne Bell race advertising. I had been running three miles a day and never ran in a race before. I didn't even know how far 10,000 meters was. I jotted down the telephone number and scooted off to work. The decision was made, though. I called and got the information and Sunday morning, at 8:00 a.m. I was on the starting line.

"Everyone around me looked like a runner. I was too embarrassed to admit I had never run over three miles in my life. I met so many women in the starting line who gave me confidence—except for one girl who I took a liking to who was also running her first race; she got very sick to her stomach at the halfway point and finished exhausted.

"I really expected that I'd drop out at three miles but there was no way I could conceive of it with all the cheering spectators. I made it four miles and thought I was going to die. My legs felt terrible. Luckily, the weather was perfectly overcast and cool, and no cramps appeared to destroy me. At five miles I knew I would finish, but I did not want to break my run by walking. One girl ahead of me looked back and started to walk. As I neared her I told her to start running. We ran along together as I explained that if she stopped again, it would not only be her undoing but mine, too, because I'd have to walk then. I know we will be friends forever after our ordeal together.

"The finish line after 6.2 miles looked beautiful to us. I cannot put on paper the feeling of accomplishment I felt after the race. I was sorry I had not told anyone I was racing, but in a way I benefited much more by meeting all these people on my own. The strangest part of the race was looking back and finding out I was not indeed the last runner. In fact, I finished 358th out of

1500, averaging about 8:00 miles. Not bad for my first real race. Maybe I *can* be the best."

JOYCE BRIGHAM
Lincoln, Rhode Island

"Running gets people in tune with their bodies."

Jayce Brigham is 21 years old and lives in Lincoln, Rhode Island. She began running five years ago when she noticed a number of men running around the lake in a nearby park. "I used to think that they were pretty amazing," she says. "How could they do it?" Jayce began to gain an awareness of physical fitness, and began doing exercises, biking, and ballet. Her younger sister began running and Jayce would try to do it with her. "From then it was a slow, gradual process. I now need willpower not to run. I am an addicted runner and I love it," she says.

Running has become an addiction of sorts with Jayce's family. Her mother, sister, and brother run—and now her father has started.

She has had three pair of Nike Waffle Trainers; before that she used the Adidas SL-72s. Her longest run has been a 15-miler.

"I first began running to get into shape," Jayce says, "and to lose weight. I now run because it is a part of my lifestyle, and I could not imagine not running. It does help me stay in shape and helps me maintain an ideal body weight, but the main reason I do it is because I love it.

"The only thing to stop me is injuries, and I hope to avoid them even though they have a tendency to sneak up on you. Running gives me a natural high, and I look forward to that time spent running each day.

"Running makes me more alive and energetic—I am less tired than if I don't run. It makes me happy. It is good for my heart, lungs, and my entire body. It enables me to take time for myself to escape the noise and tensions of the day and to go out and explore my environment. It enables me to go places and see things I would have never seen if I didn't run to them. It enables me to smell the crisp, fresh air and hear the birds. I can also observe the different seasons throughout the year. It gives me the chance to meet many other healthy people who run (especially at races, where there are tons and tons of healthy specimens from all ages).

"Running gets people in tune with their bodies and enables them to feel their body better—both the occasional pains and the parts of it that feel great that day. Because of the second-wind effect, it makes you feel whole and good inside: strong and with different levels of euphoria. It helps you run your worries away from you at least for a time. For example, if I'm at school and I have a lot of homework and demands on my time, if I take a run I can at least momentarily escape these pressures and out there I find the inspiration to deal with them better when I get back. It clears the mind. I could just go on and on about the benefits of running. But I've got to go run now."

Jayce reports that she has been splashed frequently by cars and that cars seldom will move over for a runner. She is bothered by snowmobiles and big trucks—and by dogs, which have often scared her but have not bitten her yet.

Jayce has had no foot problems, but she has suffered with tendonitis in both knees several times, and has consequently been laid up for 60-90 days, which was very depressing. "I would try to swim to stay in shape," she said.

She has no formal coach, but reads as much as she can on running to keep current with training methods.

This is Jayce's speech on running to our hypothetical audience of 1000 women:

"I would like to explain that running is someting that should be started slowly, especially if you are out of shape at the start. There is frustration and some discouragement at first, but if you keep at it long enough, you will pass the hard part and you'll reach a place where it feels good, where it comes easier, where it is occasionally smooth, relaxing, trance-like, euphoric.

"Start with one mile and do this for several weeks, then gradually increase your mileage over weeks and months and years.

"Do warm-up exercises before the run, and cool-down exercises after the run. Eat well-balanced meals and get lots of sleep. Be consistent with your running, attempting to do it six or even seven days a week. Train, don't strain. Be able to talk while you are running. Listen to your body and if you feel something hurting, stop. Do hard-easy days in your training; don't do the same run over and over every day. Be sure to buy good running shoes; this is your single most important investment."

JUDY CARR
Corte Madera, California

"For women who feel they are too old to run, any book on running has stories of women champions in all age groups."

Judy Carr, 38 years old, from Corte Madera, California, used to go to the track to keep her husband company while he worked out. "I saw how running had reshaped his body and I saw the enthusiasm he had for running. I wanted to see what running would do for me. After I overcame the embarrassment of running (I felt inferior to regular runners because I had to do so much walking mixed with my running), and I increased my distances, I felt more confident, and became hooked on running. Each day I could run another lap on the track or I could run a lap faster than I ever could before and this was exciting. . . sort of like getting a present—I was the giver to myself. I know I felt good about running when I could run not only on the track but in my neighborhood and on Fun-Runs and races." Judy has run races up to eight miles. She runs two races a month.

Her husband and her two sons (11 and 13 years of age) and her daughter, seven years old, run in local races. Her husband has run a marathon. Her 11-year-old son ran in the Pepsi 20-miler last year.

Judy runs in Nike Ladies Cortez shoes in a suburban environment or at a local high school track.

Her medical problems are associated with severe increases in training. She developed a sore calf about a year after she began running and could not run for a month, doing stretching exercises to alleviate the tenderness. She also developed a strain in her outer knee when she began running over six miles at a time. The strain seemed to begin when she took a run almost straight uphill by ascending a fire trail about six months ago.

The biggest shortcoming Judy sees about running is having to prepare dinner for the children when she gets back from a run. It seems to take more time than usual to get dinner made after a run, she feels. She also finds that it is difficult for her to run in the heat. Her goal, though, is to build up her mileage on her daily runs. She hopes to be able to do the Pepsi 20-miler in Sacramento.

Her soapbox speech to other women is as follows:

"Don't give up. Don't get discouraged.

"Everyone starts at the beginning. Very few are born with the gift for running. When you are just starting out, don't be self-conscious and don't feel everyone else is better than you. When you see people running faster than you, don't feel put down. They could be running just a short distance at a fast speed.

"If you are finding you are having a hard time running, try running at different times of the day; some people run well in the morning, while others do so in the evening. Vary your time until you find a time that suits you best. If you are having trouble getting yourself going, find someone to run with. If you are lacking in enthusiasm, read a book or an article on running that can be very inspirational. For women who feel they are too old, any book on running has stories of women champions in all age groups. Running is not an expensive sport, either; all you need is a good pair of shoes; anything else is just extra. You can be as plain or fancy as you want. When you run you will see people running in everything and anything. Once you take those first steps, though, you won't want to stop."

Judy has two very memorable runs, both races. One is the Bay-to-Breakers race in San Francisco:

"I hadn't planned on running the Bay-to-Breakers because I had never run that distance (7.6 miles) before. My husband and sons did the practice Bay-to-Breakers race and I followed in the car. After seeing the course I started to think maybe I had the ability to do it, after all; I could walk to the finish line if I had to. As the day approached, I knew I didn't want to be left behind. It was the best decision I could have made. I felt no pressure before the race because I didn't feel it was going to be competitive. The feeling before, after and during the race was one of festivities and comradeship. Everyone was enjoying themselves. The miles just went by and then we were at the beach. What a great feeling of accomplishment and fun. My first words were, 'I can hardly wait until next year.' It was just great."

The second memorable race was the Bonne Bell 10,000 meters in San Francisco's Golden Gate Park:

"I felt this race to be the most important one I've run. I sent for the entry form the same day I read the ad for it. I felt it would give me a chance to see how I could run in comparison to other women, both young and old. I worried about the course and the six miles; I had only done six miles twice before. I was nervous and proud that I was entering the run. I picked up my race packet and watched the movies of other Bonne Bell races. I was very excited by the time Sunday morning arrived. The course is two loops around the pole field area. After doing the first loop, I wasn't looking forward to running the second, as I was tiring. I felt I had an inner strength to finish and I did. The cheering and encouragment from my family along the sides of the course gave me a tmememdous high. I finished 377th out of 738 and that was my greatest reward."

ANNE HAMILTON
Millbrae, California

"Some girls I've talked to think you get big hearts or big muscles from running."

"When I run I feel I can relax and go on a kind of 'trip' somewhere," says Anne Hamilton of Millbrae, California, a 17-year-old track and cross-country runner. "I can work out solutions to problems and no one is bothering me. At the same time I am meeting my goals that I've set for myself and I feel a great sense of accomplishment when I run. I know that what I'm doing makes me feel good and is good for me.

"I feel that I am temporarily leaving everyone and everything behind, which does feel really good for a while. I feel in a way that I'm on top of the world and no one can pull me down or stop me from what I'm doing."

Although she does not stress distance runs, she has run as far as 25 miles. She usually runs her distance workouts alone, and her intervals with the track team. Her runs are done in a suburban environment, on high school or college cross-country courses, in city streets and at the track.

Her family's attitude toward her running is typical: Her father says she is a 'running nut'; her mother says 'she can do anything she wants to'; and her brothers call her a 'running legend', their pet nickname for her.

Her training pace is a blistering 6:30-7:00; her fastest mile time is 5:02; her fastest two-mile is 11:00; she's done 10 miles in 65:00. The shortcomings of her training program center on having no means of transportation with which to get to training areas outside of her neighborhood and her studies, which sometimes occupy much of her time.

I hope to be better every year (so far I have) and to be the best I can possibly be as my training advances," she says about her goals.

What would she tell other women about running?

"I would tell them not to feel that running is just a man's sport because the benefits one derives from running are not just intended for one sex. You're only cheating yourself by thinking that way. Some girls I talk to think you get big hearts or big muscles from running. Well, maybe my heart is bigger, but it is probably much stronger and healthier than theirs. As for muscles, in comparison with my friends, I see no particular muscles that stand out in excess on me; in fact, I am much skinnier than they are.

"If you ever have wanted to get away for awhile, put some spark in your life, or just lose weight, then running could be a definite asset in your life. The benefits are uncountable and some you cannot even explain. I don't think I could ever stop running for good. . . and even if I stopped running in races, I would still jog around. I have found running so beneficial that you could say I'm addicted to it. You should give running a chance to be a part of your life."

Anne sees the increased number of women running in America as a source of quality runners for the United States. "From any mass group comes higher quality," she says. "There's more potential to choose from when international competition comes along."

She has no plans to run a marathon, preferring the shorter distances.

Her most memorable run came in the summer of 1976. "It was on the Prefontaine Trails in Eugene, Oregon," she recalls. "The trails are made of packed wood pieces and feel kind of springy. There are three different trails, as I recall, a three-miler, a four-miler and a five-miler. Something like that. It also has a Parcourse. The scenery is very pleasant. However, the highlight of the trip there was seeing and talking to Frank Shorter for about 60 seconds. Wow!

"The weather is very nearly perfect—not too hot but comfortably warm. There were about 15 other runners on the courses. I wish they had something like that near where I live. I think it was the best place I ever ran, but I'm not sure that many other runners would appreciate it as much as I did."

CAROLYN SAWYER
Pittsfield, Massachusetts

"My husband has urged and encouraged and supported and babysat and stood at finish lines and run with me and discussed my running endlessly."

"I started running to escape from two small children and because my poor, 30-year-old body was in awful shape," says Carolyn Sawyer of Pittsfield, Massachusetts. "I ran, off and on, for about two-and-one-half years for these same reasons.

"Then, for Valentine's Day 1977 my husband gave me not one perfect rose, but a pair of Brooks Villanovas, and I began getting more serious about running. That spring, a friend and I entered the Bonne Bell 10,000-meter race scheduled for Boston in October and spent the whole summer training for it. I was hooked.

"Running (and the progress I've made from a quarter-mile of huffing to 20 miles of relaxed jogging) is something I've done by myself. Other people encouraged and advised me, but I've done the running and the sweating—alone. It's unlike anything else I've ever accomplished, and it's given me a kind of self-confidence and pride that's unique in my life. Delivering two children by the Lamaze method was physically more satisfying and graduating from Mount Holyoke College was intellectually more fulfilling, but neither has done for my self-image what running has done."

Carolyn's training schedule is ambitious. She rests Mondays, does five miles Tuesdays, 8-10 on Wednesdays, five or rests on Thursdays, five on Fridays, five or an occasional race on Saturday, and a 15-20 mile overdistance run on Sundays. She runs most often in the morning and does a minimum of exercising before embarking on her run. She runs alone, except for her long run, which she shares with friends. Her husband runs "about the same amount I do, but considerably faster."

Her family is great about it and thinks her running is a good thing, "though my six-year-old son wishes I could be the 'real winner' in a race and 'not just do your best.'"

Her training program is formed from intuition, reading, and friends who run. Joan Ullyot's *Women's Running* is her bible.

What if she had to lay off her running for a period of time? "It would bother me tremendously. Physically, because I've grown accustomed to feeling in shape. Emotionally, because I get such feelings of accomplishment from it. Also, as a New Englander, I'd feel guilty for not doing something I'm commited to."

How does she evaluate what running can mean to women? "Most women my age reached junior high school and sat down—stopped doing physical exercise of a really strenuous nature. Running gives women an experience most men have had—working hard to get in shape, being in touch with what one's body can do, realizing that sweating can feel good."

The shortcoming of her training program is that, with two small children, she could use more time to train—and she also wishes she had someone whose advice was absolutely reliable.

"My immediate goal is to do a marathon in New Hampshire in October. I want to run it in under four hours. I'd also like to work on speed to improve my times at the 10,000 meter races I've been running."

Her husband has been the person with the most positive effect on her running. "He has urged and encouraged and supported and babysat and stood at finish lines and run with me and discussed my running endlessly."

Her most memorable run was part of her training for last fall's Bonne Bell in Boston. "It was a beautiful, sunny, 70-degree September day and I tried 6.2 miles with the stopwatch running.

"The first five miles were pleasant but not spectacular—my watch said exactly 45 minutes. Then I realized how much energy I had and how much harder I could be running. I had that feeling I've already described—of such great physical well-being that for a minute or two I felt very high.

"I started running much faster and felt like I flew the last nine home—smiling most of the way. I ran that mile at 7:00 pace. . . unheard of for me.

"But what has stayed with me is not now pleased I was at running a seven-minute mile, but how happy and excited I felt as I *began* that mile."

BARBARA WAYNE
Alameda, California

"Unfortunately, so many adults have lost the ability to play."

"Just what does running mean? Basically this: If you don't enjoy doing it, why continue?" asks Barbara Wayne of Alameda, California. "Try participating in another sport or recreational pastime. After all, there are many other activities worth pursuing that provide adventure, challenge, and exercise. Running simply may not be a suitable activity for everyone.

"If, however, you are willing to persevere and commit yourself to running on a regular basis for at least a month, it can facilitate the development of self-knowledge, self-awareness, and self-expression. Plainly speaking, running can evolve into an intriguing adventure into self-exploration and discovering one's psyche. Skeptical?

"Running is as natural as breathing, eating, and sleeping. Ancient peoples had to hunt and gather food to survive. Sometimes they would trail game for days—on foot. We can observe the games, activities, and social interaction of children and plainly see now significant running is to their lives.

"Unfortunately, so many adults have lost the ability to play. How many of you can recall that exhilarating feeling of frolicking joyfully through a field of tall, overgrown summer grass or racing across the damp, rain-soaked earth of a forest shortly after a brief, unexpected thunderstorm?

"As human beings, it is important to reach out to this 'free' child spirit, regaining that sense of spontaneity, imagination, and joie de vivre. Running can and does provide some of life's greatest essentials and pleasures. In essence, running germinates the seeds of energy and strength. The runner reaps all of these benefits, for the door to a greater freedom of consciousness stands ajar. In time our internal responses to the world undergo an intellectual, physical and spiritual transformation, enabling the runner to lead a richer, more meaningful, and fulfilling life.

"And you don't necessarily have to run a marathon to be successful. Just place one foot in front of the other consistently."

Barbara is a 5'2" blonde, the wife of Ron Wayne, a world-class marathoner. She has been running "inconsistently" for five years, inspired to take up the sport by her long-distance spouse.

She occasionally enters races, but not frequently. Her daily training course is 3.2 miles, and it runs parallel to the San Francisco Bay, offering a spectacular view of the city and the surrounding hills. Her flat course circles a yacht marina. "I love the marine environment, the clean wind, the sparkling water that becomes a different shade very day, and watching the fog roll in, particularly in the summer. It creates a thick band of whiteness as it settles in along the opposite shore, stretching from San Francisco to as far as the eye can see. On Sundays, there are hundreds of sailboats added to the scene, and lines of fishermen along the east shore of the bay. It's an inspiring place to run."

Medically speaking, her biggest problem is calf stiffness and tightness; it has remained a chronic problem. The pain is not apparent when she is playing tennis, which she does 10-14 hours a week. The discomfort only comes about when she moves forward, as she does when running.

She gets some training advice from her husband, but usually runs according to how she feels. For her, tennis is the number one priority as far as sports go. She feels that both men and women receive the same benefits from running: good health, recreation, weight control, and psychological benefits. Most women *do* experience a decrease in menstral flow and menstral cramps because of running, which a man can't claim.

As far as the woman's potential in running is concerned, she feels that women will never be able to run as fast as the elite male runners—in any event. She is equally convinced that a person does not have to run a marathon to get special benefits from running. "I've never run a marathon," she says, "nor do I ever plan to."

JODY MEIER
Wilmington, Delaware

"I run competitively for the excitement."

Jody Meier of Wilmington, Delaware, began running a year ago with a friend; they were both curious about running because of the increasing number of magazine articles on the activity. Now Jody, 15 years old, runs races between a quarter-mile and four miles each Thursday night at her local Fun-Run...in addition to a three-mile training run Thursday afternoon. She runs approximately three miles every day, and six miles on Saturdays.

Her training runs are done primarily in the afternoons during the school year, and she runs with her mother. Warm-ups are donc with calesthenics that stress stretching the leg muscles. Her father occasionally runs a mile. Jody's training is done in Puma Rockettes. The training is done either on the local high school track or along the roads in the suburbs.

"I run to stay fit, to look good in a bikini, and to have a natural high," Jody says. "I also run competitively for the excitement. From running, it is possible to feel part of America because you know that almost everyone runs. It seems like the best 'all year' type of physical fitness and it can be done in many interesting ways."

To get her training runs in, Jody merely runs out the front door; she doesn't find it necessary to travel anywhere far from home for her runs.

She reports that dogs have occasionally tried to attack her and people in cars have shouted obscenities or invite her into their cars. Other people she sees running are friendly, she reports.

Her only medical problems are blisters and the traditional black toenails.

Jody runs with the school track team and has a coach for the 880, but she is her own coach when it comes to long-distance training.

If she had to be laid up with an injury and could not run for a time, she says that it would bother her tremendously because she looks forward to running's natural high. She also thinks a long lay off would cause her good muscle tone to vanish and have her feeling weak and flabby. She feels men do not derive anything different from running than women do.

Her training is done at an 8:00-9:00 pace, and her race pace is 7:00-8:00. She feels her biggest shortcomings are lack of self-confidence and proper incentive. But, she hopes to run a marathon someday and keep running for the rest of her life.

Her speech to other women on running is short and to the point: "Ladies, don't just sit there like bumps on a log; do something for yourself. Run! Wouldn't it sound exciting to you to begin a race right now? Doesn't the thought of it make your blood rush faster? There are so many of you who running can help. It will make your day seem fantastic. Try it!"

Jody feels that the increased interest in running by women will positively effect America's showing on the international front;

she also feels that the potential of the woman runner will allow her to equal the accomplishments of male runners. Her mother, she said, has been the greatest positive influence on her running.

The Bonne Bell 10,000-meter race around Potomac Park in Washington, D.C. was her most memorable race. "It was a dark, misty, coolish morning," she remembers, "and there were 1,400 women runners. This was the first time I had ever run six miles and it was a completely flat course. The race was very exciting because of the crowd. Gayle Barron was also running in this race. I loved every minute of the race; it made me feel fantastic!"

ELS TUINZING
Mill Valley, California

"There was nothing really mystical; just feeling good and thankful to be there."

"I run because it keeps me in shape," says Els Tuinzing of Mill Valley, California. "I feel good after a run and have more energy, although during a run, especially an uphill run, it is hard to keep going. Afterward, it gives a sense of satisfaction. I also do it because the runners are fun people to socialize with. On the weekends we often have breakfast runs and potlucks afterward. I live halfway up Mt. Tamalpais with the most beautiful trails right at our front door."

Els, who is 57 years old, was introduced to running through her son, Kees Tuinzing, a coach for the Institute of Health Research. Els races occasionally in 10-kilometer races; she does quite a bit of mileage, most of it hilly: six miles on Sunday, 6.8 on Monday, five on Tuesday, seven on Wednesday, seven on Friday and a 12-mile run on Saturday. Thursday is her "day off." Most of her training is done in the morning.

Her son Kees does 100 miles a week, and between them, they have gotten Mr. Tuinzing interested in running—he does 30 miles a week. Els trains in Brooks Villanovas and races in Nike Elites; her longest run has been 14 miles.

Although encountering no major problems in her running, Els has been chased by dogs on occasion and was bitten once. Medically, she pulled a hamstring muscle which healed with a combination of massage and rest. "The ball of my left foot hurts," she reports, "especially while running on pavement." Her training is guided by advice from her son and reading of magazines and books. If she had to lay off running for any period of time, Els reports that it would bother her quite a bit, "because I really need the exercise." She feels women derive nothing different from running than men do.

She says she has felt the fabled runner's high, especially on a beautiful run on the Bolinas ridge. "There was nothing really mystical," she said, "just feeling good and thankful to be there."

Her runs are done at a pace of 8:00-9:00; her racing is at a 7:00 pace. She feels that her greatest shortcoming is that she needs more practice on the track in order to build her speed; she doesn't enjoy track workouts, but she is doing it once a week now.

She is building her running program slowly toward several goals, one of them doing next year's Double Dipsea race, a treacherous cross-country race up and down mountains along the Pacific Ocean. She would also like to try a marathon, if her foot problem heals itself sufficiently. And, she would like to compete in the masters' Olympics to be held in Germany next year. year.

When asked to make a speech on running to other women, Els said:

"You all must have noticed the running craze among men, women, and children and you say to yourself: I am never going to be that crazy. But then you take a good look at the runners and talk to them. You notice how well they look, how alert and how much fun they are. Before you know it you, too, are hooked.

"The beginning is very difficult and it helps to have somebody to run with and to instruct you. Before you know it you are off the track, running in the neighborhood or driving to a nice area to run. If you are lucky, you get your husband involved. You go to Fun-Runs, meet other beginners, advanced runners, and some outstanding runners who encourage you.

"And then comes your first race, which you almost always finish in a decent time. Now you are really hooked, and you feel one of the gang when you join a runners' picnic afterward. You establish close friendships and enjoy the comaraderie of the runners. You belong!"

Els feels the increased number of women runners will allow the natural competitiveness of each to come to the surface, and there will be a group of female runners that will begin making their mark on the international level.

Who has been the most positive influence on her running?

"My son, the coach, started me without pushing me. He showed patience and consideration. Also, my husband has been an inspiration; he started running a year after I did. It is such fun to run together and enjoy the social part of running together."

"There have been several very memorable runs," Els said when questioned on what runs will always stand out in her mind. "My first race on Angel Island was memorable. I was excited, of course, and only worried I would make a bad showing or not be able to finish. I even felt sick in my stomach but finished all right and felt a great satisfaction—even more so after I found that my son Kees and I had won the mother and son category.

"My second most memorable run was the AAU masters championships (10 kilometers) in Belmont, where I ran in the rain and took second place in the 50-and-over category. That was just a few days after the birth of my granddaughter.

"My third memorable run was on Mother's Day when I ran the Bolinas ridge with my husband, my son, and his friend Gordon. It was just the four of us on a beautiful day, in fantastic country with green meadows, wild flowers, beautiful trees, and a great view. That was a real high."

RUTH ANDERSON
Livermore, California

"Let the race directors know you exist and want to be recognized."

Ruth Anderson is a radiochemist at the Lawrence Livermore Laboratories of the University of California. She counts and records gamma radiation in an effort to detect the presence of various radioactive materials, including uraniums and maintains a library of radioactive isotopes. While Ruth spends her days in the laboratories, she spends many of her free hours on the roads, training for marathons. She has run more than thirty marathons and has twice been the national women's master's title holder.

A runner for five-and-a-half years, Ruth has been one of the moving forces in the effort to secure equal rights in running for women—and especially for master women runners.

"There are several messages I would like to give women of all ages, but a 'soapbox' implies the opportunity to espouse a cause. I would have to wrestle with two topics: 'An Olympic Marathon for Women' and 'Equal Opportunities for Masters Women. Since I have covered my view on the need for the marathon in the Olympics for women in the chapter on politics in this book, I'd like to take about master's women," she said, being offered the soapbox from which to talk to other women.

"Now that the numbers of women running have reached such impressive proportions, the need for peer-group competition is truly important. Men over 40 have been enjoying ten-year and even five-year divisions in major races and national championships for the past several years. It's now a matter of information: Let the race directors know you exist and want to be recognized. Women runners don't stay 39 years old—they turn 40 and 50 and even 60! There are even 70-year-olds competing. There is no age at which you are too old to run if you are physically fit to enjoy all the benefits running affords.

"So often I have been given the argument that there aren't enough over-40 women to merit a division, let alone breaking it down even further. That was more a situation of five years ago than now. Still, even when I first started running five-and-a-half years ago at forty-three, I so appreciated the consideration and recognition that some race directors gave me—just a ribbon with fifth or third place is recognition—that I encouraged my fellow masters women to support those races. I am a firm believer that rewards are a very important aspect in encouraging participation in athletic events (which isn't much different than it is in all aspects of life).
recognition but truly encourage participation of their members is in team competition. Many women who might encourage participation of their members is in team competition. Many women who might never expect to receive a medal on their own have a chance as a member of a team to score competitively. Even more important, they realize they are needed. Not everyone can be a frontrunner, but everyone should be given a chance to count. Here, also, is a real opportunity to bring out the run part of competition. Teams don't have to be for hotshots only, but rather an emphasis should be placed on participation.

"Not all areas of the country may have masters or seniors clubs where membership begins at 30 or 40 years of age. However, where these clubs do exist, it helps the women masters to organize and support each other. They are also more apt to be given the understanding and support of the male members. Nationally, the masters committee is trying to look out for the women's interests, too. National championships do indeed offer age divisions for men and women alike in five-year age groups. The world masters championships, first held in Toronto, Canada, in 1975 and again in Gothenburg, Sweden in 1977, offered excellent international peer-group competition for the women. Such an Olympics for older athletes is most inspiring and really can give women the same goal to strive as for men if they so desire."

Ruth's interest in running began when some friends talked her into running with them during lunch hour. Now, one of the most famous women runners in the country, Ruth competes virtually every weekend, in races from three miles to the marathon. (She has also done ultramarathons, having done a 100-kilometer race in 1976, and planning to do 100-milers in the future.) Her training schedule is solid but not overwhelming, proving that it is possible to accomplish much on a reasonable amount of work. She races on Sunday, runs 6-8 miles on Monday, 9.3 miles on Tuesday (she runs a cross-country course each Tuesday), 7-9 miles on Wednesday, 6-8 miles on both Thursday and Friday and 8-15 miles on Saturday. During the week she runs at noon, and takes early morning runs on Saturday.

She does a variety of stretches before running, attempting to keep herself as flexible and injury-free as possible. She also does a half-mile jog before starting on her training run. Her husband runs 35-40 miles a week, and her daughter does 10-15.

Her favorite training shoe is still the (men's) Nike Waffle Trainer. She uses the Nike LDV for hillwork, Oregon Waffles for beach running and for running on slick surfaces, the Nike Meika for 10-K flat races, the Waffle Trainers for marathons. For short track races, like the 1500 meters, she uses Nike Interval spikes.

Ruth's weekday training is done near her lab in a rural setting, including her regular Tuesday 15-K run through a hilly cross-country course in a nearby park, through a brace of redwoods and down canyons. On weekends she runs city streets, frontage roads, and slightly hilly streets.

How about injuries from running? "As a beginner runner I had more than my share of diarrhea—particularly on hot days or from the stress of longer races and runs," Ruth says. "Since I have been taking desiccated liver regularly, this problem has gone away. My only two real injuries were a separated shoulder from a fall in the Woodminster cross-country race and a fractured fifth metatarsal foot bone caused by a foot twist on the Double Dipsea race."

Ruth's main goal is to do a sub-3:00 marathon. She also wants to run in the famous London-to-Brighton 52-miler, even more so than the Athens Marathon, which is also high on her list.

As though to prove her point that women can do anything they want to do, this is the story of Ruth's most memorable run:

"It started in the dark and finished in the dark. The day after Christmas 1976 I stood shivering in the foggy pre-dawn at Lake Merced in San Francisco. Visions of 26 times around the lake danced through my head. Each five-mile circuit became a new experience. With only a handful of brave souls, about 20 in all, the field spread out quickly. I was happy for the company of my friend Barbara Carlson and my husband, John, the first go-around. Conversation certainly helps the distance get covered easier.

"The only scenery was visible by the street lamps until nearly the third lap. A whole new course seemed to open up before me with daylight and the lifting of the fog. Runners were arriving to do a lap or two with us as part of their training runs. I appreciated the chance for more company as John was now tending the pit-stop van with my supplies of hot tea (with Body Punch and extra sugar added), dry clothes and changes of shoes. It was a most welcome Mecca to look forward to after each five miles. The routine also involved a stop at the boathouse restroom and a stiff-legged return to running after these stops.

"Somehow the marathon distance went by, then 50 kilometers arrived—halfway! A real feeling of encouragement came at this point. I enjoyed the next three laps. The sun was warm (but not overly so) and a new companion in the lake even added to this illusion.

"The pistol-range became active—a new distraction—a bit scary, so I chose to hurry past that part of the course. I was surprised how I could run without too much discomfort once I got going each time—until the last mile. It was dark again and there were no runners in view. Then some friends and John joined me—a 12-minute stretch and I had completed 100 kilometers. I'll never forget that first ultra—a real trip—successful adventure, no matter what may follow."

CINDY PREBES
Tarrytown, New York

"The cheering got louder and I burst into tears covering my face with my hands."

Tarrytown, New York's Cindy Piebes, although running for only two years, is a perfect example of what a woman who wants to run can do. She's been racing everything from 10,000 meters to the marathon, usually racing twice a month. She builds her running upon a very ambitious training base: five miles on Sunday, Tuesday and Thursday, alternating to ten miles on Monday, Wednesday and Friday, and running a 10-15 miler on Saturday, doing at least 55 miles a week, a good distance for maintaining a solid training base. She usually runs alone, late in the afternoon on weekdays and in the mornings on weekends. She usually runs along backroads where there isn't much traffic to worry about; on weekends she runs the horse trails of a local estate. She lives in an area where there are plenty of hills, so she works some of them into her training.

"I started running to lose weight," she says, "but I run now for a number of reasons. Primarily, I run to stay healthy both physically and mentally. At last check, my blood pressure was 104/70 and pulse rate 55 and I'm happier in my life than I've ever been, so I guess it's working." (Cindy is 25 years old.)

"I also love the country and even though I work in New York City, my home and my running terrain is in the woods and hills of Westchester County, which makes me feel far, far away from the city. Out in the woods, in view of the Hudson, I feel very much at peace with myself and my environment. Although I am no religious fanatic, I enjoy talking to God while I run and feel very close to Him during many runs, especially those off major roads.

Her mileage has apparently given her a few medical problems. "I had some hip pain and knee pain when I first started, but ran through it until everything disappeared. I do have a bad ankle that I've twisted a number of times on uneven ground, so I have to be conscious of where I run. I did sprain it once badly enough to keep me from running for a couple of days. I developed a bruise on the head of my second metatarsal when I increased in mileage for the Boston Marathon, but I run now with an arch pad and presently have no problem."

If she could speak before an audience of about 1,000, this is what she'd tell them:

"Why do I run? Let me count the whys. If you run, I probably don't even have to tell you. You most likely already know. I run because I have seen what it has done for *me.* Not only in terms of physical and medical benefits, but in improving who I am. True, my body is more trim than when I started my running. My clothes look better on me and many acquaintances remark on how I 'glow.' And, true, my blood pressure is low. I rarely get sick, and I eat better than I have in 20 years. The perfect picture of health.

"But more important than this, running has made me best friends with myself. I get no cosmic reality from running, no ethereal experiences. I do get a better perspective of what my life is all about. What is important to me is my family, good friends, a healthy body that responds when I ask it to, land and trees and animals that aren't hurt by my 'assault' on their environs. I'm no beauty and I could stand to lose 15 more pounds. But I don't wake in the morning and wince at my image in the mirror. I've stopped trying to fit into other peoples' worlds by going out to bars and getting drunk every Saturday night and eyeing every guy that walks by as a prospective husband."

Her current goals are ambitious: (1) to lose 15 pounds, (2) to run a 3:00 marathon in New York City, and (3) to be one of the best marathoners in the metro New York City area. She feels that within the next five years a woman will run a 2:15 marathon, and that the gap between the times of men and women will continue to narrow. Cindy ran two marathons in 1978, at Ithaca and in Boston. She feels that she has been the most positive influence on her running. "I started because of me and I am the one who talks myself into continuing. Many other people have influenced me by taking an interest and really caring but I would say that I've been the most important."

Her most memorable run was, naturally enough the 1978 Boston Marathon:

"My parents, my ex-fiance's parents and two of his sisters came up to Boston to watch me run. I remember being very surprised and excited that they wanted to come, too. One of their sons had run the year before, but was not in shape for this year's run.

"We arrived in Boston late in the afternoon and after checking into the hotel and having dinner, we drove down to the finish line at the Prudential. It was really exciting seeing the timing booth and stepping over the finish line while no one was around. I swam at the Collegiate Nationals a number of years and the excitement the night before the marathon came quite close to the excitement of the big meets I had competed in. I slept well that night and we got up early the morning of the race and I had pancakes—though I really didn't want them. I was afraid they'd still be in my stomach at race time.

"We watched all the early news shows with scenes of the route and Dr. Sheehan and various competitors. I was nervous and excited. The weather was perfect for running—cool and overcast, but no prediction of showers. I dressed in my running gear—shorts, turtleneck and T-shirt with a roadrunner on the back. I remember trying to decide what T-shirt to wear—what a decision. As we drove parts of the marathon, I got more excited and my mother kept saying, "Are you sure you can do this?" I had run a qualifier marathon a month before and missed the cut-off time by 12 minutes but decided to run anyway in Boston. I also remember being furious at the morning papers that described the number of unofficial runners who were only going to get in the way and cause trouble. I was furious because the writer was talking about me! Me, who had trained so hard to get there and to whom this race meant so much, even though I had no number and who had just as much right as anybody to run.

"At the start of the race I looked for people I knew but saw no one. I went to the bathroom twice in 15 minutes and probably would have gone again if there had been time. I don't remember much of the race itself—except I felt good the first 13 miles and really enjoyed being cheered on at Wellesley College. I couldn't get over the number of people along the route and how friendly they were. They just wanted to touch you. I felt really important for some reason even though I was only one of about 7,200 people!

"I surprised myself at Heartbreak Hill because I passed a lot of people on the way up. My parents and friends were at the top and my Dad had a glass of Gatorade for me that splashed mostly in my eyes as I tried to drink it. I wanted to cry, it was so good to see him and my Mom there. From that point on I really started to go downhill. I thought it was probably from running two marathons in a month and I remember just telling my legs to keep moving, we were almost finished. With about three miles to go I had to walk a couple hundred yards and I was real impressed by the encouragement of the people who were watching as well as from the other runners. They could see how much it hurt yet they all wanted you to finish. I started running again and everybody clapped. The most memorable part of the whole experience was one of the most emotional of my life—the finish.

"As I came around the corner and up the last incline before the finish, I got a burst of energy from heaven-knows-where, and sprinted past about ten people up the hill. The cheering got louder and I burst into tears, covering my face with my hands. I couldn't believe it. As I finished, one of the officials asked if I was okay because I was still crying and I said, "Yes, just happy." I sat down on the floor of the Prudential building to wait for my father and couldn't get up from sheer exhaustion. When my father came I hugged him like I would never let him go. I'll never forget that experience as long as I live."

JUDY PETERSON
Foster City, California

"I had a real fear of limping across the finish line. . . ."

When a woman runs a marathon it literally changes her life. The accomplishment involved in running 26 miles, 385 yards gives a woman confidence that she felt was set aside for the gods. A woman's first marathon is often one of the most memorable things to happen in her life. Judy Peterson, 38 years old, of Foster City, California, remembers her first marathon vividly:

"I was relatively well-trained for it and had done a number of 20-mile runs fairly easily, so I felt I could go the distance; however, I had originally hoped to do the Avenue of the Giants, but did not get my registration in on time and therefore settled for the *Pacific Sun* Marathon in Marin. I had been informed the course was quite hilly but didn't realize how hilly until about three weeks before when I drove over part of it.

"At that point I was extremely disillusioned and was afraid I couldn't do it in my hoped-for four hours. However, after later running a good portion of the course in practice runs, I realized I would be able to negotiate the hills rather easily.

"Just one week before the marathon I developed a sinus infection with a fever of 101.4—which totally deprived me of energy. I was never sure up to the day of the marathon whether I had fully recovered from the illness.

"As the date approached, the weather was getting warmer and warmer. Finally, the day before, I had to admit that the day of the run would be a scorcher and again I got down and disillusioned, feeling I couldn't manage hills plus heat.

"On the morning of the marathon I felt confident, but still had some fears about the heat (which reached into the low 90s before noon). I decided to go for a 3:50 time and recorded the appropriate splits on my arm.

"I ran with a friend throughout the race, and she began to hurt a lot at around 12 miles—suffering from the heat. Up to that point, we chatted and felt really good. From 12-20 miles I was really worried she wouldn't make it and wondered whether I would make it without her. My boyfriend met us at 10 and 18 miles—and tried to give me my times. At those points I really didn't care and simply wanted to finish regardless of the time. I tried to encourage my running friend and to keep up light chatter but found it increasingly difficult to concentrate on things to say. Finally, at about 20 miles I went off and left her at an aid station, thinking she was going to stop. I struggled on alone, beginning to feel more and more tired and light-headed. I stopped wherever there was water—hoses, buckets, official aid stations, etc. At about 22 miles my friend caught up with me, feeling stronger than I was! The last three miles were almost unbearable—I wasn't exactly hurting but was just stiff and weak.

"At least three times I was told 'only two miles to go'; twice I was told 'only a mile to go.' Such misinformation was very discouraging and the last three or four miles felt more like 10! I was so afraid I wouldn't make it at all that I apparently picked up my speed at the end. Before entering the track, though, I said to my running partner: 'Let's be sure to reserve some strength so we can finish looking strong.' I had a real fear of limping across the finish line or looking like Joanne Woodward at the end of her marathon in the film *See How She Runs*. Finally we entered the track for one lap before crossing the finish line. I almost sprinted the last 50 yards or so, both so I could look good crossing the line and also just to get the damned thing over with!

"My boyfriend grabbed me as I crossed the line, gave me a big hug and kiss, and led me over to someone who poured a bucket of water over my head. Then I sat (almost fell) down on the ground, too tired and weak to even appreciate the fact that I had just completed one of the biggest accomplishments of my life. I remember saying 'it wasn't worth it.'

"As soon as I sat down I felt a tremendous pressure and tingling in my nose and sinuses. I was sure I was going to develop a bad nose bleed, but luckily it never materialized. The tingling persisted for about a half-hour. Also, my fingertips tingled. I drank as much fluid as I could: water, diluted Gatorade, beer, orange juice, etc. I wanted to stretch but didn't have the energy to do so by myself so my boyfriend helped me. At that point I realized I had a pulled muscle in the groin area of my left leg. I still don't know whether it was the result of running the marathon or stretching too much afterwards. I never felt the strain when running; however, I suspect it was from the running anyway.

"My official time was 3:46:35, much better than I had hoped for at any time before or during the race. For that matter, at 20 miles I remember feeling I would be lucky to break four hours. My boyfriend recorded my times at 10 miles and again at 18—and when I later figured out my pace for various legs I was startled to realize I steadily picked up speed throughout:

1-10 miles: 8:57 pace
10-18 miles: 8:28 pace
18-26 miles: 8:19 pace
1-26 miles: 8:39 pace for race

"I certainly concur with whoever said 'the halfway point in a marathon comes at 20 miles.' I couldn't believe how much harder those last six miles were than anything I had experienced before. I'm sure the intense heat was much to blame for the way I felt, though, and not just the distance. Once I recovered enough to stand and walk (about an hour after I finished), I vowed I would do another, but never again in the heat.

"Now, three weeks later, as I write this, I am running lightly—no more than 20 miles a week. I feel fine but just want to take a break from the intense training. My pulled muscle still hurts also. I will probably start training again in earnest after another month or so—I *must* run another marathon!"

Judy survived her marathon on solid training, building up to it by running a 5-7 mile race on Sundays, doing a five-mile run Mondays, a 10-miler on Tuesdays, a five-miler on Wednesdays, 10 on Thursdays, taking Fridays off, and running a long run of about 20 miles on Saturdays. She had been running one-and-one-half years before doing her first marathon.

Judy mentioned that she runs for many reasons. They include running because (1) it feels good to be outdoors exercising, (2) she has always been concerned with fitness and being in shape, (3) she gets a mental high from it (in conjunction with the good mental outlook running gives her on life), (4) the discipline involved spills over into her daily life, (5) running offers a healthy means of competition, and (6) she likes the camaraderie among runners.

ESTHER BYNUM SHARP
Cambridge, Massachusetts

"It makes my dog feel good to get out and stretch his legs with me."

Esther Bynum Sharp, 26, hails from Sumter, South Carolina, is spending a year in France, and lives in Cambridge, Massachusetts. She has been running for 15 months. She became interested in running by watching the Boston Marathon and cheering on a friend of hers who was running in it; she was, at about the same time, searching for a quick, comprehensive way to exercise her dog in the city; running clicked as the answer. She does not race frequently, and makes one long run a week (six to 13 miles), while running 2-4 miles three or four times a week in the winter, and 4-6 miles three or four times a week in the summer. Her longest run ever was 16 miles.

She does most of her running in the morning, claiming that she gets sideaches (stitches) if she runs after she eats. She does yoga exercises before her runs, and runs either alone or with a friend—but always with her dog. She is not the only one in her family who runs: her husband runs intermittently; her father runs 1½ miles four times a week; her sister runs a mile 2-3 times a week; and her brother-in-law runs 2-5 miles two or three times a week.

While living in Cambridge in the winter, Esther runs on the streets near her apartment. When she visits her parents in Sumter she runs the roads in suburban areas, or on the beach at Pawley's Island. "The most beautiful place in the world to run," she claims, "is on Mt. Desert Island in Maine. There, in Acadia National Park, are over 50 miles of beautiful gravel carriage roads that wind through the mountains by lovely lakes and streams. Flat or hilly courses can be found for any distance imaginable. The air is as clear and pure as is possible (no industries within 25 miles). Cars are not allowed on the carriage roads and you can run for hours without seeing another person, particularly in early or late summer. Whenever I run there I feel as though I can go forever without stopping."

That special feeling a runner gets is one of the reasons Esther runs. "It makes me feel good," she states. "It makes my dog feel good to get out and stretch his legs with me. I like the increased endurance I gain from running. I like the way my body feels after running, the strength in my legs. Running regulates my appetite and bowel movements. Since I started running I rarely feel an urge to eat between meals. Running makes me want to eat good, wholesome meals of fruits, vegetables, milk products, and whole grains."

Would a forced halt to her running bother her? "Yes, somewhat, but not devastatingly so. Stopping running would not bother me so much if I could funnel my energies into some other type of similar physical activity. However, no other exercise I've found is as wholesome as running."

Esther feels that men and women derive nothing different from running, that running always lifts her spirits, and that there are no real shortcomings in her current program because she runs when and as much as she feels like.

Toward what goals is she building her running program? "I've thought from time to time that I would like to train for the marathon. Given my present schedule, it seems difficult to achieve that goal in the next year. So when and if it happens, I'll be happy. If I do decide to realize that goal, I'd like to have encouragement from other people and perhaps some coaching."

Her most memorable run was her 16-miler. . . which came on Mt. Desert Island. "I started at the foot of Eagle Lake," she recalls. "Eagle Lake is the reservoir for Bar Harbor. I ran up and past the Gordan Pond, which has pure, fresh drinking water, down to Little Long Pond, around and up a hill by The Bubbles Pond. It was a clear, sunny day, with temperatures in the 70s when I started, and in the low 80s by the time I finished. At 13-14 miles my legs ached like they never had before. I passed Bubbles Pond and slowed to a walk, then sat down to get a drink. After a couple of minutes, the aching didn't stop, so I started running again. I was really glad to reach the foot of Eagle Lake again, which ended my run. I felt a tremendous sense of achievement and I felt that running a marathon was a goal within my reach. At the same time I realized how much training it takes to run 26 miles. I had taken a big step, however."

JEAN ROBERTSON
Lynn, Massachusetts

"I run because it's something I'm used to. . . "

Female runners come in all shapes and sizes—and at all ages. Jean Robertson of Lynn, Massachusetts is 11 years old, 4'10" and 74 pounds. She has run the mile in 5:39. Her oldest (of four) brothers gave a little background on Jean's running exploits before she took the stage to talk about herself.

"Jean did her first running at a local Fun-Run when she was three," 25-year-old Bill says. "It was a 1.2-mile course and she tied for first with her 14-year-old sister because she was the only one who didn't stop. She ran in local road races until she was eight and joined Liberty A. C. Under club direction she has rapidly improved. Her main attributes as a runner are mental toughness and diligence—which also shows up in her schoolwork, where she has received straight A's for the past two years.

"Jean loves races and would do them every day of the week if she could. She also likes practices with the team, but she considers other practice running to be a pain in the neck—something she endures. Once in a while she looks forward to it and is usually pleased after she completes her run.

"She *says* she is going to run the Boston Marathon within the next couple of years, but she won't if anyone in the family or her coach has anything to say about it. It just seems to me that Jean was a born runner, if that is possible. She took to it right away and has improved and enjoyed it ever since."

Jean, then, has been a runner for eight years—something most runners competing today can't claim. She races about once every two weeks, the races varying in length from a mile to eight miles. Her schedule for the rest of the week is ambitious—but structured to her age: she does her easy runs at a 9:00-9:30 pace. Tuesday and Thursday she does three or four miles of intervals with her running club. The rest of the week she does 3-5 miles easy. She does her training runs after school in the afternoon. Of her warm-ups, she says: "I do a stretching exercise of leaning against the wall for two minutes, plus some toe touches and leg stretches. I should do more but I usually don't."

Her training runs are seldom alone. She runs with the Liberty team or with her Irish setter or with her father or one of her brothers or with her teammate, Patty Murnane.

Just about everyone in the family runs. Her father, John, is 52 years old and runs about 50 miles a week; 25-year-old Billy does about 50 miles a week; 24-year-old Jackie runs occasionally; 22-year-old brother Tommy runs occasionally; all have competed in the Boston Marathon. Sister Pat, 21 years old, runs two miles a day; 19-year-old Marie runs occasionally; brother Paul, 14 years old, runs three miles a day; and sister Cathy, 12, runs occasionally.

"I run," says Jean, "because it is something I'm used to and it has been part of me for so long. It also keeps me from getting too fat. I also enjoy traveling to races with my team. The exercise helps me stay healthy, I get a feeling that I've accomplished something when I run, and I have many friends who are runners."

Most of her running is in the city. "I live a half-mile from the beach and usually run an out-and-back course there. I have other courses which include hills; almost all are out-and-back courses," she says. When she does her training runs, kids yell things at her, like "Pick up those legs" or "Run, run, run." Dogs sometimes bark at her and occasionally try to bite her. And she sometimes has troubles crossing the street because of the heavy traffic.

She had a pulled muscle caused by a speed workout that lasted two months. She also has calcaneal apophisitis, which is a condition where her bones are growing faster than her muscles, but which will likely equalize as she eventually stops growing.

For a young lady who will likely have many more memorable milestones in her life, her most memorable run came at the Dartmouth Relays in January of 1977. The race was the mile. "It wasn't really a hard race," she says, "but the worst thing was waiting for it because it wasn't until 9:00 p.m. so I couldn't do that much playing before that.

"When we were playing on one of the mats we met Jan Merrill in the strangest way. It just happened that she was leaning against the same mat we were jumping on. That is, she and her bodyguards [other girls who keep other people from pestering her]. So when we jumped on it she talked to us for the first time—or rather yelled at us.

"The race finally came and I was very nervous. Everyone had already run their races and done very well. My brother Billy, who stood watching with a broken leg, thought I was going too fast. The clock they had was a big digital one that was hanging on the wall. Most of the girls in the race were in high school. When the race started I was in about fifth place, but on the seventh lap I was in first place, but on the last half of the eighth lap I was passed. When I was running I looked at the clock and right below the clock I saw my brother jump up and down with his crutches out to his sides so I guessed he was happy.

"My time was 5:39, which wasn't bad. As a matter of fact, one of my teammates, Sandy Cullinane, said to me that I was the best runner there. All my teammates crowded around me. That made me feel good. When we left the track to go to the motel it was snowing, but I couldn't have been happier."

ELEANORE SCHOLTE
Jamaica, New York

"The marathon will always stand as one of the high points in my life."

"I run because it's a way to remain fit. It feels very good, especially afterwards," says Eleonora Scholte, a Pan-Am flight attendant. "It is a beautiful way to clear the head, arrange one's thoughts and sometimes to float away. It is a moment to be really with yourself.

"I love to go running right after a flight. The body is yearning to go out in the fresh air to cleanse itself from the unwholesome air of smoke-filled cabins.

"From running, I have lost some weight, my body has become firmer and I feel stronger physically. The appetite seems to naturally gear itself more towards fresh fruit (and juices) and raw foods in general. The urge to fill myself up on heavy meals is practically gone.

"Sometimes it is difficult to explain why someone wants to run. There is a certain mystique about it which only the runner feels and knows for him- or herself."

Eleonora is from the Netherlands and now makes her home in Jamaica, New York. She has been running regularly for nearly two years and races six or seven times a year, from four-milers to the marathon. Her training consists of six miles on Mondays and Thursday, eight miles on Tuesday and Friday, ten miles on Saturday, and she takes off on Sunday and Wednesday.

She usually runs alone and because of her schedule with the airlines has no set time in which she does her training.

When she does run, it is often in some foreign country at the other end of a flight. "My job carries me to different countries, environments and climates all the time," she reports. "My running varies from city centers like Tehran to some very isolated beaches, such as the western coast of Africa." When she runs at home she merely steps out her front door and turns either right or left.

Eleonora, like most runners, is self-coached. She gets advice from other runners and reads the literature on the subject. Also, like most runners she finds that she would have difficulty if she had to lay off. "The body gets very jumpy after absences," she says.

She feels that there are some benefits women get from running that men cannot share. "I think that most women who don't have much self-confidence gain it through their accomplishments in running. Also, from a physical standpoint, there seems to be less vaginal problems (less cramps during menstruation; reduced discharges) when a woman runs."

The goals Eleonora set up for herself when she took up running were not competition oriented. "I won a few mixed races for women in my age-group, but I want most to be able to run regularly, sensibly, and for the rest of my life."

Her most memorable run was the Baltimore Marathon. She remembers it this way:

"A lot of runners got together the night before in one of the city hotels, which gave us a discount for accommodations. A special meal (the typical carbohydrate-loading type) was prepared for us. I had about three plates of spaghetti.

"The following day I was a bit nervous and chewed slowly on a breakfast of pancakes and coffee. It was a crisp day. We took the car to the outskirts of the city, with plenty of time to make the start of the race.

"When the gun sounded and a few thousand runners surged forward, I asked myself what I had thrown myself into. Trying to keep a very slow pace at the beginning so as not to use all my energy up at once, my friend stayed with me until the halfway point, at which point he took off on his own.

"The scenery was beautiful; the course had a lot of hills, especially at 18 miles—but I walked that one. For the remaining seven miles it was hard to start running again. But I did.

"The people along the side of the road were beautiful and encouraging. At five miles out I stopped once again, this time to have my knee massaged. My leg was starting to disobey my commands and I kept telling myself: 'You have to finish, you have to finish.' They were giving all finishers a jacket and I really wanted to earn one. So for this silly jacket I struggled through the last miles. I finished in 4:04 and I was elated that I had managed to stay with it until the end. It will always stand as one of the high points in my life."

CATHY SCHUTT
Cambridge, Massachusetts

"I space out and feel timeless, perfect, absolute, at ease, and loved."

"I run for a number of reasons, and the more I run the more sense it makes to me," says Cathy Schutt of Cambridge, Massachusetts. "I'm studying for an advanced degree in community health—and am especially interested in the state of being well, motivation theory, compliance, and self-discipline in health care. In addition to finding answers to helping people find their best level of health maintenance, I experiment and work with my own body to find answers. I've become convinced that illness is a result of not participating throughout life in regular physical, emotional, and psychological exercise. Because I am in touch with what is happening to my own body, when I care for, teach or counsel others, I can come from not only a theoretical background, but also from one of experience.

"Physically, I like the way my body looks since I've begun running. I feel good and look good and enjoy working with my body to achieve its potential. I fantasize about being athletic throughout my life—being a role model to others in their 80s and 90s.

"But mentally, I'm really hooked. I can't *not* run. If I don't run I feel sluggish and down. If I have something on my mind or am wondering how it's all going to work out, I go for a run and the answer is there spontaneously, without effort. And no matter what else I've done, running caps off the day and makes it all worthwhile. It's a special thing I do in my own special relationship with myself."

Cathy, 32 years old, and a trim 123 pounds at 5'8", has been running seriously for two years; she had been jogging for a mile or two a day for two years before that. She now runs 25-35 miles per week, taking one day off per week. She usually does her running in the afternoon, but has run at 5:00 a.m. and at midnight. "Getting the run in is the priority," she says.

She does 10-15 minutes of stretching before running and she also does progressive relaxation stretches several days a week. She runs both alone and with friends, preferring to run alone when the mood strikes her; running with friends can provide an opportunity for some good-natured competition midway through the run, she feels. Her uncle and cousin are marathoners, and they regularly run 50 plus miles per week. She has many friends who are runners, and is finding that more and more of her acquaintances are becoming runners.

Cathy has no great medical problems from running beyond the usual shin splints. She's never had to stop training due to an injury.

Her family and friends support her running, many of them taking up running after seeing how much it has helped her. "I look healthier, have great energy and endurance, and greater powers of concentration," she says.

She currently listens to her body for indications that her training might be going in the wrong direction; she reads about proper training and discusses it with other runners, especially her uncle; she plans to get a coach soon.

She feels that she gets the same things from running that men do. "I'm glad women have the opportunity to run or be athletic and physical. All human beings need that," she says.

When questioned about "experiences" while running, Cathy was very affirmative about them. "I have them all the time. I space out and feel timeless, perfect, absolute, at ease, and loved. Really, all is great when I run," she says.

"My most memorable run occurred last July at a wildlife sanctuary outside Concord, Massachusetts," Cathy relates. "It was on a warm, humid, rainy afternoon. I ran eight miles through and around the reserve in company with plants, flowers, birds and other animals. We seemed to mesh perfectly, for nothing scurried away from me as I approached. Everything allowed me to come among it without recoiling in fear of me.

"I remember feeling free, exalted, perfect, and timeless in a meditative state. It left me disoriented for hours afterward. I felt that I had gone somewhere outside the normal realm of most of my experience and I labelled it heaven. I mean, what else could I call it with that feeling?"

JOAN FOX
Sunnyvale, California

"I need time alone and running is perfect for fulfilling this need."

Joan Fox of Sunnyvale, California, a 17-year-old cross-country and track runner in high school, observed running from the perspective of just recovering from an arch injury that caused her to miss a very promising track season. "I would have had an excellent track season," Joan says. "I was getting stronger every day and was in great shape." She feels that her arch strain is pretty well under control now, though, and she is working hard to get back into shape. Her getting-back-into-shape schedule includes running in the Fun-Run at Foothill College on Sunday (all three races), doing eight miles on Monday, five or six on Tuesday, a fast three or four on Wednesday, five to eight miles on Thursday, eight miles on Friday, and either another eight miles or rest on Saturday.

For someone who races as much as Joan does, the layoff was a bit frustrating. She normally does road racing all year long and takes part in all-comer track meets in the summer. She had also hoped to compete in the San Francisco Marathon in July, which would have been her first, but was unable to because of the need to ease back into shape after the three-month layoff.

Joan started running in March of 1976, and has had quite a bit of encouragement from her parents, both of whom run.

In her normal training, Joan likes to do interval workouts with friends, but usually does her roadwork alone. She runs in the late afternoon during the school year, and is pretty flexible during the summer, getting her run in whenever the spirit moves her. She does a full slate of warm-up stretching exercises before getting onto the roads, where she does her mileage at a 6:30-7:00 pace; during races she is usually competing at about a 6:00 pace. Her best time for the mile is 5:20.

Because of her arch problems, she trains in Nike Elites because she needs shoes with no arch supports. She also trains in Adidas Countries with orthotics added. She races in the Elites and on the track in Tiger Spartan B spikes. Her longest run has been 18 miles.

She lives in a suburban environment, but within two miles she can be in a rural setting, which is where she prefers to run. She works out a lot of her problems during her runs without even thinking about them. "You learn your priorities while running," she says. "Also, I need time alone and running is perfect for fulfilling this need. It is a great source of freedom just to walk out of the house and go wherever you want to. I know that no one can stop me. This is something in my life over which I have complete control. No one but myself can force me to run 18 miles.

"Running also helps control weight. I find that I never really feel like eating after running. When I was injured I swam to keep in shape and that made me eat all the time. But running builds more muscles and I don't eat as much. Also, with swimming you just had the bottom of the pool to look at. It was so boring. I could only stand it for up to 20 minutes. But with running you get a variety of scenery and it's possible to run with someone else and talk to them while you're doing it if you want."

Joan has a coach in high school. She also has a coach on the AAU team she recently joined—the San Jose Cindergals. She had no sooner joined the Cindergals, though, than her arch injury occurred; she plans to return to the training swing with the Cindergals, though. According to Joan, the Cindergals' coach is excellent and she follows what he says they should do. During the summers, Joan coaches herself from intuition and experience.

The most memorable run in her life occurred last Thanksgiving when Joan and a friend ran so that they wouldn't feel guilty about stuffing themselves with all the Thanksgiving goodies. They ran toward the Perham Ranch, which is 7½ miles round-trip. "There's a mile and a half on a busy street, then a couple more miles on a not-so-busy street," she says. "Then you're practically in the country. Perham Ranch is great. All these trees on the sides of the path and a little creek. The trees were all the colors of autumn. As you go farther up the road you come to the farmhouse and barn and some animals—then you have the option of two paths. One follows the creek and is in a forest while the other goes toward the meadows; they're both uphill runs. I forget which one we took that day, but going past the barn and all the animals on Thanksgiving, just talking with a friend, was great. It gave me a contented feeling for the rest of the day."

SUNDARI MICHAELIAN
San Francisco, California

"I said to myself: Now I'm a marathoner! If I can do that I can do anything."

"I run because of my spiritual life first and foremost," says San Francisco's Sundari Michaelian. "In high school I hated track and most athletic pursuits.

"Sri Chinmoy was a great athlete in his youth and still is very athletic. He learned the tremendous value of physical exercise in mental and spiritual well-being, as well as just making the body strong and fit.

"He encouraged us to participate in sports and three times a year when we go to New York to see him, we have a miniature Olympics among ourselves (there are about 700 of us in all).

"At first I didn't enjoy it much, but a friend of mine, who loves running, helped me to appreciate the real joy of running, and now I'm really hooked.

"In my spiritual family, first we concentrated more on field events—now the emphasis is shifting toward long-distance running. Sri Chinmoy wants to have 300 of us run in this year's NYC Marathon.

"It's very inspiring to get so much joy out of running and to be with a group of people who share that."

Currently Sundari is running 35 minutes on Sunday, 40 on Monday, 25 on Tuesday, 40 on Wednesday, 25 on Thursday, 40 on Friday and 25 on Saturday. This is not, she stresses, typical of her week.

Before running, Sundari does toe-touching, calf-stretches, bent-knee sit-ups, hamstring stretches. Although she runs alone on most training runs, her sister runs and so do two other girls she lives with. When they run, the girls in her spiritual group wear hand-made nylon shorts that are very loose and comfortable, but long enough to be modest. She had been training in Nike Waffle Trainers, but when she became injured she changed to Brooks Vantages. Her longest run has been the New York City Marathon.

She reports that when she runs near her home or in Golden Gate Park, dogs never bother her. People seldom do, either... "only an occasionally overly friendly guy will be annoying. I don't enjoy the encouraging comments men make as I run by." Her main complaint is cars, and then her complaint centers on their exhausts.

Sri Chinmoy is her only coach, although she uses her intuition and reads whenever she has time. Her normal daily training runs are done at an 8:20-9:30 pace; her fast training runs at 8:00; and her fastest single mile was at 7:00.

She hopes to be able to get in enough training to run in the next NYC Marathon. She sees women being able to run a 2:20 marathon and feels that ultimately they will be able to run just as long, or longer than men.

When asked about her most memorable run, her first marathon experience in New York City was quick to come to mind:

"My friend and I had trained for three months and this was our first marathon. We were excited and scared at the same time.

"We flew to New York to be with Sri Chinmoy and the 31 other of his students who planned to run. For most of them it was also the first marathon. We were so excited, we had our uniforms all ready and each of the girls had a friend called an 'inspirer' who would join us at mile 19 (where we thought 'the wall' would come), and inspire us to the finish.

"We all drove to Staten Island in a bus giggling nervously, praying that we'd make it and whatever else might help us through at that moment.

"The huge crowd assembled, a cannon sounded and we were off. I'll never forget that experience. As I ran along I sang a song written by Sri Chinmoy for this marathon and it was very inspiring.

"As the song went on and on in my head the thousands of smiling, encouraging faces streamed by waving, slapping hands, offering drinks, giving advice and always encouraging. It was pure joy! At 19 miles I still felt strong; my inspirer joined me and we entered Central Park. The day was sunny, clear and about 40 degrees. By that time the slightest incline was a real hill to me. The last four miles were really endless and there was a point when I really didn't care if I even finished. I just kept praying that I would make it. I think I smiled the whole way, because the crowd was smiling and they loved it when we runners smiled back. They clapped and cheered. But for the last mile or so there was no smile—just determination to keep putting one foot in front of the other.

"Finally we rounded the last corner and I saw the finish banner. Devadip (Carlos Santana) and some other disciples of Sri Chinmoy's were playing electrified versions of some of Sri Chinmoy's songs right near it.

"Then just as I reached the final stretch, I saw my guru smiling at me and taking pictures as his 33 children passed. At that moment it all made perfect sense. I put on my biggest smile and charged up that final hill and through the chute to be handed a medallion, get wrapped in a space blanket and given gallons of Perrier.

"What a feeling! What a sense of accomplishment! I said to myself: Now I'm a marathoner! If I can do that I can do anything.

"It was one of the most significant experiences of my life."

CAROL L. IRVINE
Upper Marlboro, Maryland

"Women runners of all ages are helping to change the 'ideal woman' from a soft, fragile painted doll to a strong, natural human being."

Carol L. Irvine of Upper Marlboro, Maryland, is 31 years old and has been running off-and-on for four years, consistently for four months. Like many women, she began running to get in shape (which included losing weight). Similar to other women who have tried running, Carol found very quickly that one could very well run for running's sake and accept the benefits as a bonus. "I am still trying to lose more weight (I've lost 25 pounds, 15 of it while running), and I'm now trying to lose inches and become firm and lean.

"Since I started running," Carol explains, "I have enjoyed better health and a more positive outlook on life. I would like to be a runner all of my life. I have always enjoyed the outdoors and running takes me there. I am an explorer, and running helps orient me to my surroundings. I sleep better, eat more nutritionally, and enjoy relaxation more. If I eat foods that are wrong, it hurts my run, and knowing this makes it easier to avoid fattening foods.

"My boyfriend likes to see me as a runner. He doesn't run, but he encourages me to run, because he sees the good it does for me.

"When I meet someone for the first time, and learn that they run, I automatically feel like there is a bond. Other runners, for example, are very unlikely to smoke, so I'll not have to worry about that. Other runners are more likely to be healthy, which I enjoy, and also they are usually more stable and independent. These characteristics are an indication that any potential friendship will be comfortable and sound. And it's important to *be* the kind of friend you want to *have*."

Carol has been competing regularly in six and 10-mile runs in the Washington, D.C. area. She trains every day, doing four miles on Sunday, five miles on Tuesday, Thursday, and Saturday and eight miles on Monday, Wednesday, and Friday. During the week her training runs come in the afternoons, and they are done on weekend mornings. During the summer she runs in the evenings when it is cooler. Before training runs, she does slow toe-touches, wall presses, and side-leg stretches. She usually does her runs with her high school cross-country team; she is one of the coaches. She runs alone on weekends.

When she lived in a townhouse in Washington, D.C., most of Carol's runs were tours of the national monuments. "I ran around the monuments," she says, "from the Capitol down the mall, past the Smithsonian building, to Washington Monument, Lincoln Memorial, Kennedy Center, across the bridge to Arlington Cemetery, then back. Now I run at school to the Oxen Hill Manor & Children's Farm, down a mudslide to the banks of the Potomac River, along the river to a trail up to a subdivision and through the subdivisions back to school. During the summer we meet at Cosca Regional Park and run around a lake and up the power lines right-of-way or along the fire trails. There are farmlands and woods on that run. At home, I run along woods to a golf course or through the suburbs or down a highway past tobacco fields." She has run along highways, but doesn't like the exhaust fumes or the noise or the road surface.

How about the matter of women deriving something different from running than men? "I don't know. . . it seems that women aren't as vocally competitive as men, but they can still get many similar benefits—a feeling of strength, health and peace. Women runners I talk to are sounding like they are gaining in self-confidence, that here is something they can do as well as men—maybe not in speed, but in getting fit. When I run in women's races, I feel like these are my sisters, and that we're all working together to help one another."

Carol's training runs average 10 minutes per mile; her fastest mile time is 7:30—during the first mile of a Bonne Bell race.

Her goals are to run a marathon someday and to increase her speed, so she's competitive in her age group.

We asked Carol to prepare a speech that she might give to women:

"Today, we often hear women speaking out for women's rights. Stereotyping is a major obstacle to the liberation of people, the liberation to do what feels right or natural to them. The feminist movement is not trying to make all women leave behind their previous roles, as much as it is encouraging each woman to do what is most satisfying to her as an individual. Women runners are successfully demonstrating the logic of doing what is natural for them. As women break through barriers that were arbitrarily set up (such as running long distances), they are proving that not only are some women talented athletes, but by their numbers, they are showing that many women are strong, fit individuals. Women runners of all ages are helping to change the 'ideal woman' from a soft, fragile painted doll to a strong, natural human being. Once women are commonly accepted as physically capable of feats of endurance, perhaps then it will be easier to bring down obstacles in the world of work and family. With our health comes a new, stronger self-confidence, and a willingness to speak up for our rights. It may be the runners of America who bring about a new consciousness and a new zeal to American society."

JUDITH A. KELLEY
Washington, D.C.

"I run for the mental benefits. The physical ones have come along free of charge."

"My husband was already addicted (to running) and I wanted to share some of that time. Also, we were living in Eugene, Oregon, at that time, so it was practically *de rigueur*. We lived very close to Hayward Field and used the track often. We decided to participate in a Jog-a-Thon to raise money to resurface that track, so I trained for two months with that initial goal in mind," says Judith A. Kelly, who now lives in Washington, D.C.

Training runs now come whenever it's possible to fit them into a flexible schedule between jobs. "I run from Foggy Bottom in Georgetown to the Lincoln Memorial or the Washington Monument or across Memorial Bridge to Virginia and back, or to Iwo Jima Memorial or Roosevelt Island or up the C&O Canal towpath or up to the National Zoo," she says. "Our proximity to Rock Creek Park makes it very pleasant for an urban environment. I am originally from northeastern Pennsylvania, though, so when we go to visit my parents, we run in a beautiful rural setting, with huge hills and remote fields where deer and other animals stare at us in wonder. We're the only runners in the area, I suspect."

Why does Judith run? "I am a complicated, screwy person who can worry about nothing, stew about everything, imagine the worst, carry on about the nonessentials, and otherwise make myself miserable," she says. "I create barriers for myself constantly.

"But on the other hand, I am a bright, creative free spirit who can get so buzzed up about an idea or project that I won't be able to sleep or I'll forget to eat. I like to try to say I project a positivism about my life and inject that in others.

"What running helps do for me is make the disparities between those two personality factors more even, more consistent. When I have problems or tensions or emotional blocks, running acts as a release and a purifier. It can be a great calming force and a great renewer.

"I run for the mental benefits. The physical ones have come along free of charge. I have toned up considerably, lost some weight; I do have more energy and sleep more soundly. I have more confidence and believe in myself more."

Any problems while running? "Not really," Judith says. "I'm a cautious person by nature and try to avoid any situations that might cause a problem (i.e., solitary males on an isolated trail, stray dogs, etc.). I wear a whistle on my wrist and try to avoid routes where I will have to cross heavily-traveled streets."

How about support from the family and friends? "Many of my friends are runners, and I might be considered the hostile one because I am more sensitive to my inadequacies as compared to them. Most are stronger, faster; I'll probably always be a back-of-the-pack runner. My parents and siblings think it is quite rare for me to be doing this, I think. I remember buying a subscription to ***Runner's World*** through my sister's high school magazine drive and my mother remarked: 'What could they possibly say in a whole magazine about running?' "

Does a woman derive something special from running that a man does not? "The feeling of success and control over one's body is a very positive aspect that is probably new to many women (and perhaps some men). Many men, however, having participated in sports in their youth, know the exhilaration and self-confidence this instills."

There are some benefits unique to women, though. "Physiologically, I know my digestion is better and my menstrual cycle is more even. I experience little periodic pain when I have run on a regular schedule for the previous month. This month's erratic schedule resulted in horrible cramps, so my body is definitely giving me strong encouragement to exercise regularly."

As far as the fabled "runner's high" goes, Judith has her own version: "The closest would be a run Bill and I did in Pennsylvania this past spring. There is an old dirt road that snakes through the woods in a big five-mile loop that Bill has run often. Even though it surrounds my father's land, I had only been on it once before in my life. We started running at about 7:00 p.m. It was almost dusk and I did not plan to run all the way around. But I kept going, even though it was getting really dark. We were deep in the woods when it seemed like a storm was brewing. The wind howled through the hemlocks; the other bare trees swayed wildly; the dead leaves scurried across our path. Bill was really excited. Thunder cracked; lightning flashed. He loved it. I was uneasy but tried to drink it all in. He took my hand and reassured me. We darted through the rain. We did two huge hills and finished in triumph."

FRAN CRAWFORD
San Francisco, California

"There is a thrill to meeting goals and pushing to the limit."

"My most memorable run was the 1978 Dipsea [a grueling cross-country run up and down mountains in Mill Valley, California]," says San Franciscan Fran Crawford, who ran her first marathon (Avenue of the Giants in 4:37) a month earlier. "This was the third time I've run the race, and the most exciting thing about it this time was that I could really see how much improvement I've made in running. I was so much stronger, and I ran much more than the first time (there's always a lot of walking at the Dipsea).

"The best part of the run was when I was going downhill—and just flying—the hills and stops were behind me. It's such an indescribable feeling—because I feel so loose, free and powerful. I had to go as fast as I could because people were behind, wanting to pass and there was only room for one on the trail. I had enough strength and running experience so I was able to push more on the whole run—and even more so on the downhills. The weather was perfect this year, too—foggy and cool."

Fran is 27, 5'8" and 131 pounds; she's been running for 3½ years. Reluctant to give in to her sister's encouragement that she run, she finally did so and now races as much as 46 weekends out of the year, primarily with the local running club, the Dolphin South End Runners.

"At first I ran to keep in shape," Fran admits. "I was losing weight and wanted to firm up. I didn't enjoy it, except for the feeling of exercising and working out that I knew was doing me good. I couldn't even run ¾-mile. I don't know how I managed to keep it up. It was over six months before I started to look forward to running.

"Now I don't even think about my running. It is something I do, like brushing my teeth. It is something I manage to fit into my life because I want to do it. It makes me feel so healthy and strong—I can't describe the feeling—it's hard to imagine myself overeating and having hangovers like I did before. I feel empty if I go without running for too long—and I get so envious of other runners I see who are able to run better than I do.

"I don't always get the runner's high that is so talked about, but I do get a tremendous calm after a good run. So many problems disappear or lessen in importance. I am so proud of my achievements in running. It has given me a tremendous amount of confidence. I have never done anything to be proud of before. Running is something I did for myself.

"There are so many benefits I could talk about. One of the best is being able to consume *tons* of food without gaining weight. I've lost some weight, but the main effect on my body has been in toning up: my thighs are firm like they've never been before. My veins are larger so I have an easier time giving blood. My circulation has improved so I don't have cold hands and feet all the time."

Fran's training includes seven-mile runs on Saturdays and Sundays, Fridays off, and four-mile runs Monday through Thursday. She trains at an 8:30 pace, runs races at an 8:00 pace, and does her fastest miles below 7:30 pace.

Given a soapbox from which to speak to other women, Fran Crawford says she would stress the following four points:

"Stick with it. Don't expect the 'runner's high' at first. You have to build up to it, and it is a lot of hard work if you're unathletic and out of shape. Just do it gradually and increase the speed and/or distance at a rate that feels comfortable for you.

"Make a commitment to running. Strive to get enjoyment out of it. You have to do it for an extended period of time. You can't go out for a week or two and expect a great experience from it. Even if you are only running a few times a week for short periods, be consistent in at least doing *that.*

"Don't think or worry about your running. Just get out and start doing it. That's the hardest part. After that you can start worrying about the proper shoes, running styles, and all those other details.

"Listen to your body. Run according to how you feel. Don't think you have to follow a schedule from a book or a friend. You're the one who has to enjoy it. Don't make it an ordeal."

By approaching running with the correct attitude, Fran feels that more and more women will enjoy the sport and that the natural talent that has been untapped in most women will surface to bring a groundswell of good, competitive runners to the fore—runners who will push records down drastically, especially in the marathon.

Fran's prime inspiration in her running has been Walt Stack, 70-year-old president of the Dolphin South End club, even though, she says, he doesn't remember her face. "First of all he created the DSE which has been the biggest factor in my improvement in running and in sticking with it. He is always encouraging and positive—especially to the slower runners like I was at first, and especially to woman runners. He has also been a goal to beat; he still beats me in the longer runs. He is always an inspiration because of his enthusiasm, warmth and his disregard of age."

WENDY SAYRES
Auburn, Maine

"Two years ago, I couldn't imagine running a 9.2-mile race, much less a marathon. Who knows?"

Wendy Sayres of Auburn, Maine began running four years ago. Her husband gave her a pair of running shoes for Christmas; she ignored them for six months, and they gathered dust in the back of a closet. There was no way a pair of running shoes was going to lure her into running like her husband had been doing.

Curiosity about running and the frugal New England spirit that told her there was something wrong with allowing a perfectly good pair of running shoes go to waste got Wendy onto the rural roads around her house. Now she says it would be a letdown to have to skip running. "It really would take something out of daily living—that feel-better-all-over feeling that comes after 45 minutes of fresh air and sweat," she says.

She trains usually six days a week, doing three miles on Monday, Tuesday, and Thursday, five miles on Friday and 5-8 miles on Wednesday and Saturday; Sunday is usually a day of rest or racing. Wendy's run races from three miles to 15 kilometers; she races 10-12 times a year. Training runs come at 5:50 a.m. during the week and during the afternoons on weekends. Her warm-up consists of the Royal Canadian Air Force exercises, level three, and several of the *Runner's World* stretches. She runs alone, although her husband puts in 35 miles per week during down periods, more when he's training for a marathon, while her son does 95 mile per week training. Wendy's longest run has been 10.5 miles.

The only trouble she's ever encountered on runs were two

inebriated boys who threw rocks on one occasion, and an occasional churlish dog. The only injury she has had is a periodically recurring sore Achilles tendon.

Wendy is a voracious reader of running material and rates the inspiration she gains from reading about running right behind her husband's encouragement as the moving force in her running and as her coach.

As far as women gaining different things from running than men do, she feels that there's little truth to that. "Perhaps," she adds, "the fact that a few years ago most women never dreamed of running three or five or ten miles easy each day, much less competing in road races with men, makes women's running a little special. In the sports programs of my generation's schools and colleges, running was never even mentioned."

Special runs to her are those on which she encounters Maine wildlife or in which dramatic weather systems sweep through Maine while she is on the run, which happens in three out of the four seasons. One such weather pattern moving in provided her most memorable run:

"Perhaps the most memorable run was an eight or nine mile perambulation with a friend of mine down the eastern side of Isle au Haut (eight miles out to sea off the Maine coast) along the island's solitary road. We were nearing the halfway point of the run, where we planned to turn around and head back toward home, running past a pebblestone beach called Boom Beach, when a terrific thunderstorm came up. There were no houses within two miles and no large trees to hide under and I was scared to death. My friend was not bothered in the least by the flashes and crashes while I was anxiously counting each second between sighting the lightning and hearing the thunder.

"We reversed directions and were heading back down the road when the welcome sight of a 1950 Ford Customline coupe greeted us. The car contained my husband and my friend's husband. Wet and grateful for rescue, I jumped into the back seat. That's one day I didn't mind ending my run early."

Wendy's training runs are done at approximately 8:00 pace, while her latest mini-marathon was done at a 6:00 pace. Her goal is to be the best woman runner in her age group (40-50) in the state of Maine. She says she has no immediate plans to become a marathoner, but she has not discounted the idea a little farther along in her career. "Two years ago I couldn't imagine running a 9.2-mile race, much less a marathon. Who knows?"

The first and foremost influence on her running continues to be her husband. "He cheers me on at races, gives me hints and encouragement—and even flattery. Joan Ullyot is pretty super also as far as inspiring the woman runner," she concludes.

PAT JENNINGS
Oakland, California

"I run to break out of my shell. Out of my conventional self."

Pat Jennings of Oakland, California, is 35 years old and has been running for a little more than two years. She came to running through the back door, having become interested in exercise first, and then deciding to go running with some of her female friends who were using running as one form of exercise. She now runs a race each week, anywhere from four to 15 miles in distance.

Her weekly training mileage is considerable. She runs 7-8 miles on Monday, Wednesday and Friday, 8-9 miles on Thursday, 10 miles on Tuesday, races on Sunday and uses Saturday as a rest day. She does her training in the afternoon and uses the pre-run stretching sequence from the May 1978 issue of *Runner's World*, which is being accepted as the standard by most runners. Most of her runs are alone, but she does run with friends twice a week.

Pat's husband runs about 20 miles a week and takes part in the races; her middle son, who is nine years old, races up to eight miles but trains very little; and her youngest son, seven years old, runs up to five miles in the races "when the spirit moves him."

Her training runs are done in an urban environment, usually near the University of California. "Because I run alone I like to run where other people are running," Pat said. "I regularly run on a track and do two or three miles there as part of my run. I run fire trails but enjoy them more when I have a running companion."

Why does Pat run? "I run because I *can do it*. I have never been athletic and running is a perfect sport. I can improve in distance and speed simply by putting in the miles," she said. "It's a game I play with myself. How much can you run? Every day? How far? Does it hurt? How much does it hurt? I write everything down in my log book. I like to add up the totals each month. I like to see where gaps occur and why.

"I run to break out of my shell. Out of my conventional self. I put on shorts and a shirt in colors and styles I do not normally tolerate and run places I'm self-conscious to walk through. Running is my alter-ego. It makes me feel good. It's an accomplishment. Amaze your friends and family. That's me. Besides, it keeps me in good shape—and I enjoy being able to eat and drink what I want without worrying about gaining weight."

How do her family and friends react to her running? "My mom questions my sanity. She thinks I should be improving my bustline and not my legs," she says.

Pat feels that women *do* derive certain things from running that men do not. "I need to get away from the kids, from the laundry, from the dishes," she said. "I need to be rejuvenated every afternoon. I need to be younger, more beautiful, trimmer."

As far as memorable runs go, Pat says that her most memorable is a *bad* memory. "That was the Pepsi 20-miler last November," she explains. "I *thought* I was prepared, but I had never run over 15 miles (and had done 15 miles only three or four times). The day was overcast with the sun pushing through—one of the ugliest light situations as far as I am concerned. The course is *flat* out and back, and I don't like flat. It was 20 miles and by 13 miles I wanted to stop. My calf muscles were exploding. Aid stations were out of liquids. By 15 miles I was walking/running. Walter Stack passed me. By 18 miles I was sitting on the edge of the road, needing my 'mommy' for the first time in many years. I wanted to cry. The rest got me another mile with relatively little pain. I passed some folks. Then the pain began again. Had anyone offered me a ride I would have taken it. Vans were carrying weary runners to the finish line, but I couldn't *ask* for a ride. I would have accepted a ride with 400 yards to go! As I was coming over the finish line, I heard someone comment that they (meaning we slow runners) are like the ones that finish a marathon at 4:30. That was a crushing statement. I hurt just as much as a fast runner. I ran just as far. And it was harder. Give me credit. Give me a Pepsi. Give me another chance this year."

SUSAN PARISH
Syracuse, New York

"It was an experience comparable only to losing my virginity."

"I began running for all the usual reasons," says Susan Parish of Syracuse, New York. "I began to run to lose weight, to tighten muscles, those kind of things. However, after a couple of months my reasons began changing. My attitude then was to see how much my body could do, how much longer and faster could it go? Now, after almost a year, my daily run has become the focal point of my day. I look forward to it. It helps me run out the tensions of the day—to have that time alone to think. But the physical side is important, too. To be outside in any kind of weather makes you really appreciate the subtle changes of seasons and the world around you.

"I guess the greatest benefits I get from running are the good feelings about myself. I look better, I'm more relaxed, and I have a good concept of who I am and what I can do. I run because I have to run. I don't feel complete without those daily runs."

Susan began running informally in the fall of 1976 when the pools and the beaches closed. "I felt some kind of rigorous exercise was needed every day." She has since run two 10,000 meter races and one 5000-meter.

Her daily training schedule follows those set down in Joe Henderson's book, *Jog, Run, Race* (World Publications, 1977): 45 minutes Sunday, 15 minutes Monday and Tuesday, 30 minutes Wednesday, 15 minutes Thursday, 30 minutes Friday and a rest day Saturday.

Most of the people in Susan's life support her running, although her mother thought that a bit of insanity had crept into the family tree when Susan contemplated her first race. Susan's boyfriend is sometimes annoyed by the time she spends running, but he has recently bought a pair of Nikes and occasionally joins her on a run.

Like most runners today, Susan has no coach, but picks up advice from reading *Runner's World* and good running books.

On the matter of her reaction to laying off running for any amount of time, she is quite emphatic. Would it affect you? "Yes!!!" she answers. "I've never been able to lay off more than two or three days at a time. I've run half-miles when I should have been in bed from being sick. But the running made me feel better. It bothers me to stop running because I feel that I'm losing or getting behind in my training. Even though I know that sometimes it really can be more harmful to go out and run. I get very bitchy and my schedule gets all upset when I can't run. I don't know what to do with the time running fills," she says.

Susan also has some strong feelings on what women can—and should—get from running: "I feel that basically women derive many of the same things that men do. Personally, I feel that running gives me the freedom to be more feminine. Many women today are concerned with being tough and they feel they have to dress and act manly to prove it. I am tough. When it's ninety degrees or nine degrees, when it's raining or I've got shin splints to my ears, I'm out there doing it, and you can bet I'm tough. But when I come home it's to the bath oils and perfume, clean hair, and clean from head to toes. My toughness is internal. I love to wear dresses. I love being a woman."

When it comes to memorable runs, Susan's first race comes to mind. "It was the Bonne Bell mini in Boston on October 9, 1977," she says. "I wasn't really prepared for this race, having only run about 1¾ miles as my longest run—and that was only for two nights prior to the race.

"But it just happened that I would be in Boston on that day, so I entered. It was very cool; I was uncomfortable in shorts and shirts. I was also nervous. But the mood at the starting line was great.

"Once the race began I knew it would be okay. I seemed to get right in the groove. But the best part of the race was the spectators. They lined the entire course and gave moral support the whole way. They really kept me going.

"I'm still not certain of my time. Something around 64 minutes, I think. I was tired but felt great and just kind of walked around in a daze for a while. It was an experience comparable only to losing my virginity. That race changed my attitude from being a fitness runner into being a runner to be a runner."

LINDA PALTER
Washington, D.C.

"I loved to run as a child, and I've rediscovered it as an adult."

Linda Palter of Washington, D.C., 31 years old, found herself taking a long, honest look at herself 2½ years ago when someone asked her, "When's the last time you ran across the street?" and she couldn't remember. "I felt that I was too tired to go for a walk and I knew something was very wrong," she said. "So I decided it was time to run, to do something physical with myself."

Linda takes her running very personally, races occasionally for fun, getting most of her benefits from the autonomy it provides her. Despite the fact that she does not race, her training is as regular as runners who race every weekend. She runs two miles on Monday, three miles on Tuesday, Wednesday, Friday and Saturday, 4-5 miles on Thursday and 6-7 miles on Sunday. "I try to take one day off every few weeks," Linda says, "but it's difficult!"

She runs at noon and sometimes trains after work near her health club close to the Potomac River, a very scenic route that provides some good bike paths. She also trains at the American University track, seldom on concrete surfaces.

Preparatory to her training runs, she does a variety of stretching exercises, including calf-hamstring-body stretches, yoga plow, touching toes, etc. She always does 5-6 minutes of stretches *after* her runs. She usually runs alone, but is sometimes joined by a friend during her lunchtime runs; in the evenings she runs alone, unless she has a track session. No one else in her family runs.

When asked why she runs, Linda was prepared with several reasons: "If you eat a proper diet, you enhance your physical body and your health. If you get a good education, you take advantage of your experiences and take responsibility for your own learning and development, you enhance your mind. If you live in the present, accept others as they are and learn to love and share that love through communication, you enhance your spirit. At least that's what I'm told. But, if you run, you do all three. You balance your body with your mind with your spirit. It seems almost magical.

"A man once told me he related to the 'sportsperson' in me. It nearly blew my mind. No one had ever said that before! I developed a self-confidence that at times seems virtually indestructible. After running 10 miles, I know I'm okay.

"Other people have been motivated to engage in a physical fitness program just by observing my increased energy level. My office-mates are favoring fresh fruits and veggies instead of Big Macs and some report daily their latest running accomplishments. It's all quite a compliment.

"Running decreases my nervous appetite; running increases my healthy appetite. Running equals more oxygen equals more vitality for life.

"Running feels good. It's never difficult to feel what's right if you're in tune with yourself; let the right thing you're doing take over. Running is right."

Linda has had shin splints and one stress fracture—which is why she gave up training exclusively on hard surfaces. She has learned from her injuries, however. "When I fractured my foot, my family was more concerned about my physical well-being while my friends were concerned with my mental well-being." She pays attention to the difference between the pain of challenge and the pain of injury. "One can only tell the difference by being in touch and not asking another person," she says.

Linda's runs are done at an eight-minute-per-mile average and she sometimes dips down to a 7:30 pace. Her primary goal is to keep running without getting major injuries that will disable her; her secondary goal is to get others interested in running. "I'm careful not to push my trip on others," she says. "Not everyone likes apple pie or aspires to motherhood. If you know what I mean."

What was Linda's most memorable run? "About six months before I turned 30, I had set myself a goal of running five miles on one run. I was running about two or three miles at a time. And, as I recall, the plateau I was about to go beyond was seemingly impossible to me. If the 3-5 mile plateau was going to be as hard to accomplish as the 0-2 mile plateau, it was really going to be a challenge.

"The run, which I did five months later, was begun. Expectation ridden, I had decided *this* was the day. Carefully computed fractions of a course I had run many times before would finally add up to *five*. First time around no big deal. Second time a real challenge. Third time, could I manage it? A surprise was in store. All of a sudden there was strength. I finished my five miles stronger than my second lap. It wasn't just the run that was so significant, but the implication that there are levels of plateaus—and one of them is in the mind."

ANNE H. PATE
New York, New York

"As women move toward achieving equality with men, their biggest handicap is their own self-image."

Ann H. Pate of New York City is thirty-six years old and has been running for fifteen months. She originally began running in an attempt to increase her stamina for her karate classes. Since beginning to run, Ann has competed in four races, two of them 6.2-milers, one a four-miler and another a five-miler. During the course of a week she does between 13 and 14½ miles of training; she does one mile on Monday, between one and one and a half miles on Tuesday, Wednesday and Friday, and three miles on Sunday, Thursday and Saturday. Her runs are done in the early morning, around 6:00 a.m.

Preparatory to her training runs, Ann does deep knee bends, does bounces on each leg with legs spread, and does hamstring stretches. She usually runs with her two dogs. Her boyfriend usually runs with her three times a week. She trains in Puma Easy Riders, but prefers Nike Cortez; she races in Tiger Jay-hawks. Her longest run to date has been a seven-miler.

She usually does her training in Central Park and around Great Lawn. She starts her run when she leaves her door and hits the street.

Most of her friends are supportive of her running, as they, too, are into sports, mostly karate. Her son calls his mother "Super-Jock." Other people and coworkers are mildly disapproving and her mother tells her, "you're going to kill yourself."

As far as women deriving something from running other than what men derive, she feels that their realization that they can be physical just as men can is the main difference. She trains at a nine-minute pace and hopes to be ready to compete in the New York City Marathon.

Given a soapbox from which to address other women, this would be Ann's speech:

"As women move toward achieving equality with men their biggest handicap is their own self-image. Women can be as smart, as strong, as sharp, as fast as men, but if they do not perceive themselves as capable of achievement they won't achieve. One of the most important ways to achieve a positive self-image is through running. Running increases the sense of self. A woman learns that if she can control her body she can control anything. Running increases your health—you feel terrific and you look terrific. You have enormous stamina. You can keep going all day.

"Another thing about running is that anyone can do it. If anyone had told me five years ago that I would be able to run six miles I'd have said they were crazy. I couldn't run a couple of blocks, much less a mile. But learning to run has taught me that with work, training and perseverance, I can do anything. I had always known that I could make intellectual accomplishments but to learn that I could be strong physically was a revelation.

"Running gives you a tremendous sense of accomplishment. You learn that you aren't going to die from a little pain in your chest or your legs. You will be less sick, have fewer colds, sleep better, though I never had a problem there. The most sedentary endomorph can be a runner. I had never had anything to do with sports in high school or college and was in pretty sloppy shape five years ago.

"You should also think of racing. That really blew my mind. It was incredible the things you perceive. Racing with men is important, too, in order to learn to be less afraid of competing with them in other fields. Who knows how the world might change if all women started running. . . ."

Ann sees her boyfriend, who makes her run fast and who encourages her to race, as being the person with the most positive influence on her running.

She here describes her most memorable run:

"The best run I had was the first time I ran over 1½ miles. My boyfriend, Charlie, and I were visiting friends in New Hampshire over Labor Day weekend last year. Charlie and I decided to run down to the town and our friend Joel agreed to drive down and meet us. The plan was for us to have breakfast at the Coffee Shop and Joel would drive us back to the house.

"It was a beautiful, clear day, warm but not hot, between summer and fall. I was really scared starting out since I'd never run that far. We took my dog, Bow, along too. We started out together and after a mile Charlie was well ahead of me. Bow ran back and forth between us but finally stayed to keep me company. In the car it had always seemed downhill to the town, but there sure were plenty of hills on foot. I counted six and each one was a struggle. Twice dogs came out barking and snarling at me. I thought one was going to get Bow but the owner called it back. I was really getting tired and kept looking for the sign marking Hillsborough town limits.

"I was determined to reach the town before Joel drove by. Finally, I hit the town's sidewalks and I knew I'd made it. I ran on down the five or six blocks to where Joel and Charlie were waiting. They said they'd just gotten there. Charlie was amazed I was so close behind him. We put Bow in the car and went for breakfast. I couldn't eat anything but wanted lots to drink—water, tea, orange juice. I felt rather spacy for a while but terrific.

"This marked a real turning point in that, for the first time, I felt I could be a real runner. The next month, with Charlie's encouragement, we went to Boston where I ran my first race: the Bonne Bell Mini-Marathon."

ALLAIN SCHNABLE
Brookline, New Hampshire

"When you criticize another woman and her attempts to be happy, you may ultimately be putting yourself down."

"I run for me," says Allain Schnable of Brookline, New Hampshire. "I've always enjoyed sports (in summer camp I was fond of archery, volleyball, sprinting) but was always short of breath. I had to be taken out of half-court basketball games.

"My husband encouraged me to run, but I'd try and I'd get so tired I'd hate it and give up. I'm also stubborn and won't do something just because someone wants me to. After several attempts at beginning, I got very excited about running after seeing a track meet up close (a winter, indoor meet). I went home and began using a 1/8-mile loop from my front door. It was difficult at first but I enjoyed it.

"I continued and during a year's training, extended it to one mile with a tough hill. No other women in my neighborhood ran, although some later began running under cover of darkness. I wasn't really interested in upping my distance. I'm very slow (four years later, I'm doing 10-minute miles), but the breathing got easier and my legs became stronger.

"I found another woman to run with, but she wanted to do more distance, races, etc. I increased my distance somewhat and had run in one three-mile race when I met her. I sometimes felt competitive with her, but I realized, too, that my own abilities at that point would make it impossible to keep up with her. In subsequent races and longer runs I learned to accept my inability and to compare myself only with myself. I think that I'm probably very competitive down deep, but my common sense in knowing my level of ability holds me back and allows me to accept running for what it does for me."

Allain reports that she trains inconsistently because of her work and night school schedule. She usually takes Saturdays off, while running three miles on Sundays and Fridays, two miles on Mondays and Wednesdays, four miles on Tuesdays and five miles on Thursdays.

Most of her training is done in the evenings, especially in the winter months. Before her runs, she does toe-touches without bouncing, hamstring stretches, 10-15 sit-ups and a variety of stretches for the Achilles tendons.

She prefers to run alone now, but liked to have company when she was starting. Her husband runs about 60 miles a week; her sister runs about seven miles a week. She is partial to Nike training shoes, currently doing her training in the Waffle Trainer. Her longest single run was 8½ miles.

Her courses are primarily rural. "I vary the course," she says. "From my house I go up the main road 1/8 mile to a housing development, do a ⅔-mile loop and come back. Or I go up the road 8/10-mile, move onto some wooded trails in the conservation area, and go 2½ miles, then back home—or continue from there onto another road and then home (which is 3½ miles total). There are a variety of courses available to me by running out my front door."

If she had to stop running, Allain feels it would bother her quite a bit because she likes being more physically fit and keeping her body in shape. She also feels that running dissipates stress that can build up at work, and that is a very important aspect of running. Running is an individual thing, and what a person gets from it has nothing to do with his or her sex. The greatest shortcomings in her running program are that she feels she does not have enough talent and that she doesn't push herself as much as other people do. Her goal, however, is to continue running for the rest of her life.

If given the opportunity to address a group of women, this would be Allain's speech:

"I'd like to speak to you this morning on a very important topic—us. It seems that we are being divided into factions and I'd like to try to clear the issues a bit. I hear women calling each other names—unfeminine, aggressive, homewreckers, weirdo, etc. Frankly, I don't understand it. Yes, I do understand it in my own way, and that's why I decided to talk to you.

"If ever in the history of womankind, we should feel closer now. Why? Because now we have choices. You and I can, to some extent, be more of what each of us wants to be as individuals. We don't need to look at our sex first and then map out a life's course. So, come on, let's give each other the freedom and growing space we're finally taking for ourselves. Let's not be so quick to judge another lifestyle. If your neighbor has always wanted to be a bricklayer, hurdler, mother, physicist, and she reaches her goal, be happy for her. Because, you know, when you criticize another woman and her attempts to be happy, you may ultimately be putting yourself down."

Allain describes her most memorable run:

"I started out at four o'clock on a September afternoon. It was going to be dusk by the time I returned so I started up the two-mile hill near my house. I tried to keep loose and jog extremely slowly as the trail is always a killer for me, especially just starting out. As I moved along I was surprised at how quickly it was going by and believe me, I knew just how many corners, up and downs there were on the course.

"When I arrived at the far end I was elated. I felt it was too dusky to go back into the woods because of the difficulty in seeing branches that a runner could trip over, so I took the alternate route (three miles around). No one was on the dirt road that night as I headed downhill. It was so quiet at that moment in time, just the early part of the evening, one of my favorite of all times, and I jogged slowly and peacefully. I felt my conditioning all come together that day. At other times I'd reach the top and have to stop until I could catch my breath and stop my pounding heart. I continued my way home, finally coming down to the main road, which, blissfully, was uncrowded.

"I wasn't flying, but just going along, comfortably, and I knew that when I got home I'd have done five miles and not be wiped out. That was pretty exciting. When I did get home, after running the *entire* way, my husband said he'd noticed it took a long time to go up and back on the trail. When I told him I'd gone all the way around, I enjoyed the shocked look on his face."

JOANNE ERNST
Medford, Oregon

"Certainly women should be allowed to run distance events (marathon included) in the Olympic Games. What an injustice!"

Joanne Ernst, 19 years old, of Medford, Oregon, has been running seriously for four years. "I always liked to run as a child and experienced success in grade school competition," she said. "So, when I had the opportunity to join an AAU club in Boulder, I did. I run collegiate cross-country now on Stanford University's varsity team. I run the scheduled meets and also enter some road races in the off-season, averaging about one a month."

Her fairly typical schedule of training for the off-months (i.e., when there is no cross-country competition) includes either a rest day or a long run on Sunday, 6-10 mile runs on Monday, Wednesday and Friday, 10-15 miles on Tuesday and Thursday, and sometimes a race or another long day on Saturday. She always runs according to how she feels. "I feel very guilty if I don't run, but I don't force myself if I'm not looking forward to it," she said.

She usually trains in the morning because of the cooler temperatures and because there are less people about in the early morning. During cross-country season she trains in the afternoon with the team. She does various stretches from a standing position, concentrating on relaxing the back, hips, and legs; she also does the hurdle-stretch and sit-ups. Her training at school is usually done with one other person, while at home she trains either with friends or alone.

Her brother, also 19 years old, lives in Boulder and runs five days a week; he is building toward running a marathon. Joanne's training is done in Nike Waffle Trainers, which she's found good for her needs during the past 2½ years. She runs cross-country meets in Nike Oregon Waffles and runs on the track in Nike Intervals. Her longest run has been 15 miles, which she's done repeatedly. Most of her longer runs are done at Stanford University in a fairly suburban/rural environment. "I often run past freeways, but tend to stay on less frequently traveled roads," she reports. "I really hate running with car exhausts. In Colorado, my favorite runs were in the hills or mountain trails outside Boulder."

Running, Joanne feels, helps her make it through the day. "It relieves the tensions which build up inside of me. I feel good physically and emotionally when I run. I feel more confident about myself, and like myself better."

She reports that when she has to lay off running she suffers mental anguish. "I become irritable without training, even after a day or two. I begin to feel fat and this makes me even more irritable. And then I know it will hurt to get back in shape again. But it's mostly mental anguish.

She has had no "supernatural highs," "but I have often felt as if I were just floating above the road, with no consciousness of the physical effort I was making."

She trains at a pace between 7:00 and 8:00 per mile; her fastest timed mile was as a senior in high school when she did a 5:30.

Her goal in running is to continue running forever. "Life without running would probably send me to my death faster than anything else I can think of," she said.

Her speech to women is short and to the point: "If you are tired of being fat, run. If you are weary of boredom, run. If you want to gain some self-respect, run. For me, running is probably the most satisfying part of my life. Its benefits are both physical and emotional. In every aspect of my life I find that running increases the pleasure I derive from it. So, if you are willing to expend some energy for a self-made miracle, put on some running shoes, step out the door, and run."

She feels that the tremendous increase in women runners will increase this country's chances of a good showing on the international level. "The popularity of running brings out women with hidden talent and encourages women with known talents to keep up their efforts. The majority of women runners do run for recreation, but this leads the women with talent to the right places."

She feels, too, that women runners are just beginning to realize what they are capable of accomplishing. "Certainly women should be allowed to run distance events (marathon included) in the Olympic Games. What an injustice!" she says.

The person who has had the most positive effect on Joanne's running was Roger Briggs, her high school cross-country coach. "I was the first girl to go out for the team and he encouraged me to do my best. He also was the first person to emphasize to me the goal of running all through my life."

Joanne reports that she does not have a most memorable run. She does, however, have a favorite location for running. A location where the runs have blended together into one run she likes to think about. "The location is the Mesa Trail, above Boulder. It is a hilly (mountainous) run. I would run there in the morning or in early evening. The rhythm of the hills would put me into a floating state. The trees and wildlife were fantastic. I often saw deer. I loved to run this area with one or two other people, and we would just drift along peacefully. I was always sad to come back down to the roads after this run. And, I think about it often. It is kind of my dream run when I'm away from Boulder. Try it sometime. It's great!"

MARY ANNE McBRAVER
Houston, Texas

"Love is a husband who runs at your pace."

Mary Anne McBraver of Houston became involved in running in a rather unique way. Her husband, who had been running for some time, put a note in her Christmas stocking one year asking her if she'd please give running a try. It had become a very big part of his life and he wanted her to share it. That evening she joined him and it has played a prominent part in both their lives since then. That was 6½ years ago.

Mary Anne enters at least two races per month except in the summer when it's too hot; the races are usually 10 kilometers or over. Her typical training week (when she's not training for a marathon) consists of a ten-miler on Sunday, five miles on Monday and Thursday, six miles on Tuesday, Wednesday and Friday, and seven miles on Saturday. She usually has no normal time for training—she does it when she feels like it. Through the summer months she always runs in the morning in order to avoid the heat. She does pre-run stretches, mostly using yoga postures. Most of her training runs are alone; on weekends she and her husband join friends for a run. During marathon training, though, Mary Anne and her husband run together in the evenings. There are very few people, Mary Anne reports, who are runners in her neighborhood. Besides her husband running, four of their five children do running in spurts, the three girls usually doing it when they feel as though they've had a "fat week."

Mary Anne trains and races in Brooks Villanovas. She is on her third pair.

The longest distance she has run is the marathon, but she more frequently does 20-milers.

When asked why she continues to run, Mary Anne had many reasons. "It has become both a physical necessity and a mental balm. Physically, I know I am in excellent shape; my resting pulse is 38-42; my cholesterol and triglycerides are low; my weight is lower than it was in high school, even though I must still watch what I eat. I can gain weight very quickly even running over fifty miles per week. It's disgusting, but that's the way my metabolism works.

"So there are a lot of reasons to keep running. I forgot to mention the social aspect. We have certainly added to our acquaintances and friends, and have made some really good friends. Running is something my husband and I can share; we have some really great talks during long training runs. It is our time to ourselves. We find time to share the days during running. He is very good about running at my pace, and to me, love is a husband who runs at your pace."

Mary Anne has had some very real problems on the run. "Two German shepherds jumped me one day and I really thought I was going to be mauled. However, a man stopped his truck and came running, swinging a chain. Another time while running on a very busy street, two men in a pick-up tried to grab me. Both of these experiences left me quite shaken. On the second occasion I was able to run into a building and call a friend to come and get me."

Mary Anne does not have a coach. "I run by how I feel," she says. "I am a firm believer in listening to your body. If you don't, you're in trouble. I don't really like running fast; I am not overly fond of racing. I like to compete against myself. I do hold several records for women over forty in the Gulf AAU, but they will soon be broken. I tried running intervals with my husband for several weeks, but it felt so bad I couldn't see what good they would do me. I don't want a coach. They would take the good out of running for me. A coach would make it too much like work."

When asked whether she has ever experienced the "runner's high" or any other heightening of consciousness while running, Mary Anne was quick to respond: "I have many times experienced a 'lightness of spirit.' The awareness or heightening of consciousness is often present. I had the most beautiful experience of my life while running—my spiritual life, anyway. I met God on top of a hill in Waco, Texas. It was during a race, and all of a sudden I was alone on top of this hill, I looked out to see how gorgeous everything looked, and felt an immense presence with me. The clouds seemed to pull back from the earth and everything glowed. A happiness invaded me and remained for hours. I finished this most difficult race feeling wonderful. It is really difficult for me to describe this experience. I've never tried to write it before, but I shall always remember it. There has never been any question in my mind about God's presence."

When asked what kind of speech she would give to a gathering of 1,000 women on the subject of running, this was Mary Anne's response:

"It is not difficult for me to speak about running. It has become a very important part of not only my life, but my family's life. At times it seems as if everything revolves around it. Our children have learned to accept these times and are proud of the fact that we can and do run. They are included whenever they wish to be, and particularly delight in helping with the races, especially the marathons.

"It is my opinion that research will confirm that running will prolong the onset of menopause. The activity will stimulate the glands to produce longer. You younger ladies may not like the idea of prolonging the onset of menopause, but look at it this way: you won't have to wrinkle quite so early.

"The other factor in running is personal. We all want and need different things from our running. I cannot tell you what it will do for you in these areas, but I can tell you what it has done for me.

"Several years ago I was taking twenty-six pills a day—all prescribed—for everything from chronic constipation to rheumatoid arthritis. Believe me, I think twice now before taking an aspirin. I certainly have no signs of arthritis even though a few joints do creak at times. I have come to believe that for me arthritis was mentally-induced, probably due to boredom and a 'poor me' attitude. Oh, I always kept busy with five children and all of their activities: I held every office in the PTA, was Room Mother for years on end, worked in Brownies, Cubs and Girl Scouts, drove all the field trips. But there was really nothing stimulating in all of this. I had the cleanest house in town, some of my friends called me Mrs. Clean. Running got me out of the house, got my blood circulating, brought new friends, brought new activities that were not child-oriented. It gave me energy when everyone thought it would be draining energy. So much of being tired is a state of mind.

"My running has brought me closer to God than I have ever been. It is impossible to run out the door on a crisp fall morning and not feel His presence. And on a busy street you surely cannot help but talk to Him and appeal for your safety and the sanity of the drivers. I have felt His presence and His hand many times during my runs. Too, running brings an awareness of surroundings at times which manifests the presence of God.

"Running has given my husband and I another common interest. It occupies much of our time now, as we are involved in putting on races with both the AAU and the Road Runners Club in our area. We can and do help one another. We train together for marathons, we each run about two marathons a year. He is a truly loving husband for he will train at whatever pace I can manage. I'm sure it has slowed down his times, but he maintains he would rather keep it this way. He has qualified for Boston for several years, I have not (3:35 is my best time). I could go to Boston on his shirt-tails, but we don't have the desire yet. We did go to a marvelous marathon in Ottawa, Canada in May. We stayed a week in Canada; this was the longest we had ever been away from home.

"Socially, we have made many new friends. You will find that long-distance runners have much in common. We occasionally travel to runs with friends and without the kids you don't have to act your age. We have made many beautiful friendships through running."

JEAN COOPER
Marietta, Georgia

"When I first began running, I was embarrassed because I was very poor at it and shy."

"I began running because I was in poor physical condition and my figure was out of shape," said Jean Cooper of Marietta, Georgia. "In about three months I began to really like to run. Now it is a big part of my life—my favorite time of day.

"Running has changed me in many ways. I feel better physically, mentally, and psychologically. I have gained confidence in myself because I look better. Also, it is something that I do for myself and by myself if I choose to. I really enjoy running alone most of the time. I use the time to clear my mind and relax mentally.

"When I first began running, I was embarrassed because I was very poor at it and I was shy. But I continued because I felt I had to for my own sake.

"It is difficult to put into words what running means to me. Some of my friends ridiculed me at first, and it was impossible for them to understand why I did it. Now they look at me and know why I did it and what benefits I have derived from it. I don't really feel I have to explain it anymore, but I just tell them I enjoy it tremendously."

Jean has been running for 1½ years and although she has raced only twice in the past year, she trains every day, measuring her training by time rather than by mileage. On Sunday and Thursday she trains an hour; she does thirty minutes on Monday and Friday; ninety minutes Tuesday and Saturday and forty-five minutes on Wednesday.

Jean trains in the afternoon and includes a fairly ambitious stretching and exercise routine before her runs. Her longest run was 6.2 miles, which was a Bonne Bell race. She does most of her running in a suburban neighborhood with some speed work at the local track. Jean's neighborhood is hilly and wooded and very conducive to running. She reaches her training area by walking out her front door.

She reports having had a few problems with dogs, but says she is not afraid of dogs unless they seem ready to attack. "A couple of times this has happened, and I was frightened," she says, "but the owner came out and called the dog off. A few people made remarks to me when I first began running, but now I might get a whistle now and then but I have no real problems."

Medically, she has had a few ankle pains, some pains in the feet and legs, but she found that they were due mostly to running incorrectly; the problems cleared up when someone showed her the proper way to run.

Jean has no coach, but she reads a lot about running and is not shy about asking questions. Most of her training is done by intuition.

She reports that she would really be bothered if she had to lay off her running for a long time; she would miss the exercise and keeping in shape, and the mental relaxation. Jean thinks women who run continue to do it because they come to love it, while men who do it do not really like it but they do it because they feel that they have to do it.

She also reports experiencing the "runner's high" many times during her running. "This does not happen every time I run or even every week," she said. "The first time it happened was one night at the track when I ran for a long time with friends. I seemed to be as light as a feather, and I felt that I could run forever."

She feels the biggest shortcoming in her program at the moment is her lack of a coach. "Lately I have felt that I am at a point where I am not improving but maybe going backward a little bit. I still enjoy running but feel something is wrong."

The speech on running she would give to an audience of 1,000 women is short and to the point: "I wish that you could know what running has done for my life. If there were some way that I could flash back to my former self before running, you would understand my evangelistic fervor about running. Before I began running, I felt tired most of the time and not only could not run at all but walking was also difficult. Now I have a lot of energy and look better than I have in years. I like the feeling of being in shape and feeling good. I am 42 years old, but I feel like a 20-year-old. Running is something I can do on my own and for myself. I don't need anybody to do it with me, although I do enjoy having a companion at times. When I realize that I could run six miles after working for less than a year, I knew that I can do anything I want to in life."

Jean thinks the increase in women runners will have a very positive effect on our country's chances for success on the international level. "Running in the schools in our country will do a lot to encourage females to run. It is getting bigger each year. Five years ago there was almost nothing for girls in track. I do think that most of the women involved in running do it more for improving themselves than to get into competition, but the fact that more women are running will interest young girls."

Jean describes her most memorable run: "It was one Saturday morning when I was running through my neighborhood. I felt really good that day and didn't seem to tire at all. So I continued to run longer than usual and took a route I had not taken before. It was a cool morning and clear. I had the feeling that I could run forever and felt light on my feet. My mind felt clear and my mind just drifted."

ANN RANDLE
Birmingham, Alabama

"If I didn't have running to rid myself of tension, I would be filled with anxieties."

Ann Randle was in the process of getting divorced four years ago and she felt she needed something positive in her life to help get her through it. She took up running as both a mental and physical balm. A resident of Birmingham, Alabama, Ann has taken her running therapy through several phases until she is running primarily because she enjoys it.

She enters races about once a month, usually 10,000-meter races. And her training shows how serious she is about something she likes. On Sunday she does a long, slow run of eight-twelve miles, four-six miles on Monday and Tuesday, three miles in the morning and four in the afternoon on Wednesday, intervals on Thursday, four-six long, slow miles on Friday and five-eight miles on Saturday. Most of her running is done in the late afternoon and she warms up for it by doing wall push-ups, toe touches, and side stretches. (Ann says that she never really stretches as much as she should, a shortcoming that seems to be common to most runners.)

Although she occasionally runs alone, the majority of her runs are with her boyfriend. No one else in her family runs regularly, although her two daughters, sixteen and twenty years old, have run in the past (on the high school track teams). She says that both of her daughters are "positively wonderful natural and strong runners" but that it breaks her heart that she cannot motivate them to run regularly.

Ann wears Nike Waffle Trainers for running and racing, and thinks they are the best shoes she's worn. In the summer she runs in shorts, a T-shirt, and usually a bra, but not always; in the winter she wears a warm-up top, hat, and gloves. She doesn't wear long pants in the winter unless it is extremely cold.

"I run," she says, "for pleasure. I also run because I know I am improving the quality of my life. Who wants to live to be old if they are in poor health? Not I. Running gives women a whole new lease on life. Physically and psychologically. I run because I love it!"

Ann's longest run was an abortive try at a marathon; she injured her foot at the 15-mile mark and continued painfully along to 18 miles where she dropped out. Her longest regular training run was 15 miles.

She almost always trains in an urban environment, but loves running along beaches and in rural areas whenever possible. Despite her running in urban areas, she reports no trouble with traffic, dogs, or hecklers.

Medically, she can cite only the foot problem in the marathon attempt, which she attributes to a 10-mile descent down Monte Sano Mountain in Huntsville. "I think constant downhill is extremely hard on the front of the thighs, knees and ankles," she said.

How would Ann feel if she had to lay off running for any period of time? "If I have to lay off for any more than a day, I feel horrible. . .really lousy and bitchy," she said. "I get very uptight, depressed, and nervous. I have to run. It helps me in everything I do. My disposition is much better since I've become a runner. I work in a very stress-filled job—real estate. I'm also residential sales manager of my company, and if I didn't have running to rid myself of tension, I would be filled with anxieties."

Ann averages 8:30-9:00 miles in her workouts and about 8:00 per mile in competition. She once ran a seven-minute mile.

She reports that her biggest single shortcoming is her weight problem. "If I could get my weight down, my times would improve dramatically," she said. "I can't seem to find the incentive or motivation to lose the weight. It's very disheartening." One of her goals as a runner is to still be running when she's ninety years old.

As far as the potential on the international level of the women of the United States, Ann feels that the incredible interest in running is going to help develop the best women runners in the world in this country. She also feels that women will never be able to beat men in speed, but that in endurance they may ultimately be able to go farther. She feels that both men and women meet on a common ground when they run and that they both derive a sense of well-being from it. She plans to run a marathon next year—to vindicate herself after last year's failure to finish during her first try.

She describes her most memorable run: "It was the first run I attended at the Birmingham Track Club. This was four years ago. I was recovering from a partial hysterectomy. The surgery had been four and a half weeks before the run, and of course, I hadn't been training, but I ran two miles in seventeen and a half minutes and one mile in 8:30.

"My second most memorable run was the *Birmingham News*-Birmingham Track Club 10,000-meter run in November of 1976. The reason for the thrill of this run is the fact that I was meet director and had gotten the *News* to sponsor our run. Another aspect of running that I feel women are shy about is the direction of large runs. How many female meet directors are there in the country? Not many, I'm sure. This will be my third time as meet director for our run, and it's a pretty big run. Bill Rodgers and Ed Leddy will be back for the third year.

"I feel we have kept running in the proper perspective. We are not promoting a product, just running, and I think it is greatly appreciated.

"The reason I got into our runs here is that I was tired of seeing them disorganized and with no sponsor. So I called on the *Birmingham News* and got their sponsorship and then I volunteered (yes, *volunteered*) to be meet director.

"It has been one of the most rewarding and thrilling events of my life. I feel if meets (runs, et al.) are properly done, they will give the runner encouragement, motivation, and incentive to continue running and improving."

YVONNE GREEN
Flint, Michigan

"Whenever I see my ex-boyfriend with another woman, I run farther."

Yvonne Green of Flint, Michigan, 24 years old and 5'3", 125 pounds, has been running for a year. She started because she wanted a convenient, inexpensive form of exercise. She does not race and is currently using a very simple, basic training program of running three days a week: one mile on Wednesday and Saturday and a 1 to 3 mile run on Sunday. She trains whenever it is convenient and has not yet developed a preference to either morning or afternoon or evening sessions.

As a warm-up to her runs, she does jumping jacks, toe-touches, side bends, and does a 1/8-mile fast walk. She runs both alone and with friends. Her older sister runs up to four miles a day several times a week.

She usually runs in a warm-up suit or, when it's hot, in cut-off jeans and a T-shirt. She has not yet purchased running shoes because she does not consider herself good enough.

Yvonne runs because it helps keep her weight from going up, it relaxes her and makes her happy, and it helps her lose unwanted inches. She reports that her longest run has been a two and a half miler.

She usually runs in an urban environment, on either an asphalt track or on a golf course. She sometimes runs on an indoor track in cold weather. She does her training runs about one and a half miles from her home and reports never having had any real problems with traffic, dogs, or people.

Medically, she has had some knee pain, but she cured it herself by applying alternately heat and cold. She receives support of her running from her family; her parents have given it a try, as have her seven sisters. She trains mostly on intuition, doing very little reading on the subject. She plans to spend more time reading so she can be a better coach to herself, because she currently does not have a coach although she would like to have one.

Having to lay off running would bother her, she reports, and at one point she took a run when suffering from a fever. Although her running is moderate, she enjoys running enough to feel addicted to it.

She thinks men derive much the same things from running that women do, but that women derive the additional advantage of being freed by running from the embargo against strenuous activity that society has long placed upon them.

In a speech to 1,000 women, Yvonne would stress the following good points about running:

Running helps you lose weight and to keep it away once it's off; it helps take off inches where needed and helps firm up the body; it improves the person's ability to concentrate; it relieves tensions; it increases self-confidence; it decreases the amount of sleep needed by making the body more efficient; it helps clear the skin complexion; and it decreases the use of cigarettes.

She feels the biggest shortcoming in her training program is a lack of incentive. Her goals in running at the moment are to lose fifteen pounds and seven inches. She would also like ultimately to run more than five miles four times a week.

Who has been the person with the most positive effect on her running? "My ex-boyfriend. Whenever I see him with another woman, I run farther," she says.

Her most memorable run was her first two-miler; afterwards, she says, she felt invincible.

CAMILLE DEE SIMPSON
Houston, Texas

"Every time I run I can use the time to think about the day."

Camille Dee Simpson, twenty-four years old, began running three years ago. She began when her boyfriend gave her a pair of Nikes and a sweatsuit for Christmas. He was an everyday runner; Camille began running to keep up with him and she soon found that she was very much enjoying the running for its own sake. She now competes three or four times a year. She runs five miles Sunday, takes off Monday, does four miles Tuesday, two miles Wednesday, three on Thursday, takes off Friday and does four on Saturday. On weekends when it isn't too hot in Houston and when she has the time, she takes a longer run. To get her runs in before the heat, she usually runs before 9:00 a.m. or after 7:00 p.m.

To prepare herself for her runs she does about five minutes of stretching, concentrating on the legs and back. She runs with her German Shepherd and sometimes runs with her boyfriend or one of her sisters. Camille has managed to lure three of her sisters into running. One of her sisters, twenty-seven years old, has just started running and has gotten up to a mile a day, another, twenty-three years old, goes two miles a day, and the third one, nineteen years old, goes between two and five miles a day. The twenty-seven-year-old sister, Camille reports, just had a baby and is running to get back into shape.

Camille has tried Nikes (and finds them good), Brooks shoes (which she finds okay) and Adidas TRXs, which she has nothing but praise for.

Her longest run has been the Dallas White Rock Lake Half-Marathon in December of 1977.

She usually does her training runs in the campus area around Rice University where it is very shady. Occasionally she'll go to one of the city parks where there are several jogging paths; her third choice is around the neighborhood streets, dodging cars and animals.

Camille talks about her running: "The real reason I began to run was that my boyfriend ran four to five miles a day with a group of men from the YMCA, and that was all they talked about. I gave it a try and worked *slowly* up to two miles a day. I discovered the ten pounds that I could never get rid of had been lost! I also enjoyed a new means of getting exercise.

"I started reading articles concerning running, mainly in *Runner's World.* My interest in the sport grew and I kept up my own program. I would set a goal, for example, an upcoming city fun-run of a longer distance, and work for that distance. To keep working on a program requires *some* discipline, and I was able to keep on my program, work on new goals, and achieve them. This was a definite benefit as far as self-improvement went.

"Another benefit is the good feeling from helping others stay on an exercise program or contributing help in some form in putting on runs for others. I wish I had more time for that.

"Every time I run I can use the time to think about the day, or think about a problem or any situation. This is the most important benefit as far as I'm concerned. I value my time to myself and I enjoy running alone. However, if I'm running with someone else, the feeling you share while running is always a good feeling!"

Camille reports that because she usually runs with her dog, she is rarely bothered during her runs. Traffic is not usually a problem, although she hates to stop for a light when she has a good rhythm going.

Camille has strained muscles in her ankle and knee, but no serious injuries to date. She usually pays close attention to her stretching and is careful to not overexert herself until injuries are healed.

She gets a lot of support from her family and her boyfriend, although she says some of her friends seem to be jealous of her ability to enjoy running so much.

Her boyfriend, who belongs to the local AAU club, is her coach and helps her with her running. She also tries interesting advice from magazines.

Having an interruption to her running would bother her.

"Once I stopped for 10 days because of a flu and I had so much stored-up energy! I felt I needed the rest, so I didn't run, but it definitely bothered me," she said.

Camille's best time for a mile is a 7:45; she usually does her training runs at an 8:30 pace. She reports that whenever she runs continuously for an hour or more, she seems to achieve a level of awareness such that she can keep going for as long as she'd like to. She reports that at those times she feels very relaxed and that the feeling holds back the onset of fatigue.

Her speech to 1,000 women would go something like this:

"Running, or jogging, can do more for you than exercise your body to lose a few pounds. This is important and probably one of the main reasons a lot of women start to run. But there's more. Running can make you aware of lots of everyday things that you usually have no time to think about. Use your running time to get to know yourself. Ideas become clearer when you make the time to think things through. On the other hand, if you need a friend, get out and make friends with fellow runners. They make the best friends! Together, get out and about, and see new sights. Enjoy just being able to get out and run. There are lots of people who are not so fortunate.

"Remember, not everyone is cut out for speed or endurance racing. Some are, and perhaps we are envious. But *run for yourself!* Keep running on a level where you can appreciate the benefits that it can give to you.

As far as her own running goes, Camille sees the lack of time as the greatest shortcoming. "Work schedules and mostly hot weather in this area cut down on running time. If only a day were twenty-six hours long," she laments.

Her goals at the moment are to build a solid base and, hopefully, try a marathon within the next few years. Until she gets time to train properly for a marathon, though, she plans to keep close to her current schedule.

Camille talks about her most memorable run: "It was at the Dallas 1977 White Rock Lake Marathon. I participated in the half-marathon. The morning was cool, about fifty-five degrees, and sunny. The weather was perfect. I had never run more than ten miles before, and was both excited and nervous about the attempt. Everyone was excited and that kind of feeling spreads. For the first few minutes of the race everyone was packed together but we began to spread out over the first miles.

"The beautiful course runs around the lake and we 8:30-per-milers could see the leaders taking off across on the other side. The weather held up cool and crisp. It was very easy to keep on my pace. People kept encouraging each other to hang in there. As the leaders circled back around, we all cheered, and kept on, determined to finish.

"The cool breeze off the lake helped a lot, as the morning warmed up. The aid stations appeared at the right time. I had no trouble keeping pace and was right on time the first loop: about eight and a half miles. I felt really strong even at ten, and I knew I would finish my half-marathon. Even though I set no speed records, it was a great feeling to know I could achieve the goal I had been running toward all fall. Running toward the finish, and afterward, with my little trophy, I felt so proud of my personal accomplishment. My time was 2:02, certainly no speed record. But what a good feeling! Really a beautiful day!"

WILLIE ANN ALBEA
Anniston, Alabama

"I run because I enjoy the feeling I get for the rest of the day."

Willie Ann Albea, 56 years old, has been running for five years. She began by jogging with an exercise class at the Anniston, Alabama YMCA for ten minutes three times a week. She raced nine times last year (between three and 6.2 miles) and hopes to do fifteen races this year.

Willie's typical training week is as follows: Sunday is her rest day, Monday, Friday and Saturday she runs five miles, six miles on Tuesday and Thursday, and seven miles on Wednesday. Her runs are usually done in the mornings. She does various stretching and loosening-up exercises before she runs, changing them to fit her needs, and adds 30 sit-ups to her routine to build strength. Some of her runs are alone, while others are with friends. No other members of her family run.

She has five pair of running shoes: her first pair were the Adidas ROM, which she wears only occasionally because of their stiffness and poor cushioning. She also has Nike LD-1000s and Waffle Trainers, Tigers and a new pair of New Balance that she has worn only twice.

"I run because I enjoy the feeling I get for the rest of the day," she says. "I'm much more energetic now. I no longer have a tired feeling upon rising each day. My bladder and kidneys are better than they have been in years. My weight is better distributed and body is toned up. My resting heart rate ranges from 50 to 64, but it used to be approximately 68-84. I'm not as irritable as I was, except when I find myself running too much. Other people admire my perseverance and dedication to my goals—which are those established for joggers by the National Jogging Association. I started that particular program in 1976 and have continued ever since."

Willie usually runs inside the YMCA, and is only lately beginning to run more in the open. She takes part in a five-mile Fun-Run on the first Saturday of the month at a nearby Army installation, where she frequently encounters quail and other animals she enjoys seeing along her runs.

She does feel that women derive different things from running than men do. "For one thing," she contends, "women tend to build up more extra weight in the hips and the thigh area than men do; but running keeps my hips small. Running has strengthened my muscles in the pelvic area, in the legs, back, and stomach, primarily because of the sit-ups I do to get ready to run."

She has, on occasion, felt pleasant sensations when running that make her feel like she can continue running forever. "All the aches would suddenly leave the back of my legs and I would be moving along so effortlessly," she said.

She does her training at a 10-minutes-per-mile pace and races at about an eight-minute pace. She reports that she currently has plenty of time to train, and is now working to become faster. She plans to continue to run for running's sake and to participate in many more races, because she feels good when she does.

This is her speech to a group of women: "Ladies, I'm a runner because I enjoy running. It helps me to feel good about myself. It gives me a good self-image. I meet friends every day who say, 'How far did you run today?' 'Eight miles,' I'll say (or whatever distance I went). They'll usually say something like this: 'I don't see how you do it' or 'I wish I could do that.' I tell my friends to begin their own program—that starting small is better than nothing. My favorite saying is: 'The way to get a job or task done is to get started.' I write my goals down each day (that helps give me something very real to strive for) and some days I just think to myself: 'How can I run six miles?' An inner voice will answer: 'Do it just one step at a time.'

"I remember picking cotton as a child and seeing acres of white, fluffy cotton (we didn't have a cotton-picker machine) and we gathered bales of cotton but only one ball at a time. Same with shelling butterbeans or picking berries. We filled our berry buckets with tiny huckleberries one berry at a time.

"Running has several advantages over other physical fitness and I do explain that to my friends who ask. I do tell my friends to be kind to their feet by getting a good pair of shoes."

As far as the future of women's running goes, Willie feels that women in the future will be doing times that the best men are doing now, while men's times will be pushed even farther down.

Her most memorable run was the Gadsden, Alabama 10,000-meter run on May 20, 1978. "We had a loop in the course," she remembers, "which took us downtown, across a river, and back. My friends called out to me. My son, and grandson, were both running in the race and I got to see them run. (I also got to see Steve Bolt run, he won the race.) Even though I've been in several races with my son and grandson, I never get to see them because they're out in front of me. They always get to see me come in, but at this race I got to see them racing, too, and it was a real thrill for me."

GAIL BIDDLE
Atlantic City, New Jersey

"The most important door running may open for you is the door to understanding yourself."

Gail Biddle of Atlantic City, New Jersey has been running for a year. She credits her starting to run to Norman Draper, a friend who stirred up her interest in running and who convinced her of the benefits to be derived from the sport. Gail usually runs races of five or six miles. She trains four miles every day or every other day, but has begun increasing some of her runs up to as much as seven miles. The longest run she has ever done is 10 miles.

Her training comes at various times during the day, she isn't locked in to any particular time. She does stretching exercises on the boardwalk before she runs. She says that she used to jump rope before a run, but she changed over to stretching. She usually trains alone, but sometimes trains with friends. Her younger sisters are also runners.

"When I first began running and for months thereafter I ran in cheap shoes," Gail said on commenting on her footwear. "I have since purchased Etonic Street Fighters and am very pleased with them."

Most of her training runs are on the boardwalk, which is a rather unique training environment: she is able to avoid traffic and also runs on a surface softer than concrete or asphalt. She consequently has had no problem with traffic, dogs, or people.

Medically, she reports that she did have some strained muscles in her foot after a 10-mile run in new shoes, but other than that she's not encountered any real problems. She also reports that her family is very positive about her running; they respect her interest in the sport and they feel that they can see the benefits she is deriving from it.

If she were given a soapbox from which to address other women on the subject of running, she has some definite things she would talk about:

"Running makes me feel as though I've accomplished something. It has made me begin to come out of my shell. I've always been pretty good at athletics but have always been sort of introverted. Running has changed that. I don't feel like I'm on exhibition while I run. I can run alone and feel so comfortable about doing it that it's unbelievable. It builds up one's confidence.

"I think a person can talk to a nonrunner about running, about their experiences, about what running means to them, but that other person can't feel or can't realize what running does for you until they actually go out and begin their own program.

"I don't claim to know if running is for everyone. People are individuals and what's right for one isn't necessarily right for everyone.

"I would advise people to try it, beginning slowly and working up to some distance. Give it a chance. Push yourself and you can open any door. The most important door running may open for you is the door to understanding yourself."

When asked how she would feel if she had to lay off her running, Gail had an answer ready because she's found that happening. "I recently became a Beach Jack (blackjack) dealer at Resorts International. My schedule has been nine-hour weekdays and 10-hour weekends, with only one day off a week. To say the least, it has really cut into my running schedule. And yes, it does bother me. I feel guilty when I don't run."

As far as women deriving different things from running than

men, Gail feels it's all in the mind. "I think it all depends on the individual and not on whether they are male or female. Everyone's mind functions differently. But on the whole I think running cleanses a person's mind and body, one factor contributing to that being the incredible amount of oxygen the body takes in."

As far as experiences while running are concerned, Gail reports that during the Bonne Bell mini-marathon in Boston, she felt "as though my whole body was drifting through the air."

Her training has been at a pace of one mile every eight minutes, and her races are done at a 7:30 pace. She feels her biggest shortcoming has been her job's long hours that make training regularly difficult. She says, however, that lately her hours are getting back to normal.

She feels that the number of women getting involved in running, and the increase in good high school-level programs is dramatically increasing the chances that American women will be doing much better on the international level. "Women are beginning to take themselves seriously about running," she said.

Her most memorable run was, understandably, the Bonne Bell mini-marathon in Boston. "I felt the best I've ever felt while running," she said. "I felt as though I was flying or just drifting through the air. My energy was unbelievable.

"I hadn't had much sleep prior to the race because we'd just driven from Atlantic City to Boston and we were a little wide-eyed. I averaged a little over 7:30 per mile, which pleased me very much. The race was very well-organized and the course was very scenic. The run in itself was a natural high. That sums up the only way I can describe it. It was exhilarating.

"Everyone in the race seemed to be a part of each other. We came together from all over to share in an event that would make us one."

MARY SPEAR

Winston-Salem, North Carolina

"I'm a very lazy person, so it takes my mother to get me out to run."

Mary Spear of Winston-Salem, North Carolina, has been running competitively for four years. She began running when she went to a summer camp where there were many different sports offered—one was cross-country. The coach encouraged her to continue her running and she shortly began entering AAU-sanctioned races. She currently races about once every two weeks. Mary is five feet, five inches and weighs 89 pounds; she is 14 years old.

Her schedule runs like this: Sunday—easy jog of about three or four miles, Monday—faster pace for about three to five miles, Tuesday—same as Monday but with some speed work and intervals thrown in, Wednesday—fast pace for three to five miles, Thursday—same as Wednesday but with some speed work and intervals thrown in, Friday—repeat of Thursday, and Saturday—fast pace for four or five miles. Mary does her training runs in the afternoon or evening. She warms up by doing hurdle stretches, alternate leg stretches, toe-touches, abdomen stretches, sideways stretches and a few slow laps. She runs with the track team on Tuesday and Thursday during the summer, but runs alone other days.

Her father runs every day, between six and eight miles. Her younger brother runs in races but only trains twice a week. Her youngest brother, Matthew, seven, runs but hardly does any training, "He does everything on talent," Mary says.

Mary both races and trains in Nike Elites racing flats.

Mary finds that when she runs long races she cramps up and therefore avoids running over 10-kilometer races.

Her training is done primarily in a residential area on the edge of town where she lives. "There is a large estate about two miles from our house," she says. "It is open to the public. Just about every runner around that part of town runs there. The first two miles are along a fairly busy street and on residential streets. Then I run about one or two miles on the winding trails of the estate's gardens. I run back the same way I came."

Mary explains why she runs: "I'm a very lazy person so it takes my mother to get me out to run. Until recently I suffered severe cramps whenever I ran, so I was reluctant to get out and run. Every once in a while I will get those cramps again. I find that I have to have three or four hours between the time I eat and the time I run. The main reason I run is because I love to win. My whole family is active, so I naturally gravitated to a sport. If I don't have a race coming up I don't usually run. My mother thinks it's a shame. I'm the state champion in the mile and the 880 but I don't train as hard as my opponents. This year I've trained more than I ever have before and I've done much better.

"I find that if I sit around and don't run, I'm not as alert as I would be if I did run. After a run I usually feel great and have high spirits once I get out and get the run finished."

Mary rates automobiles as the main problem with urban running. "I have to cross roads three or four times," she says. "I usually run at about 5:00 p.m. and the traffic is heavy because everyone is coming home from work. I used to have a different route, but some unfriendly dogs made me change that."

She has a coach, but the coach is the team coach and does not have time for individual attention with each member of the squad. At practice he tells Mary what to do and she does it. She usually just listens to other people and she does what she thinks she should. She admits that she should be doing more than she does.

"At first laying off my running wouldn't bother me," Mary says, "but then my conscience would begin to bug me. During the racing season it would bother me a lot. I'd worry about the upcoming race. If I wasn't able to train, I couldn't expect to do well."

In regards to having any experiences while running, Mary reports that she really hasn't had anything significant happen. "While I'm running I think a lot, about problems or about tomorrow. If I have something due in school, say a report, I write it in my mind while I'm running. During a race, though, it's strictly business. After a race I'll feel sort of elated or high."

Mary describes her most memorable race: "My most memorable race happened recently. It was the AAU Regionals. For the older runners, it was the qualifying meet for the National Junior Olympics. I was seeded first in the 880.

"The officials put two people in each lane. The seeded person and I were put in the first lane. They stagger-started us. The rest of the runners were told not to cut to the inside lane until a whistle was blown. That would be at about 110 yards. As soon as the race started everyone cut to the inside lane. I was completely cut off! I was really mad. If I had been thinking clearly I would have stopped and told the officials to start the race again. There was a lot of pushing and shoving. I pulled up to third right at the tape. The person who got second just nipped me. Immediately all the coaches started yelling at the officials. One of the people complaining was a man who had been the head of the state meet. The officials had done three things wrong: They put two people in each lane, which is illegal, the whole first lap should have been run in the assigned lanes, and they didn't stop the race when the other runners broke too soon. After an hour's debate they decided to let the results stand because the girl who placed second didn't want to run again."

JEANNE PICARIELLO
San Antonio, Texas

"Most women don't know what they are capable of, especially since a lot of us didn't have a competitive sports background growing up."

Jeanne Picariello, 26 years old, has been a competitive swimmer for years. When she began working and found that she could not attend swim workouts as often as she would like because of her schedule, she began running to keep in shape for swimming. She began to enjoy running, however, and now enters races of from 2000 meters to 10 miles once a month. She's been running for three years.

Her training workouts vary quite a bit since she is a member of the U.S. Modern Pentathlon Team at Ft. Sam Houston (in San Antonio), and she must also keep her skills sharp in the other four events besides running—swimming, horseback riding, fencing and shooting. She also regulates her workouts by how tired she is from her night duty as a nurse. She usually manages four long runs (8-10 miles) a week, two medium (4-6 miles) and one easy (three miles) per week. Her training runs are done between 10:00 a.m. and noon.

Before she runs she does stretching exercises to loosen up the Achilles tendon, does a hurdle stretch, splits, and the backbend and walkover. Her training is sometimes done with the pentathlon team. She has four brothers in high school, all of whom are middle-distance runners.

She both trains and races in the Lady Nike Waffle Trainer.

Jeanne's problems in training come from some unusual places: police hassle the team members when they train in the golf courses, but they continue to practice there anyway; she also has to deal with whistling and obscenities hurled from men in pick-up trucks, which she has learned to ignore.

She has a team coach, but she also learns a lot about running from reading ***Runner's World, Track & Field News*** and ***Marathoner*** Magazine.

If she had to lay off her running, she feels that she would be driven crazy. "I'd be paranoid of a weight gain, and I'd feel miserable and bored and lethargic," she says.

She does not feel that women derive anything different from running than men do.

This is her hypothetical speech to a group of 1000 women: "Don't sell yourselves short. You can do anything you set your mind to. I'm talking especially about being in the best physical condition possible. If you're healthy, it just radiates a certain image about you. People come to respect you more when you look and feel so good because it affects your performance in everyday life. You have more energy and therefore can accomplish more.

"Running and exercising can be fun and enjoyable. You don't have to be a competitor to benefit. Personal gains are the best rewards. Besides, if you haven't tried athletics, how do you even know what you are capable of? The real you might be waiting inside, ready to be unleashed on a 10,000-meter run."

Jeanne trains at a 7:00 pace when she's fresh, and at about 7:00-7:10 when she's tired. She runs at 5:20 pace for races from 2000 meters to 1.5 miles.

The biggest shortcoming in her running program is her job. "I'm an ICV nurse at the burn unit in the army. I requested permanent 3-11 shift (evenings), but it's invariably 3-12 or even 1:00 a.m. I'm on my feet rushing around all night. Then I have to get up early to train and do errands. Then it's to work again. The work schedule never seems to cooperate with my running. I almost always have to work late the night before a race."

Jeanne is building her training program toward qualifying for the women's National AAU 10,000-meter track championship, or the AAU Cross-Country Nationals. "If I ever get enough sleep so I can train more efficiently, I'm confident I can do it," she says. "I also want to start marathoning this year. But it will probably mean having to break away from swimming and other pentathlon sports."

How will the boom in women's running help the United States effort internationally?

"I think the best American runners are yet to be discovered," she says. "Many of our top females started out as recreational joggers and got hooked. Most women don't even know what they are capable of, especially since a lot of us didn't have a competitive sports background while growing up. Latent talents need to be developed and guided. Besides, if they start on a recreational level, at least you know they *enjoy* it and that's half the battle right there."

As for the reaches of the talents of women runners, Jeanne sees it this way: "I think in the near future we'll see top women's marathon times around 2:20, more ultramarathons and long distance and middle-distance times will be lowered dramatically. It takes more coaching and stress testing/research by exercise physiologists so that coaches may better understand the female athlete and coach her more effectively."

She describes her most memorable race: "It was the Bonne Bell 10,000-meter race in Houston in April of 1978. I placed seventh out of 750+ in my first 10,000-meter race of the year. I arrived in Houston after driving four hours, exhausted from work the night before, but very excited. It was the first race of entirely women that I'd ever entered, and I entered it to see how I fared after running against mostly guys in local road races. The fact that all women of every size and shape surrounded me totally psyched me out. We got off to a fast start (6:10 first mile) and the top seven of us stayed pretty much together except for Kathy Jackson, who won, and the second-place girl. I learned a lot that day about drafting and pacing against the other girls. There was a huge crowd of spectators who lined up everywhere in Memorial Park, especially on a bridge (overpass) that we ran under. They were really boosting my spirits. What amazed me was the number of young guys that yelled out encouraging remarks, splits and our position.

"The day was humid, typical of Houston. About 70 degrees, partly cloudy, which helped. The race started at 9:00 a.m. on the button—very well organized, and generally a lot of fun.

"It was a great feeling to be among really fast ladies. I was also impressed to see the number of young girls (6-12 years old) who ran and finished, and mother and daughter teams.

"The best part was that we weren't 'patronized' or made to feel that there was any 'tokenism.' Surprisingly, Bonne Bell didn't load us down with a lot of cosmetics and perfume, which was nice. I felt like a successful woman athlete and very satisfied."

ELIZABETH GUTHRIE
East Riverdale, Maryland

"In many ways it is an ego trip but I can't think of a better way to be egotistical."

Elizabeth Guthrie of East Riverdale, Maryland began running 2½ years ago when she enrolled in a slimnastics program at the local YMCA. One of the warm-up exercises was 7-8 laps around the gym. "After much pain and struggle, I slowly discovered that I enjoyed running," Elizabeth said. "I haven't stopped running since."

She now races about once a month and prefers running 10-milers, although she also does 10,000-meter runs.

Her longest runs have been 10-mile races: the Cherry Blossom Classic and Hecht's 10-Miler.

Her runs from home are in the typical suburban environment, but it includes some rural environment as she runs through Greenbelt Park (a national park). When she runs at work it is in an urban environment. "I work at the Pentagon and belong to the Athletic Center," she says. "I run from the Pentagon, across the 14th Street Bridge that spans the Potomac River, then down along the Potomac for a mile, around the Lincoln Memorial, across the Memorial Bridge to get back to the Virginia side of the river and back to the Pentagon. Needless to say, crossing those bridges can be unnerving some days."

Elizabeth is 29 years old and has apparently spent some of that time exploring her reasons for running:

"I guess I enjoy running purely for the enjoyment and personal achievement derived from it. I don't think anything beats that overall 'good' feeling after a good run. It also amazes me that no matter how tired I may be from work, that I always have enough energy to run and always feel so much better afterwards. The rewards of running are so numerous that it's difficult to name them all. But I'll try.

"The main thing seems to be my health. Since I started running 2½ years ago, I have had only two head colds, both of which were minor, and I was over them within a week. I used to get five and six colds a year, and each cold would hang on for weeks. Now, if I feel bad, or think I may be getting a cold, I go for a long run, and literally 'run it out of my system.'

"Running also helps clear my head. When things get tough, and the pressure of work starts to really get to me, running seems to be about the only relief. I also have some great ideas on my runs, and do some of my better thinking. In many ways it is an ego trip, but I can't think of a better way to be egotistical.

"Running also helps keep my weight down. I was always rather thin, but before I started running my weight was beginning to creep up on me. I found that I couldn't eat everything I wanted anymore without paying for it. Now, although I continue to watch what I eat, I eat more from time to time if I feel like it. I do fast one or two days a week, which helps the weight control. The only thing I eat on those days is low-fat cottage cheese, which I could eat by the barrel-full. But, it's a good feeling to know that if I do over-indulge, a good hard long run will burn away those extra calories and that extra fat."

Being in a metropolitan area has provided Elizabeth with some problems on her runs. "I think people in cars derive some sadistic pleasure in seeing just how close they can get to me, without literally knocking me over. Men seem to think that it is cute to drive real close to the edge of the road and make crude noises, or yell something off-color. I hate that more than anything. I know that the best way to handle that is to keep looking straight ahead, but sometimes I yell back at them. I really get so sick of men acting so stupidly; it's really irritating. It seems like you can never do anything without getting some type of verbal abuse from some fool."

Medically, Elizabeth has had no very serious problems. "I do have a foot problem, however," she says, "but that was corrected by the use of an orthotic. I have no arch, and running on hard surfaces gave me shin splints. I went to Dr. Myles Schneider and he corrected the situation with many running tips and of course with the orthotics. I still have to be careful. I can't push myself as others do. In other words, if I ran three 15-mile runs three days in a row, my shins would be tender. Dr. Schneider advised me to limit racing to only once a month. Any more would only strain my shins. I will also always have the problem of wearing down my heels very rapidly. I have to get my shoes resoled about once a month or so (about 150 miles to a set of heels). Apparently I still continue to run somewhat flat-footed. Because of my feet being what they are, I had to return the Brooks Vantage shoes I mentioned earlier that I had purchased. It seems that the corrective features of that particular shoe counteracted my orthotics. As a result I could not keep that right shoe from sliding all over my foot. Those shoes made my legs ache. I blame the shoe store, and told them so when I returned the shoes. The salesman should have known that since I was trying shoes on with orthotics that my feet couldn't tolerate the features of the Vantage. I purchased another pair of Lady Villanova IIs, and my feet are fine."

Elizabeth is her own coach. She reads as much as she can, and uses common sense. Her husband likes to claim that he's her coach, but since he isn't out with her at 5:00 a.m. she feels he really doesn't qualify.

Elizabeth reports that she has had "experiences" while running several times. "Well, actually more than several—maybe I should say quite a few times. I'll be running along, and it's like something else is controlling my body. Something machine-like; as if it takes no effort on my part to run, and I could just go on forever. Another sensation is as if I were standing beside myself watching me run, and feeling no strain or exertion at all."

The following is Elizabeth's hypothetical speech on the subject of running to a gathering of 1000 women:

"I believe there are no middle-of-the-road runners. Either you love running and do it, or you hate it and don't. You rarely hear a runner complaining about his sport. Oh, he may complain about the weather a little, particularly when it's hot and humid and the air quality index is in the 'very unhealthy range,' as it is so often here in Washington, D.C. (and believe me, we have good reason to complain when it gets *that* bad). A runner may complain about the usual pulled muscles and the like, but a devoted runner really never complains.

"Runners are a tough lot, too. Who else would run in weather so cold and snowy that your face freezes? Or in weather so hot and muggy that it makes everything else wilt by 7:00 a.m.? Or in driving rain where it's pouring so hard it hurts when it hits your skin? Some people (again, non-runners) think anybody who goes out in the extreme elements is crazy as a loon; but again, it's just a basic lack of understanding.

"For the female runner, it's even worse at times. Most men (again, mostly nonrunners) swear that the avid female runner will get muscle-bound, and ruin their bodies. Most women (nonrunners) feel that it is a masculine sport, and that women won't benefit from it. Most women are determined to stick out the first uncomfortable weeks of running. They don't realize that it takes their bodies a little time to get accustomed to the changes that running regularly brings about. But that with time, they can lose at least 10 pounds and become very slim and trim.

"Running is such a beautiful way to exercise. It's easy and fun, and your body and mind can derive so many benefits from it, that it is most certainly the best all-around exercise. It's obvious that more and more people are waking up to the 'jogging craze.' I only hope that it isn't merely a fad for some; or, worse yet, a fashion gimmick for others. The more men *and* women keep running seriously and faithfully, the better off we all will be for a long time to come."

FRANCES DENISON
Alexandria, Virginia

"I still marvel at how much more demanding running is than playing tennis."

Frances Denison of Alexandria, Virginia has been running for six months; she began running when her twin sister started and got her interested. To date she has competed in three races, two of them 10,000-meter races and the other a four-miler. Frances trains when she can find the time between her household duties, which means that some weeks she gets an opportunity to run four days a week, sometimes five and once in a while six. She tries to do four or five miles during each training session and prefers the evening because it is cooler.

As her warm-up for running, Frances runs the first mile slowly. She sometimes does a few stretches before she runs, but not frequently. She does most of her running alone.

As already mentioned, her twin sister, who lives in North Carolina, runs, and is currently doing 8-10 miles a day, three or four days a week. Frances's husband is taking up running, too, and does 2-2½ miles about four times a week.

Frances has three pair of running shoes: one pair of Adidas and two pair of Korean-made running shoes that she ordered from the Sears & Roebuck catalog. "I see very little difference between them," she reports. Her longest run to date has been the 10,000-meter race.

Why does Frances run? "I seem to run for the sheer enjoyment of it!! I have always been interested in sports and exercise. I studied ballet for almost 20 years of my life," she says. "I've always loved physical activities and exercise. My friends tell me how good I look and how much weight I've lost—and I laugh, because really, I've lost five pounds maximum. But from running I feel as if I've tightened up and firmed up and I feel and look much better.

"Running is actually my second love, though, as I'm a tennis nut for the past four years and no matter how much or how little I run, I play tennis every day, at least for two hours and mostly singles. The running helps me have lots of stamina and energy.

"I could probably run six miles a day and work up to much more but I'm always holding back and conserving energy for my daily tennis matches. I find that on the days I run more than five miles, my tennis suffers. I still marvel at how much more demanding running is than playing tennis."

Frances takes her training runs out her front door, since she lives in a very residential area near Mt. Vernon, which features many miles of bike and hiking paths. She has four courses laid out now, one being an easy course with no hills, one that features hills and one for rainy days that features firm footing.

Medically, she reports no problems beyond a skinned knee she suffered once when she fell on some loose gravel.

Most of her family and friends are interested in her running and are supportive, and they marvel that she can do the running and still keep up her tennis. "If they think I'm crazy, at least they have the good taste to keep their opinions to themselves," she says.

She serves as her own coach, and does most of her training by how she feels and by the philosophy of "train, don't strain." She reads as much as she can on running, finding that reading about it stirs her enthusiasm to run more.

Her most memorable run was her first race, a 10,000-meter race in Old Town Alexandria, which started at historic Gadsby Tavern, moved through the Old Town area, and then to the bike trail and through the park. "This was my first experience of running with a group," Frances says. "My first impressions were so positive because everyone was all smiles and laughing and having a good time. I had never tried six miles before and as I went around talking to other runners before the race, they were all encouraging me and bolstering me for the event.

"It was overcast and cloudy that day, and of course, just as we were moving up to the starting line, it began to rain. It was not hard rain—just drizzling. We ran along comfortably and it was cool and pleasant.

"My first experience at running in a group was very impressive to me. I had not expected such a large group and I did not see any pushing or shoving or unsportsmanlike conduct. In fact, I had the opportunity to talk to several other runners during the race and I made some new friends.

"The funniest thing happened at about the four-mile point. I could hear a man coming up from behind me and as he got closer I heard him laugh!! So, as he came up beside me I asked him if I was so pitiful that it was funny. He laughed again and was quick to explain that he was laughing because of the way I was carefully dashing around and avoiding all the large puddles. 'How can you make time like that, lady?' he asked, and I got a laugh out of it, too. I guess you don't easily break the habits of a lifetime.

"I did the race in 53 minutes, and although it's nothing to brag about, it was my first race and was sure a thrill. I really enjoyed it and I loved everything along the way."

BERNICE ROGERS
Ayer, Massachusetts

"It is just an evolutionary thing before improving your times becomes the challenge."

Bernice Rogers, 29 years old of Ayer, Massachusetts, has been running every day since March 1, 1977; before that, she had run sporadically during the spring or fall, but never more than a mile at a time. She became interested in running regularly when a male friend of hers spent every day running and spent many weekends racing; she took running more seriously and has been hooked ever since.

"I run because I want to keep some degree of physical fitness," Bernice says. "I want to keep my weight down and still be able to eat the foods I like. I want to keep my body going so that as I get older I will still be able to do things I want to do.

"Running for me is a good discipline. I run every day so that

I will not procrastinate one day to the next. It's easy to do. You do not need a partner or a team or a time to do it. And besides, I like running. I love to run in the early morning when the world is quiet. I feel that I have the world to myself at that time.

"The sun is just coming up...the birds and people are just waking up.

"Sometimes I do not feel like running—but I do—and after I get going it's all worth it. I can work out any problems that I've had the previous day: plans, trips, workouts. I can think about anything I want, or I can look at the trees, the sky, the grass, the lakes, ponds, mountains, homes...whatever.

"After I finish my run, I feel great! I'm ready for the day. I'm happier. I feel I have worked my muscles and lungs.

"I guess it's comparable to some people having their first cup of coffee for the day."

Bernice does not race extensively yet. She has only entered three races officially: one three-miler and two 10,000-meter races. Her training schedule has been rather ambitious; she does five miles Monday to Friday, 3-10 miles on Sunday and 3-5 miles on Saturday.

Her pre-run warm-up consists of the stretching sequence carried in the May 1978 issue of *Runner's World.*

She does most of her runs alone, but runs with friends on weekends. No one else in her family runs, although her father did run track during his college days.

Bernice's longest run has been an 11-miler. She arranges most of her courses so that they go through trails, which makes the runs almost like exploring. She likes to run on roads with curvy layouts and lots of trees. "Most of my courses combine roads with trails," she says. "I run through some back streets in nice housing districts."

Dogs, she reports, used to startle her and they still do sometimes, but she's getting used to them. "I have learned from a friend that if you stop, face the dog, talk sweetly, pat the dog, it usually calms him...or he keeps barking but does not attack." She reports that most people in cars are usually considerate and they usually stop for her at crosswalks.

"When I first started to run," she reports, "I tried to run too much in a short period of time. My right heel became sore just enough to notice it, and the outside area of my right knee became a little swollen with a little accompanying soreness. I consulted a local doctor and have been putting heel pads in my right shoes. It has since gone away."

Although she has no coach, she takes advice from the male friend who got her started. She also reads as much as she can and she has certain intuitions about what's right.

She does not see any significant difference between the reasons men have for running and those that women have.

Bernice trains at a nine-minute-per-mile pace, and has run as fast as 7:30 pace during a race. About her goals in running, she says this: "At first I wanted to be able to run five miles a day. Now I think I would like to run the Boston Marathon since I've already accomplished my running five miles a day. I eventually would like to try longer races (for fun). I would like to be able to run 15-milers in practice."

Bernice feels that the interest in running by women is going to have a very positive effect on the performance of Americans in international competition. "There are a great many woman runners who are seriously running and winning races...improving their times all the time. I think women have shown a fine competitiveness which increases as they become more physically fit. You start out recreationally, but it becomes fun to race and to try to improve yourself. It is just an evolutionary thing before improving your times becomes the challenge."

The person who has had the most positive effect on Bernice's running is her friend Skip Dunlap. "He runs with me at my speed, sometimes deceptively increasing the pace, encouraging me to take on longer and longer runs. He always praises me and encourages me and is always understanding."

Bernice describes her most memorable run: "It would be the 6.2-mile race I entered recently. My previous race of 6.2 miles was in the fall. I had been training all winter. I was running five miles a day. I did longer runs from time to time.

"A week before the race I ran a 10-miler by myself. I was having difficulty pushing myself past whatever daily distances I ran. But I did this day—and my second five miles was faster than my first five. It was great. That gave me confidence that I was in better shape for this race.

"I started at the back of the pack as I usually do—and I just started passing people. After two or three miles I picked up the speed. My legs felt great. I increased my pace at the five-mile mark. My legs still felt great. But I wasn't used to running at that pace. My stomach tensed up a little; I think I started to get a stitch. I thought at the last hill I would die a little, but I felt stronger going up the last .3 mile, and passed a girl who looked lean and trim. So I kncw I was close to the end but still wasn't sure about sprinting until I heard some steps behind me and I took off like a shot. I didn't realize I did have so much left. I felt good in that sprint. I had finished in 50 minutes in my fall 10,000-meter. This time I finished in 45:40. I was proud, happy and excited!"

AVON
25
Marathon
SAN FERNANDO
AVON
4

Appendix: Women's Marathon Records

All-Time U.S. Top 50

Time	Name	Year
2:36:26	Julie Brown	1978
2:37:57	Kim Merritt	1977
2:38:19	Jacqueline Hansen	1975
2:39:11	Miki Gorman	1976
2:41:31	Patty Lyons	1978
2:41:38	Celia Peterson	1978
2:44:50	Sue Peterson	1978
2:44:52	Gayle Barron	1978
2:45:32	Julie Brown	1976
2:45:34	Penny DeMoss	1978
2:46:15	Martha Cooksey	1978
2:46:23	Diane Barrett	1976
2:46:34	Leal-Ann Reinhart	1977
2:46:46	Irene Griffith	1978
2:46:54	Sue Kinsey	1977
2:47:22	Jane Killion	1978
2:47:20	Patricia LaTora	1977
2:47:26	Janice Arenz	1978
2:47:34	Doris Heritage	1976
2:48:07	Cindy Dalrymple	1977
2:48:40	Lauri Pedrinan	1978
2:49:30	Marilyn Paul	1976
2:49:40	Cheryl Bridges	1971
2:50:22	Nina Kuscsik	1977
2:50:40	Judy Leydig	1977
2:50:47	Dorothy Doolittle	1977
2:50:48	Lora Cartwright	1976
2:50:48	Jill Hanson	1977
2:51:11	Sue Rossiter	1978
2:51:12	Marilyn Bevans	1977
2:51:13	Lisa Lorrain	1977
2:51:15	Joan Ullyot	1976
2:51:37	Kathrine Switzer	1975
2:51:38	Marjorie Kaput	1974
2:52:09	Tena Anex	1977
2:52:37	Phyllis Hines	1977
2:53:09	D. Anderson	1977

2:53:14	Vicki Bray	1976
2:53:38	Sue Peterson	1977
2:53:40	Teri Anderson	1973
2:54:28	Judy Ikenberry	1974
2:54:34	Lisa Matovcik	1977
2:55:12	Anita Ayers	1977
2:55:22	Beth Bonner	1971
2:55:33	Karen McKeachie	1977
2:55:40	June Chun	1977
2:55:59	Ann Forshee	1977
2:56:07	Lili Ledbetter	1975
2:56:25	Susan Mallery	1976
2:56:40	Marie Albert	1977

All-Time World Top 50

Time	Name (Country)	Year
2:34:47	Christa Vahlensieck (WG)	1977
2:35:15	Chantal Langlace (Fr)	1977
2:36:26	Julie Brown (US)	1978
2:37:57	Kim Merritt (US)	1977
2:38:09	Manuela Angenvoorth (WG)	1977
2:38:19	Jacqueline Hansen (US)	1975
2:39:11	Miki Gorman (US)	1976
2:41:38	Celia Peterson (US)	1978
2:41:31	Patty Lyons (US)	1978
2:42:24	Liane Winter (WG)	1975
2:44:50	Sue Peterson (US	1978
2:44:52	Gayle Barron (US)	1978
2:45:32	Julie Brown (US)	1976
2:45:34	Penny DeMoss (US)	1978
2:46:15	Martha Cooksey (US)	1978
2:46:23	Diane Barrett (US)	1976
2:46:34	Leal-Ann Reinhart (US)	1976
2:46:46	Irene Griffith (US)	1978
2:46:54	Sue Kinsey (US)	1977
2:47:16	Beverly Shingles (NZ)	1977
2:47:20	Patricia LaTora (US)	1977
2:47:22	Jane Killion (US)	1978
2:47:26	Janice Arenz (US)	1978
2:47:34	Doris Heritage (US)	1976
2:47:38	Chris Lavallee (Can)	1978
2:47:50	Claire Spauwen (Hol)	1976
2:48:07	Cindy Dairymple (US)	1977
2:48:22	Sarolta Monspart (Hun)	1976
2:48:40	Lauri Pedrinan (US)	1978
2:49:30	Marilyn Paul (US)	1978

2:49:40	Cheryl Bridges (US)	1971
2:50:22	Nina Kuscsik (US)	1977
2:50:26	Elisabeth Richards (Aus)	1976
2:50:36	Silvana Cruciata (It)	1976
2:50:40	Judy Leydig (US)	1977
2:50:47	Dorothy Doolittle (US)	1977
2:50:48	Lora Cartwright (US)	1976
2:50:48	Jill Hanson (US)	1977
2:50:55	Christine Readdy (GB)	1976
2:51:09	Lockley (GB)	1978
2:51:11	Sue Rossiter (US)	1978
2:51:12	Marilyn Bevans (US)	1977
2:51:13	Lisa Lorrain (US)	1977
2:51:15	Joan Ullyot (US)	1976
2:51:37	Kathrine Switzer (US)	1975
2:51:38	Marjorie Kaput (US)	1974
2:51:41	Annick Loir (Fr)	1977
2:52:06	Tena Anex (US)	1977
2:52:33	Irja Paukkonen (Fin)	1976
2:52:37	Phyllis Hines (US)	1977

References

ORGANIZATIONS

Amateur Athletic Union (AAU). The AAU sponsors frequent local and regional events, and a full series of national championships from cross-country to ultramarathons. Securing an AAU card (a testament of membership)—is a prerequisite to competing in an AAU event. It can be obtained at any AAU-sponsored race. It is, however, more practical to join before the race, since many events have entry deadlines and some have age or time restrictions. Yearly AAU dues generally are less than $5. The following are major AAU contacts:

- National Headquarters—AAU House, 3400 W. 86th St., Indianapolis, Ind. 46268.
- Long-Distance Running Committee Co-Chairmen—Bob Campbell, 39 Linnet St., West Roxbury, Mass. 02132; and Vince Chiappetta, 2 Washington Square Village, Apt. 9-D, New York, N.Y. 10012.
- Standard Committee (Course Certification)—Ted Corbitt, Apt. 8H, Sect. 4, 150 W. 225th St., New York, N.Y. 10463.

The national headquarters in Indianapolis can provide a list of its "associations"—the districts in which runners register. Association chairmen can give details on competition and clubs in an area.

Road Runners Club of America (RRCA). The RRCA chapters sponsor a variety of distance runs on a regular basis. These generally are less formal than AAU races and usually are less expensive to enter. The RRCA charges an annual membership fee similar to the AAU fee. The national president is Jeff Darman, 2737 Devonshire Pl., N.W., Washington, D.C. 20008. There are also five communications directors who can give regional information on competition and clubs:

- Ray Gordon, Route 2, Box 1037, Front Royal, Va. 22630.
- Nick Costes, Dept. of HPER, Troy State University, Troy, Ala. 36081.
- Bob Martin, 5834 Stoney Island Ave., Chicago, Ill. 60637.
- Steven Ryan, 9804 W. 12th St., Wichita, Kan. 67212.
- Herb Parsons, 170 Rosario Beach Rd., Anacortes, Wash. 98211.

PUBLICATIONS

A growing number of periodicals cover the booming sport of long-distance running. These range from international to local. The leading publishers are:

• *Runner's World,* P.O. Box 366, Mountain View, Calif. 94042—publisher of *RW, Marathoner* and the Runner's Book Series.

• *Track & Field News,* P.O. Box 296, Los Altos, Calif. 94022—publisher of *T&FN, Track Newsletter* and *Track Technique.*

• *Running,* P.O. Box 350, Salem, Ore. 97308.

• *Running Times,* 1816 Lamont St., N.W., Washington, D.C. 20010.

• *Runner's Gazette,* 102 W. Water St., Lansford, Pa. 18232.

• *Yankee Runner,* 19 Grove St., Merrimac, Mass. 01860.

• *NorCal Running Review,* P.O. Box 1551, San Mateo, Calif. 94401.

BOOKS/BOOKLETS

These publications relate closely to the material covered in *The Complete Woman Runner.* All are available from World Publications, P.O. Box 366, Mountain View, Calif. 94042. Write for a book catalog.

• *Beginner's Running Guide,* by Hal Higdon.

• *Complete Diet Guide,* edited by Hal Higdon.

• *Dr. George Sheehan's Medical Advice for Runners*, by Dr. George Sheehan.

• *Jog, Run, Race,* by Joe Henderson.

• *Runner's Training Guide*, from the editors of *RW.*

• *Running with the Elements,* from the editors of *RW.*

• *The Complete Runner,* from the editors of *RW.*

• *The Running Body,* by E.C. Frederick.

• *The Running Foot Doctor,* by Steven I. Subotnick, D.P.M.

• *The Self-Made Olympian,* by Ron Daws.

• *Dr. Sheehan on Running,* by George Sheehan, M.D.

• *Training with Cerutty,* by Larry Myers.

• *Van Aaken Method,* by Ernst van Aaken, M.D.

• *Women's Running,* by Joan Ullyot, M.D.

List of Contributors

Ruth Anderson, a graduate of the University of Nebraska, is a radiochemist at the Lawrence Livermore Laboratories in Livermore, California. She is a former national women's marathon title-holder; she has run more than 30 marathons, including Boston three times. She is also a pioneer in women's ultra-distance events, and capped her accomplishments in that field in July of 1978 by running a 100-mile track race in a time of 16:50:47. When she slows down long enough, she contributes to the "Women's Running" column in *Runner's World.*

Richard Benyo has worked as a newspaper editor and as editor of *Stock Car Racing Magazine.* He is managing editor of *Runner's World Magazine.* His two books to date are *Superspeedway* and *Return to Running.*

Dr. Gerald Besson is an internist and a Fellow of the American College of Physicians. He is also the chairman of the sports and fitness committee of the Santa Clara (Cal.) County Medical Society. He is married and has five daughters; his wife and four of his daughters run.

Grace Butcher is an English professor at the Geauga campus of Kent State University in Burton, Ohio. Her running experience stretches out for some 30 years—from a Junior Olympics hurdles championship through several US half-mile titles and into masters competition. Grace's most recent book of poetry, *Rumors of Ecstasy... Rumors of Death,* is in its third printing.

Ellen Clark, since taking up running again after a long layoff, has done a five-kilometer race in 21:16, the 10-kilometer in 43:15, and the marathon in 3:16:57. She is also a world record holder with six other West Valley Track Club women, who ran 214 miles, in a 24-hour relay race in 1975. She is married to Olympic marathoner Bill Clark.

Mark Cockrill left a highly lucrative position as the senior vice-president of a mortgage brokerage firm to become a major shareholder and co-manager of Hawaii's first running store—owned and staffed by runners. Since then, he has become an adviser to a women's running group, works as a liaison between race directors and sponsors, is helping to develop a specialized line of warm weather running wear, and continues to struggle to keep his weight down and his mileage up.

Jacqueline Hansen has won a Boston Marathon women's title, was an AIAW national mile champion, claimed a six-mile world record, won a national AAU one-hour run championship, bettered the women's marathon mark twice, and is most proud of her pioneering efforts in the name of women's distance running. Currently, Jacqueline is running for the San Fernando Valley Track Club.

Nina Kuscsik has completed nearly 50 marathons in the past decade; her best time is 2:50:22. She has also completed a 50-miler in 6:35:53, which was the fastest time ever run by a woman at that distance. Nina's accomplishments in running were predated by her accomplishments in other sports: roller skating (national one-mile speed skating champion for 1959 and 1960), ice skating (International Silver Skates championship all-around title in 1961), and bicycling (New York State champion for women). She works as a patient representative at the Mount Sinai Hospital in New York City. Her proudest accomplishment, however, is in the area of women's rights in running; for the past decade she has been fighting to overcome antiquated rules within the AAU that have held back sanctioned participation by women in long-distance events.

Nick Marshall, a writer and runner, lives in Camp Hill, Pennsylvania. He specializes in running ultra-marathons. In 1977 Nick had the sixth best 50-mile time in the US. Also in that year he traveled to Lake Tahoe for the annual 72-mile run around the lake, Nick's first experience with running at altitude; he won the event.

Dusty Rhodes was born in Philadelphia and now resides in Boston. She holds two degrees from Penn State University, where she was an honors student and also captain of the field hockey and tennis teams. She was assistant general manager of the World Football League. She worked for two years as a player's representative in professional hockey, basketball, baseball, and football. In 1974 she was on the sports selection committee for the Emmy Awards. Dusty is founder and president of the New England chapter of the Women's Sports Foundation, and is also president and founder of Conventures, a company that specializes in management and promotion of special events, particularly in the area of women's sports.

Dr. John W. Pagliano is a running podiatrist. He has run a sub-2:29 marathon and usually runs them in the 2:30s; his best time in the 10,000 meters is 30:10. He is a former United States AAU 50-mile champion and is ranked in the top 15 US 50-milers. He holds the position of President of the American Academy of Podiatric Sports Medicine.

Barbara Pike is a mother, wife, and part-time student. She is also a runner. She started running three years ago in a jogging class where her immediate goal was to finish a 12-minute running test. Since then she has run a 3:24 marathon and hopes to be able to get her time down to 3:12.

Sue Stricklin won the masters' division of the Avon International Women's Marathon Championships in Atlanta in 1978. A runner for four years, Sue had been the manager of a combination surfing and running shop in Hawaii. She also directed a women's running clinic and recently moved to San Francisco.

Kathy Switzer was the first woman to complete the Boston Marathon in 1967. Since then, Kathy has run a 2:51 marathon, has championed equality in athletics for women, and has been instrumental in securing sponsorship for women's events and individuals. Professionally, Ms. Switzer is the manager of special promotions for Avon Products and was in charge of the 1978 Avon Marathon-International Women's Championships held in Atlanta. She holds a master's degree in public relations from Syracuse University.

Dr. Thomas A. Tutko is a professor of psychology at San Jose State University, specializing the psychology of sports. In conjunction with Patsy E. Neal, he is the author of *Coaching Girls and Women.*

Dr. Ernst van Aaken is the former West German coach of world-class athletes. Dr. van Aaken prescribes running and endurance sports to his patients to keep them from returning to his door with more problems. In 1972, while training on a rainy evening, he was struck by a car and both his legs were amputated below the knees. He has been very instrumental in fostering the cause of women's long-distance running throughout the world, and is the founder of the annual women's international marathon championships.

Photo Credits

Page

8, 310 Lorraine Rorke
15, 31, 40, 76, 223, 261 Joseph Berke
36, 44, 256, 266 M.L. Thomas
57, 438 Bill Leung
62 Lucy Hilmer
86, 208 Courtesy Bonne Bell
94, 140, 275, 442 Courtesy Avon Products
105, 124 Mark Shearman
114, 169, 176 Jeff Johnson
131, 149 Jean Shapiro
240 Staff photo
247 Paul Felley
286 Staff photo
310 Horst Muller, Don Melandry, Lorraine Rorke

Recommended Reading

Jog, Run, Race by Joe Henderson. Leads the reader through several new beginnings—from walking to jogging, jogging to running, running to racing. Each beginning has a specific day by day progress guide. Hardback $6.95, Paperback $3.95.

Women's Running by Joan Ullyot, M.D. The first book of its kind to take a serious look at women runners. Tips on diet, clothing, injuries and other problems unique to women. Specific training routines for all levels of abilities. Hardback $5.95, Paperback $3.95.

The Complete Diet Guide: For Runners and Other Athletes, from the Editors of *Runner's World*. How the athlete can use his diet to better advantage is the basis of this book. Areas addressed: Weight control, drinks, fasting, natural vs. processed food, vegetarian diets and more. Hardback $7.95, Paperback $4.95.

Doctor Sheehan on Running, by George Sheehan, M.D. Lively, witty, philosophical, and serious, that's Dr. Sheehan. Provides delightful insight into the world of running and the world of a runner. Packed with good practical information from one of the country's most popular writers on running. Hardback $5.95, Paperback $3.95.

Run Gently, Run Long, by Joe Henderson. Henderson views running as a beautiful pleasant experience. He does not feel that there is any correlation between pain and fitness. He feels that long slow distance (L.S.D.) running can produce optimum training. A beautiful philosophy with many successful users. Paperback $3.50.

Long Run Solution, by Joe Henderson. Henderson devotes this book to the mental rewards of a sport whose popularity is now reaching mammoth proportions. More immediate than the physical benefits, the psychological effects of running are now being explored. Hardback $5.95, Paperback $3.95.

The Running Foot Doctor, by Steven I. Subotnick, D.P.M. Written for the runner rather than the doctor, this book presents the causes and cures of running injuries in more than 25 individual case studies. Hardback $6.95, Paperback $3.95.

Runner's Training Guide, by the Editors of *Runner's World*. An overview of the many training methods in practice today. Looks at the popular systems and the coaches who developed them. Paperback $3.50.

Available in fine bookstores and sport shops, or from:

Box 366, Dept. A, Mountain View, CA 94042.
Include $.45 shipping and handling for each title (Maximum $2.25).

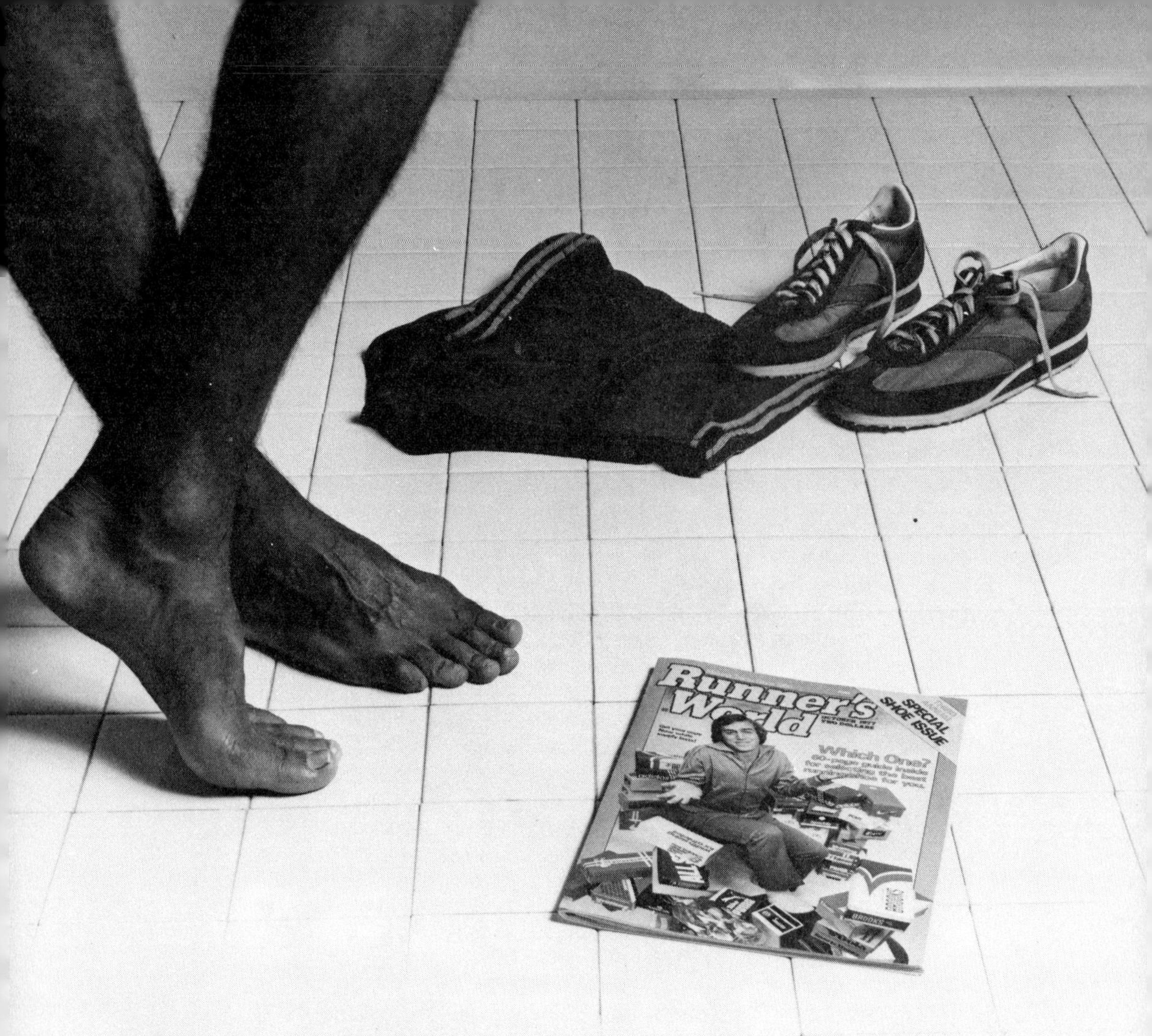

Runner's World
SPECIAL SHOE ISSUE
Which One?